CW00763523

NURSERY
STOCK
MANUAL

NURSERY STOCK MANUAL

J.G.D.LAMB J.C.KELLY P.BOWBRICK
GROWER BOOKS · LONDON

Grower Books
50 Doughty Street, London WC1N 2LP

First published 1975
Reprinted 1977, 1978, 1980, 1982
Revised and reprinted 1985

© 1975, 1985 Grower Books

ISBN 0 901361 80 1

Designed and produced in Great Britain by Sharp Print Management,
Manchester

Contents

We are grateful to Darby Nursery Stock Ltd, of Norfolk who provided the material for the front cover.

Preface

This book breaks new ground as it brings together for the first time the skills of the plant propagator and the economist. There has been much change in both areas in the last ten years. The age old art of plant propagation has been revolutionised by new knowledge and new materials such as plastics, standardised composts, slow release fertilisers and capillary beds. These enable nurserymen to simplify and streamline propagation methods and to produce uniform saleable plants in a shorter time than ever before.

To produce plants well is not enough. The days have long since gone when a man could run a nursery business simply because he liked plants. Costs are increasing rapidly and more nurserymen will be forced to look critically at their production and marketing methods if their businesses are to remain viable. Plant propagation should not be looked on as an isolated nursery task but rather the initiation of a marketing operation a few years hence. Economic management techniques can help to ensure that new nurseries are established on a sound foundation and that existing nurseries make the most efficient use of available resources.

The three authors bring a wealth of personal experience to this book. A new section on micropropagation, prepared by Dr G. Douglas, has been added to this second edition. Much of the information included has already appeared in the publications of the Kinsealy Research Centre, Agricultural Institute, Dublin and has been demonstrated there at Open Days. There is, however, need for a popular reference book wherein modern techniques are collected in a form readily available to those engaged in the day to day management of a nursery. The alphabetical treatment of the genera in Section 2 will help readers to find, in an easily accessible form, up-to-date information on the propagation and treatment of a wide range of plants.

While the book has been written mainly with nurserymen and students in mind many of the new techniques, e.g. the use of plastic in a cold frame will also be of interest to the amateur plant propagator. Coming at a time when there is increasing concern about the quality of our environment the book should have wide appeal.

D. W. Robinson
Kinsealy Research Centre
Dublin 5   v

Introduction

Traditional methods of plant propagation are being rapidly modified and developed as new techniques and materials are introduced. Any nurseryman who is not thoroughly familiar with the use of plastic structures, capillary beds, standardised composts, slow-release fertilisers etc., described in this book is likely to be a high-cost producer. He must therefore learn about these new techniques and methods if he is to compete with his rivals at home and abroad.

The student, too, can no longer expect to learn all there is to be known about nursery business from a long apprenticeship to a master craftsman. He can learn more and he can learn faster by combining his practical training with a study of the latest developments. We hope this book will be as valuable in helping him to get formal qualifications as in providing practical advice on everyday nursery work.

We could have collected much of the information in this book from other books, but we felt that this would mean describing many obsolete techniques, and that there was a great danger of including techniques that have never been really successful in practice. This means that we have written much about the genera we have investigated thoroughly, and given only a few notes about those genera of which we have little experience. It also means that the specialist may not find his own methods described in detail, for plants can be propagated in many ways and we have concentrated on developing reliable methods of producing saleable plants quickly, rather than on studying the hundreds of slightly different methods that individual nurserymen have developed for their own use.

It is important that the nurseryman should always bear in mind the necessity of making a profit, that he should not propagate any plants unless he knows he has the resources to grow them on and has investigated the market.

This book has a large section on economic planning techniques, relating to both marketing and production and these have been developed especially for nurserymen. We felt it would be pointless to take the accounting system used by a farmer, and substitute the words 'Laburnum, rhododendron, prunus' for 'wheat, barley, sugarbeet'. These planning techniques are as important to the nurseryman as the practical skills, and we feel that students, too, should make

an effort to master them.

PART ONE
Nursery Practice

1

The Collection, Preparation and Insertion of Cuttings

The importance of mother plants

It is a general principle that cuttings should be taken from young, vigorously growing mother plants, not too remote from the time when they were cuttings themselves. While the age of the mother plants may not matter so much in the case of easily rooted subjects, it becomes more important when dealing with those which are more difficult to root, since the capacity of cuttings to generate roots tends to decrease with increasing age of the parent plant.

While it is sometimes possible to dispense with special mother plants by taking cuttings from young specimens in the nursery (e.g. *Ceanothus*, p. 96), in general it is desirable to set aside plants specially for the purpose of supplying cuttings. Obviously such specimens must be true to name, but it is worth stressing that they must also be of typical form and colour; with conifers in particular it is possible unwittingly to propagate from an inferior form or strain. With some genera e.g. *Magnolia* (p. 154) it is essential to have separate mother plants because of the special treatment necessary to get early cuttings; with others, e.g. *Prunus* (p. 171) it is desirable to have mother plants that can be pruned hard to give suitable material for cuttings.

Stock or mother plants should receive every care in the way of pruning, manuring and weed control, for only if they are properly looked after will they remain in good condition for a period of years. The aim should be to keep them, as far as possible, in a strongly vegetative condition. Properly treated, mother plants tend to retain much of the juvenility of recently propagated plants and, in this connection, it is often important that the cuttings should be removed at the proper time each year, even if they are not used, as an annual cutting back has a strong influence in maintaining the juvenile state as, for example, with *Magnolia*, (p. 154) where the annual production of long shoots is required.

Types of cuttings — definitions

Softwood cuttings are those taken early in the season, soon after shoot growth has commenced, and before any degree of lignification (i.e. hardening) has taken place. Examples to be found in this book include magnolias, Japanese maples, *Prunus incisa* and deciduous azaleas. Such cuttings wilt rapidly unless inserted promptly under mist or in the warm bench with plastic.

Semi-hardwood cuttings are at a later stage of development, when the young shoots are starting to firm up at the base. Examples are numerous, as in many species inserted in June in the cold frame with plastic method. The obvious examples of *hardwood* cuttings are those inserted in October–November, like *Salix* and some species of *Cornus*. A special type of hardwood cutting is the mallet cutting, which consists of a shoot of the past season's growth with a short section of the parent stem attached.

Other things being equal, a large cutting is preferable to a small one provided they are both at the same physiological stage of development, and here we may refer back to the importance of the treatment of the mother plant as discussed above. A good example is *Chaemaecyparis*, where the annual extension growth can be but a few millimetres long in old trees. In contrast, younger specimens will give cuttings of the past season's growth 3–4 in. (7.5–10 cm) in length.

Fig. 1. Nodal and leaf bud cuttings of *Camellia*.

It is necessary to point out the meaning of *basal* cuttings as used in this book. Such cuttings are taken by cutting with a sharp knife through the base of the young shoot where it joins the parent branch. At this point there is often a slight swelling ('pulvinus'). The cut is made by slicing through this swelling. In contrast a *heeled* cutting is (by our definition) made by tugging off the young shoot with a downward motion bringing away on its base a more or less triangular piece of the wood of the parent branch. This piece has generally to be trimmed up afterwards with the knife. The term *nodal* cutting is used in its usual sense, i.e. making the cut at right angles to the stem and passing through the latter immediately below a leaf bud. Usually a joint in the stem is discernible at this point. An *internodal* cutting is prepared similarly but is sectioned between two joints.

By *stem cuttings* is meant those clipped off the mother plant without reference to whether the cut comes at or between nodes, the only criteria being that the cuttings are of the right length and age.

Leaf bud cuttings are used in a few instances, e.g. *Mahonia japonica*, where the habit of growth is not conducive to the production of the usual types of cutting, and *Camellia*, where leaf bud cuttings are useful if propagating

4

material is scarce. Only vigorous shoots with well-developed buds should be selected. Each cutting consists of a short piece of the main stem, cut just above a leaf and again between two nodes, resulting in a single leaf attached to the stem and having a leaf-bud in the axil. Such cuttings may be wounded, but root promoting substances used so close to the bud tend to delay the subsequent development of a shoot from that bud and so they should not be used unless known to be necessary. The short length of main stem is pressed into the rooting medium. Overlapping of large leaves may be a problem. Shortening of the leaf is often practised but should be done only when really necessary and as little as possible, since it cuts down the photosynthesising area of the leaf.

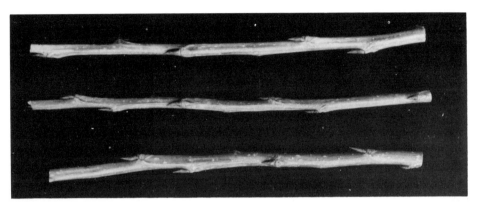

Fig. 2. Hardwood cuttings root best from stout material.

For some subjects *root cuttings* are a means of propagation. From the many genera recorded as having been raised in this way *Romneya, Clerodendrum, Rhus, Robinia* and *Ailanthus* can be mentioned as responding readily to this system. Just as for cuttings from the above ground parts of the plant, it is necessary to have vigorously growing mother plants on their own roots. Pieces of root excavated at random from old specimens often fail to grow. Starting close to the main stem, the root is severed with a straight cut. Make the next cut about 1½ in. (3.7 cm) down the root. This should be a slanting cut so that top and bottom of the severed portion of the root can be distinguished. If the material is suitable, two or more cuttings can be prepared from one length of root. With some species the first section tends to form shoots more readily than the rest. Small numbers of cuttings can be placed upright in pots containing equal parts moss peat and sand, covering the surface with a layer of sand so that the top of the cutting is just below the surface. Most species may be started in moderate heat. For larger scale operations a cold frame can be used. Root cuttings of woody plants are taken during the period between late autumn and early spring. The cuttings should be dusted with fungicide before being planted.

Collecting and preparing the cuttings

As they are collected, all cuttings should be dropped into a plastic bag or sack which should be tied at the mouth if it is to be transported any distance. At no time should the sun strike on this bag as this would very quickly cause an excessive rise in temperature within. If the cuttings cannot be dealt with quickly after collection, they may be stored overnight in their plastic container, keeping the latter in a cool place.

The actual preparation of the cutting will depend on whether it is to be a basal, nodal, internodal or stem cutting, or perhaps a leaf bud cutting. A very sharp knife should be used. The way in which the cutting is prepared should be clear from the definitions given above and information on the type and size of cutting will be found under the different genera in the succeeding part of this book. Here it is well to stress again the need for choosing good material, all of similar physiological age, and making from it cuttings of uniform size. Only in this way can one expect a smooth production line, cuttings all rooting together and proceeding together through the stages of lifting, potting or lining out and growing on. The end product to be aimed at should be a batch of evenly sized plants.

The leaves should be trimmed off that part of the cutting which will be below the surface of the compost. They should be removed with a sharp knife, as should the thorns from *Berberis* and other spiky subjects. Often, though, it is sufficient to strip these leaves off, provided they come away cleanly without tearing the stem.

Wounding and dipping the cuttings

Wounding the stem of the cutting has been found to stimulate rooting in many species. The operation can be a light wounding, as in azaleas, where it is little more than a scrape on one side of the stem, removing the minimum of bark. Heavy wounding implies the removal of a slice of bark and a little of the underlying tissue, as in evergreen rhododendrons (Fig. 3). The wound is generally up to 1 in. (2.5 cm long) cut downwards to the base of the cutting on one side (single wound) or on two sides (double wound).

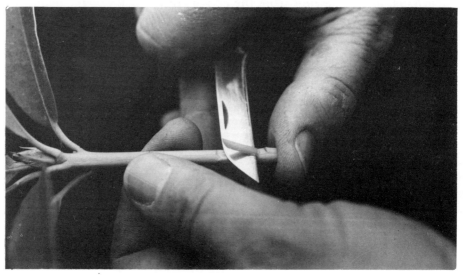

Fig. 3. Heavy wounding of a rhododendron cutting.

The effect of wounding has been attributed to several causes, such as a greater proliferation of new cells which in turn can develop into root initials, greater absorption of water, easier penetration of root promoting substances, and, in some cases, the removal of physical barriers to root emergence such as thick walled cells. In at least some cases it may be that wounding releases some sort of root promoting stimulus, perhaps of a chemical nature, as a reaction to the wound.

Whether the cuttings be wounded or not, it is recommended that they be next immersed completely for a few seconds in a solution of fungicide whatever system of rooting them is being followed. This inhibits the development of moulds and, over and above this sanitary function, may have a stimulating effect on rooting. The cuttings are then allowed to drain for a few minutes before the next step, which may be the application of root promoting substances.

The use of root promoting substances

These now have an accepted place in the rooting of cuttings and are readily available either as the specific chemical itself, in the form of proprietary powders of various strengths, or as tablets which can be used to make up solutions.

The most generally effective of these substances is IBA (indolebutyric acid). NAA (naphthaleneacetic acid) is effective on some species. In a few cases, mixtures of these chemicals have been found to give improved results and there may be further developments in this line in the future.

At present the powder forms are widely used and are very convenient. Certain precautions should be followed. There is a paucity of information on the shelf life and storage conditions of these preparations but it is common

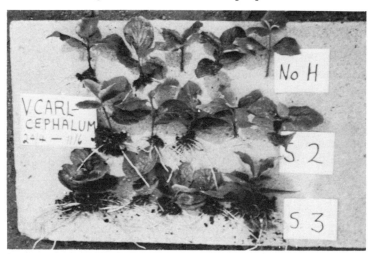

Figs. 4 & 5. Root promoting substances are helpful in rooting *Viburnum x carlcephalum* (above) and the easier *Choisya* (below).

sense not to buy more at a time than can be used up within a few months and to keep the container in a cool dry place. Deterioration is more likely to set in under the warm humid conditions of a glasshouse.

Care should be taken not to contaminate the bulk of the powder. Tap out as much as is likely to be required into a separate shallow container (*not* the lid of the tin in which the powder is stored) or onto a piece of cardboard. Any left over should be destroyed; never return it to the tin. Always keep the latter tightly closed. When inserting treated cuttings into the rooting medium, use a dibber, as pushing the cuttings into the substrate may displace much of the powder.

Sometimes liquid preparations are preferred, and for a few subjects may give superior results. The *dilute solution soaking method* entails standing the cuttings with the bottom inch (2.5 cm) of the stem immersed in the solution for 24 hours. This should be done in a cool but not cold place to avoid concentration of the solution through evaporation. The concentrations used vary from 20 ppm (parts per million) for easy rooting subjects to 200 ppm for the more difficult kinds. To prepare 1 litre of a 100 ppm solution disolve 100 mg of the chemical in about 10 ml of ethyl or isopropyl alcohol and then add water to make up to 1 litre. Dilute liquid preparations have a short life of only a few days, even in a refrigerator.

In recent years the '*quick-dip*' *method* has been developed for use with some more difficult to root hardwood cuttings. A concentrated solution of the growth promoting substance is used, ranging from 500 to 10,000 ppm, though 4,000 ppm is a generally used strength. To prepare 100 ml of a 4,000 ppm concentration dissolve 400 mg of the chemical in 100 ml of 50% ethyl or isopropyl alcohol. Such concentrated solutions will keep for a long time so long as they are not contaminated, though, as a precaution, they should be kept in tightly stoppered brown bottles in a cool place.

In using these concentrated dips decant off as much as is required into a beaker and use it immediately. Do not treat the cuttings by immersing their bases in the solution. Touch the surface of the liquid with the cut surfaces for a moment only. It will be understood that this must be done in a cool atmosphere as the alcohol evaporates quickly. Discard the used solution.

Root promoting substances not only increase the percentage rooting in the more difficult genera but are found to be advantageous also with many easily rooting cuttings. When using equipment such as mist units, warm benches or even cold frames, quicker rooting and hence a better throughput can be achieved with many species and cultivars.

Timing in relation to the rooting of cuttings

It is well known that some species of trees and shrubs can be rooted over an extended period between spring and autumn and that others can only be rooted during specific stages of their annual development.

In the case of easily rooted subjects, the time to take the cuttings may be determined by the method of rooting to be followed. Cuttings of *Prunus* **Otto Luyken**, for example, can be rooted in a cold frame in September or in a mist unit in March depending on the programme for the nursery. While it probably would not be economic to install a mist unit to propagate plants which can be done easily in other ways, it is useful to know what catch crops can be inserted to utilise spare bench space.

If there is a choice of times to take cuttings of a given species, is it better to take the cuttings early, root them quickly and grow them on or to take large cuttings later? With *Pyracantha* it is better to take them late (Fig. 49). Cuttings taken in May never caught up on larger cuttings taken in September, nor did they flower the following spring. *Prunus incisa* is an example of early cuttings developing quicker than those taken later in the year (Fig. 47). No universal answer can be given to the question — it depends on the species.

The genus *Prunus* can be used to illustrate another aspect of timing, for the deciduous species fall into two groups (a) those represented by *P. incisa* and (b) the Japanese cherries. When rooted in a mist unit the first group will root readily from softwood cuttings taken as soon as they are large enough to handle, but experience with Japanese cherries has been that lower percentages resulted from efforts to root cuttings before July. Most *Chamaecyparis* cultivars show a decline in the rooting of spring cuttings inserted after mid-March. Hardwood cuttings of many deciduous species show a seasonality in rooting with peaks in autumn and spring and a low period in between.

Timing of another kind is seen in a group of plants which includes deciduous magnolias, Japanese maples and deciduous azaleas. Here the problem is that losses are high in the first winter if cuttings are taken from outdoor plants. The remedy is to force the mother plants, e.g. under plastic. This can be done by placing a temporary structure over the plants in February. Sun heat alone is sufficient to give earlier cuttings, which root well and develop satisfactorily.

For many heaths and dwarf rhododendrons the new method of striking hardwood cuttings in February enables the production of saleable plants before the end of the year, eliminating potting and over-wintering (p. 126 and p. 180).

Fig. 6. In the plastic house early cuttings can be produced by sun heat alone.

Insertion of cuttings

The rooting of cuttings in trays or boxes rather than directly in the bench is advocated on the grounds of hygiene and convenience. It is better that the rooting medium should be fresh for each batch of cuttings and go out with them when they are rooted. In any case, a whole bench of compost would have to be renewed periodically owing to the accumulation of toxins giving undesirable root systems. Each plant species can be given the appropriate substrate and can be removed as soon as rooting has occurred. Prompt removal is especially important for some genera, e.g. *Ceanothus* (p. 94) and *Acer* (p. 69) though all rooted cuttings should be moved on to the next stage without delay, be it potting up, planting out in frames or lining out in the nursery.

The use of containers also permits greater flexibility in that a tray of rooted cuttings can be removed for hardening off, leaving the mist unit in full operation for the remaining trays. The vacant space can be filled again, thus maximising throughput. The specialist raising large numbers of one species or cultivar may consider it more convenient to insert the cuttings directly, and to accept the necessity for periodic renewal of the rooting medium over the whole bench.

When inserting the cuttings the compost should not be firmed more than is needed to keep the cuttings in place. A loose compost promotes aeration, a factor in good root development. Reference has already been made to the use of a dibber when rooting powder has been applied (p. 8). All cuttings of similar type should be placed at the same depth. The peat used should be well moistened before use so that only a light overhead watering is needed to settle the cuttings without risk of leaching off the rooting powder.

In many instances the rooting of cuttings is preceded by the visible formation of callus, i.e. irregular growth of new tissue at the wounded surface. Callusing used to be thought an essential precursor of good rooting. While a degree of callusing heals cut surfaces, it is now considered to be a separate process from root initiation, though occurring under the same conditions. Excessive callusing is taken as an indication that conditions for rooting are not quite right, as rooting should have occurred before the callus tissue had proliferated excessively. Perhaps the timing was not correct, the rooting medium may need adjusting, or the rooting temperatures may be too high. Another occurrence is the production of roots high up on the stem of the cutting. This may indicate that the cutting was inserted too deeply or that the base temperature was too high or that the medium was insufficiently aerated. Too concentrated a root promoting substance can be another cause, though in this case there is usually a swelling on the stem above the dead basal portion. When using the warm bench and plastic method for rooting the cuttings, the high humidity may induce rooting near the surface of the compost with some species, but if the plastic is not left too long and is removed in easy stages (p. 14) the transplanting of such cuttings is not a problem.

2

Systems of Production from Cuttings

Mist propagation

The mist propagation system of rooting cuttings was developed first in USA in the third and fourth decades of this century. The first systems ('Continuous fog') aimed at providing a continuous fine mist in the propagating house. It was soon evident though, that too much water was detrimental, and control of the misting period evolved from the use of time clocks through evaporating pans to the 'electronic leaf'. All these are devices to make and break an electric circuit, thus controlling the on-off period of the misting.

Since mist units are now so widely used, it is not proposed to describe them in detail. Before installing such a unit a visit should be made to a nursery operating such a system. Much more can be learned this way than from a written description, so only a brief outline will be given here.

In essentials a mist unit consists of a bench fitted with electric heating cables to give bottom heat and with misting nozzles fitted above the bench. The heat is controlled by a rod-type thermostat, usually set to control the temperature at 70–75°F (21–24°C). It is important to mount this thermostat so that the rod will lie at the same level as the bases of the cuttings. Low voltage (6–30 v) heating cables, connected to a transformer, are laid in straight lines up and down the bench, about 3 in. (7.5 cm) apart. These cables are laid over a bed of coarse grit and are covered with sand to a depth of about 6 in. (15 cm) according to the depth of the containers to be used for the cuttings. The electrical loading should be 15 w per square foot. Wire netting placed over the cables serves both to protect them and to spread the heat more evenly. The bench must be well drained through the use of coarse sand and by the provision of drainage holes. It is stressed that all electrical installation should be carried out by a competent electrician as the system must operate safely in the damp conditions of a glasshouse.

The mist nozzles are of the deflector type, i.e. the mist is formed by a thin jet of water striking a flat surface. Such nozzles may be mounted on uprights from a water pipe running down the centre of the sand bed in the bench, or attached to the underside of a pipe suspended above the benches; if the latter, it is possible to arrange that pipe and nozzles can be swung out of the way when not in operation. The usual spacing of the nozzles for a 4 ft (1.2 m) bench is from 3 ft 4 in. (1.0 m) to 3 ft 6 in. (1.05 m).

The 'electronic leaf' which controls the frequency of misting consists of a piece of plastic in which are embedded two terminals connected to the control panel mounted on the wall of the glasshouse. When these terminals are wet the electrical contact is complete. This operates a solenoid valve which cuts off the water supply. By placing the 'leaf' among the cuttings the terminals dry off at a rate bearing an approximate relationship to the drying of the foliage of the cuttings. When the film of water connecting the terminals is broken the mist is activated by the solenoid valve until the film of water is complete again. The frequency of misting can be further controlled by setting a switch on the control panel, which may govern more than one bench. In this way the additional benches will be misted only every other time the first bench comes on, or once in every three, four or more times according to the setting of the switch. This is known as weaning — the first step in the hardening off of the rooted cuttings.

Under our conditions we have found it possible to dispense with the weaner. We have sufficient floor space in our glasshouses to allow us to remove boxes of rooted cuttings to the floor where they get a slight drift of mist from over the edge of the bench, but a weaning unit can be useful for large scale operations.

It is not essential to mount the soil warming cables on a bench. Sometimes they are installed in sand beds on the ground, though if they are on benches with steam or hot water pipes underneath to give air heat, this can help to reduce electricity consumption. A minimum air temperature of 60°F (15.6°C), ventilating at 80°F (26.7°C) is generally satisfactory.

The advantages and disadvantages of the mist system may be mentioned here. The obvious advantage is that it is an automatic system, self-adjusting according to the weather conditions and the humidity within the glasshouse. In this way there is less responsibility on the operator. The evaporation from the surface of the leaf cools it, reduces transpiration and induces the favourable condition of cool tops and warm bases in the cuttings. Hence rooting under mist is usually faster. Soft cuttings can be inserted early in the year without trouble from wilting, rooted quickly and have most of the growing season ahead for subsequent development. So long as the mist is working efficiently there is little danger of scorching of the foliage by the sun. This permits maximum exposure to light and hence maximum photosynthesis by the green tissue of the cuttings. This is not to say that some shading precautions are not necessary in very hot sunny weather in summer.

The main disadvantage of the mist technique is its dependence on machinery. There must be no failures in the electric current, the pump must be in good working order, and the nozzles must be kept clean and should function perfectly. The water supply must be clean and soft. Hard water soon coats the leaves of cuttings with an alkaline deposit and raises the pH of the rooting substrate. Many subjects, particularly if slow to root, deteriorate under mist. In theory there should be no leaching of nutrients from the foliage; the mist should float down and evaporate off. In practice there is often over-wetting of the leaves. Investigations in USA have shown that, contrary to what might have been expected, young vigorously growing cuttings of the species studied did not leach appreciably, but more mature semi-hard cuttings not in active growth did lose nutrients while being rooted under mist.

It is often asked whether it would be beneficial to add nutrients to the water used in misting cuttings. In experiments in USA results have by no means been straightforward. Some species responded well, especially in subsequent growth, whilst others were indifferent and some showed reduced rooting under nutrient mist. There are practical difficulties in applying the nutrients, and spraying them over cuttings, boxes, bench and floor results in the encouragement of moss and algae; the latter can even grow over the leaves of the cuttings. It seems preferable to concentrate on rooting the cuttings as quickly as possible under hygienic conditions and moving them into a fertilised compost without delay. This is not to say that there is not scope for liquid feeding in some cases, as when rooted cuttings have to be held for short periods in the container in which they were rooted.

Though the warm bench and plastic method described below is an alternative to the mist for many species, there are some for which the mist seems specially suitable, as mentioned in the section on propagation of individual genera, e.g. *Ceanothus*. In general, woolly leaved plants do not appreciate the damp conditions of the mist unit.

Mist propagation is a relatively elaborate and expensive method of rooting cuttings compared with the cheaper alternatives that are available for so many species. The nurseryman should hesitate to install a unit if he is only concerned with easily produced subjects. These are generally cheap because they are easy to root and so must be produced economically. This is not to say, however, that he is never justified in rooting them under mist. For instance, in order to maintain throughput it may be useful to know what subjects can be used as quickly rooting catch crops to utilise bench space unoccupied by the main crops.

Warm bench and plastic

Cuttings to be rooted by this system are set in trays plunged in a bench fitted with heating cables as described in the section on mist propagation, to give similar bottom temperatures. The cuttings are then covered with a sheet of thin transparent plastic (80–100 gauge). After the cuttings are watered in, the plastic sheet is laid down over the cuttings in actual contact with them, and is sealed by placing round the edges plastic laths of the type recommended for constructing shading slats (p. 15). In a few minutes the plastic sheet starts to fog up and soon the cuttings are in a saturated atmosphere, with droplets of water visible on the underside of the plastic. In this way the cuttings are prevented from wilting. It might be thought that such a warm and humid atmosphere would lead to trouble from disease but this is not so, as the propagator will use only healthy material and, in addition to this, the routine treatment of all cuttings with a fungicide is a sanitary measure.

This fogging up of the plastic is the first line of defence against scorching of the cuttings by the sun but alone is quite insufficient. If direct sunlight shines on the plastic, high temperatures soon build up. Even the low February sun can induce temperatures of 80°F (26.7°C) or more under such plastic, so as soon as the bright days come it is necessary to apply light shading to the glasshouse. A thermometer set among the cuttings is strongly recommended, to give warning of conditions becoming too warm. As the sun strengthens it will become necessary to provide further shading, e.g. by a woven material drawn along on wires under the roof.

By using the warm bench and plastic method one is independent of pumps and misting equipment, and less water is needed. To set against this, rather more care and attention is called for on the part of the operator, particularly with soft cuttings of deciduous subjects. The importance of timely shading 13

Fig. 7. Glasshouse bench with plastic (basal heat optional).

has been mentioned. In addition, periodic inspection is called for. Every ten days or so the plastic sheet is peeled back and the cuttings inspected. Any fallen leaves are removed and should any incipient moulds be noted, an overhead damping with a fungicide is given. Another important point to check is that the plunging medium and rooting substrate are not becoming dry. This can happen in irregular areas over the bench owing to the beads of moisture condensing on the plastic, coalescing and channelling away from some places. When all these points have been checked, the plastic is reversed and replaced until the next detailed inspection is due.

When the cuttings have rooted sufficiently, weaning can begin. Here, too, the judgement of the operator must be called on. The plastic sheet is slit and torn in gradually increasing fashion, but too sudden exposure of the cuttings can cause them to dry out. With some subjects (e.g. rhododendrons) the roots tend to develop near the surface in the humid atmosphere provided and special care is needed. The destruction of the plastic is not wasteful as it tends to lose its 'fogging' properties with time and so should not be used for further batches of cuttings. Once the cuttings are accustomed to full air the bottom heat can be switched off, or the trays transferred elsewhere to complete the hardening off process.

Cuttings often come out from under the plastic in better condition than from under mist, no doubt owing to the absence of leaching. However, the classical 'warm bases and cool tops' condition is not created as it is under mist and this may be why cuttings are in some cases slower to root when under plastic. The nurseryman may be content to put up with slower rooting rather than install mist.

Cold frames with and without plastic

The simple cold frame with glass lights is a long established method of rooting cuttings that has been extended in scope by the coming of plastics. It is possible to use frames for three crops in one season, i.e. September–October,
14 April and June–July.

September and October have been the customary months in which to insert cuttings for rooting in cold frames, perhaps to be left for a full year before being transplanted. Often one sees cuttings rooted in this way left until they become starved. Instead they should be lifted in April (June for conifers) and transplanted to further frames, lined out, or containerised, according to the recommendations given later in this book (p. 20). In a general way the easier-to-root, robustly-growing subjects can be lined out for growing-on (p. 21) while scarcer or more valuable subjects, including conifers, are usually better grown on in frames for a second season. Where soil or climatic conditions are not ideal, growing on in cold frames provides an opportunity for giving the plants optimum soil conditions, good irrigation, and protection as needed.

For most subjects the cold frame with plastic is not recommended for cuttings rooted over winter but this point should be checked in the section on propagation of individual genera, for there are a few for which the use of plastic sheeting at this time of year has given better results, such as *x Cupressocyparis* and *Pittosporum*. The plastic sheet used is the thin 80–100 gauge as described for the warm bench and plastic method and is laid and sealed in the same way before placing the glass lights in position.

When hard frost threatens, a protective material such as hessian should be spread over the frames and this may conveniently be held down by the plastic slatting recommended for shading the frames.

This slatting is made from second-grade electrical conduit piping and may be made at home. Holes are drilled at each end of the slats so that they may be threaded onto a nylon cord, separated by short spacers of small diameter plastic tubing. This type of slatting is much more convenient to handle than the old style heavy wooden kind; one man can carry a large roll and can very speedily lay it over the frames, almost with a flick of the wrist. The slats do not snap or rot as do the wooden kind. The roll should be securely anchored down at the ends of the runs of frames.

Even during the winter period shading should not be overlooked. It will not be necessary in mid winter but after inserting the cuttings there can be bright days, so as a precaution apply to the outside of the glass a light wash of a proprietory shading material. This will be thinned by the winter weather, so that when the sun strengthens in February it may be necessary to renew it. In any case, have the slatting at hand — it is a convenient way of giving extra temporary shading.

For the same reasons as given under the warm bench and plastic section (p. 13) shading is particularly important and the direct rays of the sun should not be allowed to strike the plastic sheeting.

As the time approaches for the cuttings to be lifted, the plastic can be gradually dispensed with in the way already described. Then the lights may be opened to a gradually increasing extent daily, choosing appropriate weather, until they are finally left off altogether.

When it is desired to propagate junipers these give very good results from cuttings inserted in April with plastic over them. They will be ready to come out in June, when a wide range of subjects will go into the frames under plastic to be rooted by September. Then we are back at the start of the yearly cycle. Obviously, shading both by a wash on the glass, and by slatting, is all-important with these April and June batches of cuttings.

If cuttings going into the cold frame with plastic are inserted in a well moistened compost it is not usually necessary to water them again until they 15 are rooted. It is easy to check those in a cold frame without plastic; they will need irrigation as winter merges into spring.

A compost found suitable for use in cold frames is that generally recommended in this book for the rooting of cuttings, i.e. two parts moss peat to one of sand. This is placed in the frames to a depth of about 5 in. (12.5 cm).

The low tunnel

This is an inexpensive and simple system for the mass production of a wide range of species. Although the subjects dealt with are relatively cheap and easily rooted, this implies that, for maximum profit, they must be propagated by the cheapest available means.

In essentials the low tunnel system consists of a long, 3 ft (0.9 m) wide tent of white plastic, 500 gauge, 50% light transmission, supported on wire hoops and sealed at the sides and ends. Sometimes the system is made more elaborate by the inclusion of a spray line and though this may be needed on some soils, in our experience it has not been necessary for the successful rooting of over 60 different species and cultivars. No doubt more could be added to our list. A great attraction of this system is that once the rooted cuttings have been hardened off (as described below), they can be left to grow until autumn to be lined out when convenient.

An open site should be chosen for the tunnel. Although temperatures will be high in sunny weather, the cuttings are surprisingly tolerant of heat in the humid atmosphere and diffuse light provided by the white plastic. We have had scorched cuttings but they made a good recovery and grew away satisfactorily. Our experience has been on a heavy loam soil and, no doubt, lighter soils would need a more careful supervision in the way of an occasional watering or, in dry situations, by the provision of a spray line. If there is any choice, select a deep, moisture retentive soil. Shallow soils can dry out too quickly.

Weeds can be a problem so choose a piece of clean ground. In a well run nursery where herbicides are used regularly at proper rates, this will not be difficult. It is sometimes suggested that ground so treated will give poor rooting. Such has not been our experience. An additional safeguard is the peat and sand that is worked into the cutting bed. This will dilute further any residues of herbicides that may remain.

Figs. 8-11. Examples of cuttings inserted in a low tunnel in June and lifted four months later.

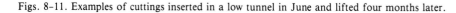

16   Fig. 8. *Philadelphus.*

Fig. 9. *Forsythia*.

Mark out with twine a bed a foot wider than the proposed tunnel, so that the plastic can be buried at the sides. Excavate a shallow trench 5 in. (12.5 cm) or so deep all round the proposed bed so that it is left as an island. This trench will be filled in when the plastic is in place.

Next spread a compost of peat and sand on the surface of the bed. The exact proportions and amount will vary somewhat according to local conditions. We find that a 1 in. (2.5 cm) depth of a two peat/one sand mixture improves the texture of our soil sufficiently, but this must be adjusted as required in other localities. An important point for the success of the whole operation is to incorporate this mixture into the natural soil. Do not leave it as a separate layer or it will soon dry out excessively. A convenient procedure is to work it in as the cuttings are inserted.

Since the tunnel is used during June and July, the cuttings will wilt quickly unless handled carefully. When gathering them from the parent plants, drop them promptly into a plastic bag to minimise water loss and at no time allow the sun to strike directly on the bag or the plant material will get too hot. At the site, too, keep the cuttings shaded all the time. For this reason have the tunnel site completely prepared beforehand with the plastic already in place at the

Fig. 10. *Hypericum*.

17

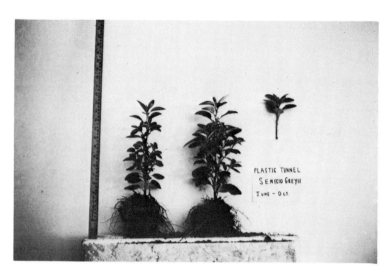

Fig. 11 *Senecio*.

beginning of the bed. A can of fungicide solution should be at hand for emergency damping down of the inserted cuttings should this be needed, and certainly for the final watering in before closing up the tunnel.

As the cuttings are inserted, follow on by drawing the plastic loosely over them, placing a wire hoop support every 3 ft (0.9 m). The cuttings will have been prepared beforehand in a cool building, and treated as advised in Chapter 1. When all the cuttings have been inserted, draw the plastic to one side and give a final watering in (see above). Seal up the tunnel by drawing the sides of the plastic into the shallow trench so that the material is stretched firmly over the hoops. Fill in the trench with soil.

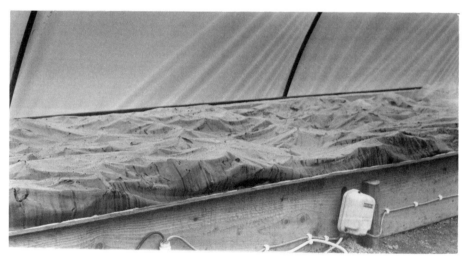

Fig. 12. Border propagation bed in an unheated white polythene house (basal heat optional).

The tunnel can be laid down during the period June to August. Since the rooted cuttings are to be left *in situ* for the rest of the season, it is advantageous to insert them early to allow for maximum growth before autumn. Rooting can be expected to occur in seven to nine weeks. During this period an occasional inspection by lifting the tunnel at the side will check that the cuttings are not getting too dry. Should mould appear – and this has seldom been the case – it should be checked by an overhead damping with a fungicide solution.

When rooting has taken place, begin hardening off the cuttings. Choose dull calm weather and first loosen the plastic at intervals down the side of the tunnel. Over a period of days gradually increase this ventilation until the plastic can be removed altogether. We prefer this system to the alternative of cutting holes in the plastic, an irreversible process. The cuttings are then left to grow on *in situ*, until they can be lined out during the autumn–spring lifting season. By then they will have made extension growth, often to a surprising degree, e.g. *Caryopteris* can make nice sized plants in flower, *Ribes* will be 9–12 in. (22.5–30 cm) long from a 5 in. (12.5 cm) cutting and *Buddleia* can grow very strongly, putting on as much as 18 in. (45 cm) of new growth.

The white polythene tunnel

A walk-in tunnel constructed of white opaque polythene has obvious advantages for the operator, particularly in poor weather conditions. Open frames may be constructed on the floor of such a structure, filled with a standard compost of two parts moss peat to one of sand. The cuttings, treated with 0.8% IBA powder (p. 7), are covered with a sheet of thin transparent plastic as for the warm bench and plastic method. Under our conditions so few of the species tried showed a response to bottom heat that we prefer to propagate these in the glasshouse.

Cuttings inserted in May have given good results (50%–80% rooting) with *Syringa*, *Viburnum* (deciduous) and *Lavandula*. These are out by July, when they may be followed by *Acer platanoides*, deciduous azaleas, *Chaenomeles*, *Callicarpa*, *Corylopsis*, *Cotoneaster*, *Cytisus*, *Elaeagnus pungens* **Maculata**, *Kolkwitzia* and *Photinia* **Red Robin**. In September–November a third batch of cuttings can be inserted. Successful genera include *Chamaecyparis*, *Cupressocyparis*, *Juniperus communis*, *J. pfitzeriana*, *Pittosporum*, *Ilex*, *Pyracantha* and *Pieris*.

No doubt further experience with this method will show its suitability for other genera, since in essentials it resembles the cold frame and plastic system, by which so many additional species can be propagated.

Cuttings in the open ground

This cheap method of propagating many species should not be neglected, particularly in those areas where the relatively mild winters are an advantage to be exploited to the full.

Naturally a sheltered position should be chosen, for the cuttings cannot be expected to do well if exposed to the drying winds which so often come in spring just as they are developing roots and starting to shoot. The site, while sheltered, should not be dark and airless, as could be the case close to buildings, for the cuttings have to stand through the rains of winter. For this reason, too, a well drained sandy soil is an advantage, though heavier soil types can be ameliorated by the addition of peat and sand. It is an added advantage to sprinkle sand along the base of the furrows before inserting the cuttings. The site should not show any tendency to waterlogging even in the wettest winter weather.

The bed should be made up to a convenient width for working from each side, e.g. 4 ft (1.2 m). On heavy duty soils it is an advantage to have it slightly raised above the general ground level.

Cuttings to be rooted in the open are not taken until October and should be from well matured shoots of the past season's growth. Their length will depend on the species and, in general, they are inserted to two thirds of their length in the soil, setting them vertically against the back of a shallow, cleanly cut trench. Sprinkle extra sand along the base of the trench before setting the cuttings. Then replace about two thirds of the excavated soil. This should be gently firmed with the foot so that the cuttings need a definite tug to lift them out; if they are too loose they will be lifted by frost. Replace the remainder of the soil more loosely.

Periodic inspection should be carried out in winter, especially after frost, to ensure that no cuttings have been loosened.

The use of rooting powders is an advantage with many species.

Growing on the rooted cutting

The process of hardening off is the first step in the growing on of all cuttings except those rooted out of doors. Details of the procedures to be followed will be found in the section of Systems of Production from Cuttings (p. 11). The subsequent treatment will vary according to the species, so reference should be made to the appropriate genus in the latter part of this book. Here the subject will be dealt with in a general way.

Cuttings rooted under mist or by the warm bench and plastic method, having been weaned from the high humidity and bottom heat, may now either be potted up or lined out in a cold frame. For some plants, such as Japanese maples and magnolias, potting up is a necessary part of the procedure for inducing the strong growth essential for successful over-wintering. Other plants such as *Clematis* and *Ceanothus* are always container grown until sold. Details appropriate to the various species will be found in the chapter on the propagation of selected genera. If potting-up is required a 3 in. pot is usually suitable as the first container. Loosen the rooted cuttings by gently knocking the trays against the potting bench. With well rooted cuttings of vigorous subjects it is sometimes convenient to eject the cuttings and rooting medium *en bloc* onto the bench by a dexterous throw, particularly if there has been any intermingling of the roots, as the plants can then be more easily separated. For more delicate subjects, it is better to lift them out one by one, using a flat piece of wood, or even a finger, inserted under each to help to lever it up. In every case, as much of the medium as possible should be left adhering to the roots to minimise the transplanting shock. In potting-up, use one of the standardised composts recommended in Chapter 6. After a few days in the propagating house the potted plants may be transferred to another house or to the capillary bed.

More robust species, e.g. most conifers, Japanese cherries etc, are lined out in a cold frame of standard compost (p. 55), after careful lifting as described. The glass lights should be placed on the frames to provide a still and relatively humid atmosphere for a few days. The glass should be shaded with one of the proprietary washes sold for the purpose with additional shade from slats (p. 15). Once the cuttings are established, increasing ventilation may be given, choosing suitable weather. Finally, the lights should be taken off. The slatting may be retained for a further period to provide shade from hot sun. The soil in the frame should consist of one of the standard composts. The frames must be fitted with irrigation lines. These can consist of plastic tubing resting on wire supports pushed in to the growing medium and carrying spray nozzles. They will be found essential during dry spells.

When the plants are lifted at the end of the season, the frame should be topped up with more of the compost to make up for material removed on the roots of the plants. This will probably be sufficient to maintain fertility for three or four seasons. After this it is advisable to give a general dressing of moss peat and fertilisers instead. Good results have been obtained by dressing such frames with 1 oz per sq yd (33 g per sq m) calcium ammonium nitrate and 2 oz per sq yd (66 g per sq m) each of sulphate of potash and superphosphate, but soil samples should be sent for analysis before deciding on the fertilisers to add.

Cuttings rooted by the cold frame and plastic method will be transplanted to other frames filled with standard compost in the case of the more delicate subjects, or to well prepared beds out of doors fitted with irrigation facilities, e.g. lay flat pierced polythene tubing or sprinklers. In the case of cuttings left to grow on after rooting in the low tunnel or rooted in the open, they are lined out as advised for seedlings (p. 26). Since this operation is carried out between autumn and spring, irrigation is not needed for establishment but temporary irrigation lines should be available to assist growth during dry spells in summer.

3
Other Methods of Propagation

Raising from seed

As a rule seeds can only be used for propagating species. Cultivars (i.e. garden varieties) will not come true from seed.

The use of home saved seed is advised wherever practicable. Purchased seed may be slow to arrive and germination unpredictable owing to drying out or exposure to various environmental factors before receipt.

Before deciding to harvest seed of a particular species it should be noted that many conifers, some maples and occasionally other species often produce hollow seed. A few seeds should be cut open to check that they are viable.

The time to harvest seed is largely a matter of observation and knowledge of the habits of the plant in question, e.g. the early flowering *Daphne mezereum* ripens in July; at the other extreme fruits of the late flowering *Cotoneaster lacteus* are not ready until December. With some species the collection of the fruits must be done promptly, otherwise they will quickly be eaten by birds, e.g. *Daphne mezereum, Berberis darwinii*. Though fruits should not be gathered while immature, in general they should not be allowed to become fully ripe before harvesting, as this may cause slower germination due to the development of *dormancy*, i.e. failure to respond quickly to conditions of temperature, moisture, air and light which are considered favourable to germination.

Dormancy is a provision of nature which helps in the preservation of a species by preventing germination at times of the year when the prospects for seedling survival are not good and, further, by staggering germination over more than one season. It makes difficulties for the nurseryman and is too complex a subject for discussion in a book of this type. It is, however, familiar to specialists in the raising of rose rootstocks and thornquicks (*Crataegus*) from seed. These growers practise stratification of the seed to overcome dormancy, i.e. mixing the seed with sand and pitting it outdoors so that it is exposed to one or two winters' cold.

The seeds are mixed with moist sand, about one part of seed to three parts of sand by volume. In order to preserve them from vermin, it is advisable to place the seeds and sand in a container. Small quantities could be stratified in a large pot or box, larger quantities in a pit. Such a stratifying pit is a useful facility for treating many tree and shrub seeds. It should be dug to a depth of about 2½ ft (0.75 m) in a well drained spot with further drainage provided by a layer of gravel at the bottom. The sides of the pit are lined with creosoted boards, weathered to free them of fumes. A further lining of ¼ in. mesh wire netting excludes rodents. Finish off with a frame fitted to the lining boards and a lid of fine mesh netting. Inspect periodically to ensure that the seeds are not being attacked by pests.

Small lots of seed can be mixed with twice their volume of sand or peat and placed in sealed plastic bags which are kept in a cold shed or in a shaded place out of doors. Examine the bags frequently from February onwards and as soon as germination starts sow the contents. In many nurseries the practice now is to sow the seeds in beds in the open and allow stratification to take place *in situ* instead of providing for presowing treatment. This method has been made possible by the advent of modern herbicides. Choose a piece of ground clean of perennial weeds. Annuals may be dealt with by means of paraquat, applied as required before the sown seed germinates, since this herbicide is innocuous shortly after reaching the ground. The first flush of seedlings can be lifted and lined out at the end of one year, leaving any remaining seeds to come up the following year. Very small quantities of seeds could be sown in pots to be plunged, (i.e. sunk to their rims in peat, sand or soil) in a cold frame. Bring them into a warm house if sufficient seedlings begin to appear the first spring, prick these off at the second rough leaf stage and return the pot of ungerminated seeds to the cold frame to go through a second winter. It is unwise to sow seeds (other than those known to offer no difficulties) directly in a warm house for this could induce prolonged dormancy. Whatever method is followed for stratifying and sowing seed, mice are a major hazard, necessitating the use of traps and poison at all times.

For the specialist there is information available on the application of alternate cold and warm treatments and the use of acids and other means of hastening germination. For the general nurseryman without laboratory facilities, these processes are rather intricate, with many points at which the programme could go wrong unless constantly supervised.

Fortunately, however, there are many species which germinate readily without stratification, e.g. *Acacia, Genista, Cytisus, Piptanthus, Pittosporum*. These seeds, and most conifer seeds, can be stored safely for up to three years in airtight containers kept in a cool place. *Spartium* and other genera of the legume family and some genera such as *Magnolia, Quercus, Aesculus, Fagus*, etc offer no difficulties, provided the seed is sown fresh, before it has time to dry out. Fine seeded shrubs such as *Enkianthus* and other members of the heather family (*Ericaceae*) usually give no trouble, nor do many conifers. There is no uniformity of behaviour even within one genus, e.g. *Cotoneaster* where some species germinate well the first spring following stratification, others germinate well the first spring but with secondary germination the following autumn and spring, while the seed of a few has to go through two winters before germinating at all.

Some seeds are easy to clean, e.g. most legumes have pods which can be left in trays in a warm place to split open. Cones will open under similar conditions. Rose seeds and some others carried in fleshy fruits need to be cleaned of the flesh which contains a dormancy promoting substance. This can be achieved by maceration and flotation. On a small scale, the fruits can be macerated in a household or laboratory blender in which the sharp blades have been sheathed by pieces of stiff rubber. On a large scale, pulping machines are used. The seeds are separated from the pulp by placing the mixture in water and decanting off the pulp, finally washing the seeds through a sieve and then drying them on paper on the bench.

For the convenience of large scale operators using sowing machines, the seeds of acers and conifers can be de-winged by threshing on special de-winging machines.

23

Sowing out of doors

Where seed is to be raised on a large scale out of doors, the soil and site should be chosen with care. The soil should be free draining, light in texture, and preferably acid (pH 5.5–6.5), especially for conifers. Much can be done to improve the texture by the addition of peat, and also sand, on the heavier soils. The site should be sheltered but open to the sun and air. Provision of water for irrigation should be regarded as essential; it will be amply repaid in steady unchecked growth of the seedlings.

The site should be roughly dug or ploughed in the autumn. This allows weathering of the soil so that it can be broken down easily in spring and thrown up into beds. A convenient width is 3½ ft (1.05 m) with 18 in. (45 cm) alleys.

On light and well drained soils it is possible to complete the preparation of the beds in autumn. This has the advantage that weeds in the surface soil can be allowed to germinate, to be cleared off with paraquat before seed sowing takes place in spring. Then it is only necessary to scarify the surface very superficially before sowing the seed, which is then covered with a layer of non-calcareous sand or grit. This layer provides a mulch, preventing drying out of the soil, as well as preventing the formation of a soil crust which might inhibit germination. Inorganic fertilisers should be forked or rotovated into the top 2–3 in. (5–7.5 cm) before the bed is finally raked level. The amounts of nutrients to be added should be based on soil analysis, especially as soil which has been in cultivation under horticultural conditions for a long time may need little but a top dressing of nitrogen when the seedlings are well up. Over-fertilisation or unbalanced ratios of nutrients will give poor results. New sites are often very low in available phosphorus and potassium. A soil test will also indicate whether lime is needed. If humus is lacking, work in peat or other organic material. Apply fertilisers a week before sowing. As a general guide, newly broken land can receive a dressing of potassic superphosphate (0-10-20) at the rate of 14 lb per 100 sq yd (7.4 kg per 100 sq m) but individual sites vary and periodic soil tests are the best guide to a logical fertiliser programme.

Before sowing, the bed should be consolidated by trampling or rolling. It is usual to sow tree and shrub seeds broadcast. Small seeds should be covered with lime-free grit to twice their own depth. Large seeds (acorns, nuts, acer seed, etc) can be covered with soil from the alleyways, again to twice their own depth. Alternatively, these large seeds can be sown by drawing out drills across the bed to the required depth.

A top dressing of nitrogen is given in mid-summer, using calcium ammonium nitrate if the soil is inclined to be acid, or sulphate of ammonia on alkaline soils. These fertilisers should be applied when the soil is moist but the foliage dry and, as an added precaution against foliage burn, any fertiliser lodging on the leaves should be dislodged by passing a brush over them. Top dress at the rate of 4 lb per 100 sq yd (2.1 kg per 100 sq m).

In cold districts it is necessary to protect the young shoots of early starters such as some piceas, beech and larch against frost. It may also be necessary to protect against frost lift in winter. On a small scale this can be done with boughs of spruce or other suitable evergreens. The use of slats (p. 15) or polypropylene mesh supported over the beds is another method.

The beds should be irrigated in dry weather by means of spray lines or sprinklers. Should there be any sign of damping off, apply a fungicide. With

24 good culture most species should be large enough to transplant at the end of

their first year, carrying this out in early spring when danger of frost lift is over. Backward or slow-growing species will be left for a second year. Lifting and lining out should be carried out gently, loosening the plants well with a fork so that they are lifted rather than drawn out of the soil. Irrigation is highly valuable for transplanted seedlings.

Sowing in frames

Where only moderate quantities of seed are involved, frame sowing is a safe way to guard against losses. Vermin can be excluded or trapped, and irrigation lines installed. Protection against frost is easily provided. It is an opportunity for filling the frame with a suitable seed compost (p. 26) which, in conjunction with irrigation and protection against cold or hot sun, will maximise growth. Seeds germinating over more than one season can be lifted in successive years.

Sowing in pots or trays

Small quantities of seed or seed of high value species can be sown in half pots and, in this case, it is advisable to plunge the pots in a cold frame until germination starts, especially with hard seeds like those of *Rosa, Cotoneaster, Daphne*, etc or in trays if germination is expected to be rapid. Fine seeds such as *Enkianthus* must be raised in trays or pots under glass. With pots or boxes kept in a glasshouse, it is standard practice to cover them with a sheet of glass, shaded in turn with a sheet of paper. To avoid the seedlings becoming drawn, watch carefully for germination and then gradually expose them to light and air. Seed sown too thickly will become drawn very easily and subject to damping off. Use a standard seed compost (p. 57). Seed in pots to be left outside should be covered with a layer of grit. As a general rule, seedlings raised under glass are pricked off into trays or pots at the second rough leaf stage into a standard growing-on compost (p. 26).

Damping-off of seedlings is due to attack by fungi at soil level, causing them to topple over in characteristic fashion, and is kept at bay by good culture such as sowing thinly, not over-watering, adequate ventilation and the use of a good compost. Loamless compost prepared from properly handled moss peat should be free of pathogens. Should the disease appear, water with one of the proprietary copper fungicides sold for the purpose. Sometimes seeds are attacked before they emerge above ground. Usually this can be detected by the presence of dead radicles (seed roots).

The growing on of seedlings

While many species are better raised in bulk by sowing in frames or out of doors, sometimes the nurseryman will only wish to raise a few specimens of a given tree or shrub annually; then, with the new techniques available today, he can hasten the growth of his seedlings to saleable size, just as rooted cuttings can be given the environment to release their growth potential to a degree formerly unrealised.

It should be noted, however, that in forest nurseries quick growing methods are being used increasingly, including the use of plastic houses and direct sowing in paper pots. The latter technique could be useful to a nurseryman raising 25 large numbers of a particular species known to germinate quickly and evenly. The pots come in concertina-like packs which are stretched out and quickly filled from a shovel of compost. They are held together by a water soluble glue and are easily detached from each other when the seedlings are ready for transfer.

Seeds of sufficient value or scarcity to be sown *in pots or trays* will be pricked off into 3 in. pots of standardised compost (p. 55), generally at the second rough leaf stage. Conifers can be pricked off when the second flush of leaves is beginning to appear. Seedlings should then be returned to the glasshouse for about seven days to re-establish before the next move. When the weather is suitable, i.e. absence of night frost, the pots will be transferred to a capillary bed within a plastic house. Potting on, generally into 4½ in. pots, should be carried out as soon as the roots have well penetrated the compost but before there is more than a slight emergence of roots from the bottom of the pot. Their subsequent rate of development and treatment will vary with the species. Reference should be made to the latter part of this book for the details under the various genera. Remarkable results can be achieved by giving seedlings this luxury treatment, e.g. *Betula* and some *Sorbus* spp. can grow 6–8 ft (1.8–2.4 m) in one year from seed.

Seeds sown *in frames* or *open air seed beds* are generally left to stand for one year after germination and can then be lined out in well prepared nursery beds. A sheltered site should be chosen on a good friable soil. Check the nutrient levels of the soil by having a sample sent for analysis in time for the results to be available before starting operations. Apply superphosphate and sulphate of potash in accordance with these results. The soil should only be worked when it is in suitable condition, not sticky and wet. On a larger scale, a rotovator may be used, but, for small operations, the site should be forked over to produce a good tilth. A tightly stretched line is set out to mark the position of the first line of seedlings. Cut out a shallow trench along the line, holding the spade perpendicular to the surface of the ground. The depth will depend on the length of root of the seedlings to be lined out, but should be sufficient to take the roots without any degree of bending. At this stage the first batch of seedlings can be lifted. They should be loosened with a fork first; often we see plants of all sizes mishandled by being drawn roughly from the ground. Even when plants are heeled in temporarily it should be the rule to use a fork as well as the hand when re-lifting. Do not lift more at a time than can be conveniently dealt with promptly, for plant roots should never be left exposed to the air. With some operators, familiarity can lead to insufficient respect for the comfort of the plants. If there is any delay, such as transport of the plants to a distant site, place them in plastic bags kept away from the rays of the sun.

A number of plants are placed along the trench at intervals appropriate to the size of the seedlings and their expected development. Each plant is held vertically against the face of the trench with the roots hanging freely. A small quantity of soil is placed round the roots by hand or with a trowel, sufficient to anchor the plant. When the line is complete, more soil is shovelled in. This is firmed with the foot before the remainder of the soil is used to level off the trench. Finally, a few strokes of the rake will leave the surface free of lumps or stones before the line is moved preparatory to opening the next trench. Lining out should be completed by early April.

The seedlings will usually benefit from a top dressing of nitrogenous fertiliser applied in early summer (May–June) during showery weather. Care should be taken to avoid scorching the foliage with the chemical. Application is safer when the foliage is dry as then any grains accidentally falling on the leaves can be brushed off. On alkaline soils or for lime hating species use sulphate of ammonia, substituting for it calcium ammonium nitrate if the soil tends to be acid for the plants being grown. Apply 1 oz per sq yd (33 g per sq m).

Layering

For many plants layering is not so important as formerly, but it is still practised for species slow or difficult to root from cuttings. It is useful, too, for nurserymen requiring comparatively few specimens of a particular tree or shrub but needing them as large specimens in two seasons — rooting the layers the first year and developing them into fully established plants the following year. It is essentially the development of roots on a stem still attached to the parent plant, then severing it and establishing it as an independent specimen. There are several forms of layering, but it is only proposed to deal with three here.

Though layering requires the minimum of equipment, the proper conditions must be provided if it is to be a successful and productive method. A well prepared site with fertile, well drained soil must be chosen. Poorly grown mother plants will never have the vigour of growth required to produce strong shoots to replace the successive crops of rooted layers. It should be the aim to provide the same sort of physical conditions in the soil as for rooting cuttings, so heavy soils must be improved by the addition of peat, sand and, if necessary, nutrients. A first-class layer bed entails the establishment and good culture of the mother plants for two or three years until they are large enough to bring into production. A layer bed should be productive for many seasons.

Spacing of the mother plants should be generous; 8–10 ft (2.4–3.0 m) between the rows with 8 ft (2.4 m) between the plants is not too much. Apart from *tip layering* (the burying of the tips of shoots used for *Rubus*), *stool layering* is probably the simplest technique. It is well known as a means of propagating fruit tree rootstocks. Young vigorous mother plants must be established for at least one year. In this type of layering they can be 1 ft (30 cm) apart in rows 4 ft (1.2 m) apart. During the winter the established mother plants are cut down to a stump about 1 in. (2.5 cm) high. This stump sends out vigorous shoots which are gradually earthed up during the growing season with soil from the alleyways, starting when they are about 5 in (12.5 cm) high, working the soil well in among the shoots. Repeat this earthing up when the shoots have made another 5 in. (12.5 cm) or so of growth, completing the operation by the end of July. After leaf-fall, fork away the soil, cut off the rooted shoots as close as possible to the original stump, which is left exposed to sprout again in spring, thus re-starting the cycle. A well managed stoolbed should last in good condition for 15 years or more.

Simple layering

Here the shoots, instead of being earthed up, are bent over and pegged down into the soil and brought up again in such a way as to form an elbow or bend as nearly right angled as possible. This bend is covered with soil — sometimes staking is required — and interrupts the flow of sap, and it is an inducement to root formation at this point. Sometimes further interruption of the sap is

27

needed, as in less easily rooted species. This can be done by twisting the stem at the bend before pegging it down or, still more, by girdling it with copper wire. Sometimes a tongue is cut on the under side of the bend.

Fig. 13. Simple layering. Rooted layers of *Viburnum tomentosum* **Lanarth**.

The covering of soil, in addition to keeping the buried part of the stem moist, excludes light and this also encourages root formation. Further earthing up is carried out as necessary during the summer. Meanwhile, another crop of shoots springs from the centre of the plants. These are allowed to grow freely to form the material for next season's layering. At the end of the season the layered stems are carefully lifted from the soil with a fork and severed from the parent plant, to be lined out for a further season's growth.

In preparation for the next season's layering, all weak shoots should be removed from the mother plants, which can be given a top dressing of calcium ammonium nitrate at 1 oz per sq yd (33 g per sq m). Phosphorus and potash should be given also if the soil is known to be low in these nutrients. Heathers can be layered by pinning down the shoots in spring with lengths of wire and filling in the centre of the plant with moss peat. The whole plant is lifted in autumn and cut into rooted pieces.

French or continuous layering

A modification of simple layering whereby the annual crop of shoots is pinned down horizontally close to the ground early in the new year, so that the buds all along the shoots break into growth and develop into upright shoots. When these are a few inches long they are covered with soil, a second earthing over being given in summer. After leaf fall the branches are uncovered and cut up into sections, each consisting of a shoot with roots.

Serpentine layering

A method adapted to species producing long annual stems such as *Clematis Vitis* and *Wisteria*. These long shoots are brought down to ground level and buried at intervals along the stem in snake-like fashion, leaving at least one bud on each above ground section. A shoot should grow from each bud and roots from the buried portions. The stem may then be sectioned and young plants lifted when well established on their own roots.

The plants adapted to simple layering include *Magnolia, Corylopsis, Hamamelis, Parrotia, Corylus, Fothergilla* (in August). *Stachyurus,*

Fig. 14. French layering. Rooted shoots of *Cotinus coggygria* before separation.

Celastrus, Cercidiphyllum, Chimonanthus (in July/August) *Tilia, Viburnum tomentosum, Wisteria.*

Among the plants which can be French layered are *Cotinus coggygria, Viburnum farreri, V. x bodnantense, Hydrangea paniculata, H. quercifolia.*

Grafting

Grafting is a well documented subject and there are several books available which deal very comprehensively with all its aspects. Thus it is not the intention here to elaborate on the finer points of grafting but simply to outline the principles of the operation and to mention the forms most commonly used in commercial nurseries. Although there is a tendency for researchers to concentrate on cuttings for the difficult subjects through the use of modern aids, there are still many plants more easily produced by grafting. In addition, the management systems of some nurseries incorporate grafting periods in their programme and thus grafting is likely to continue irrespective of the strides made in producing the same plants by other methods of propagation.

The operation of grafting, whatever the method, is concerned with uniting part of a plant (a scion or a bud) of desirable characteristics with a seedling rootstock. Both species must be compatible, i.e. closely related, so that a union can form and stock and scion develop into a single plant. The influence of the rootstock on a scion is often required, e.g. the dwarfing effect of apple-tree rootstocks, and it is always necessary in these cases to plant the union above the ground so that its effect persists. In other cases, e.g. *Picea pungens* 29 cultivars, the root-stock is used as a 'nurse' and serves but to maintain the scionwood in a good state of active growth until after planting the graft union below the soil level. The scion will make its own root system and the rootstock can then be cut away.

Often the outstanding disadvantage of grafting is the subsequent growth of 'suckers' once the plant has become established. Unless these shoots are removed very close to the rootstock, they will affect the general well-being of the scion. A particular difficulty arises where the sucker is not identified as such. It will grow on strongly at the direct expense of the grafted cultivar and in time will supercede it.

The economics of grafting are obviously important. By its nature, it is a little more painstaking and time consuming to graft than to prepare cuttings. The success rate of each system of propagation is very relevant, as is the amount of time required by the product of each system to reach saleable size. The provision of heat for grafting in a glasshouse in winter months is expensive but the difficulty of propagating by alternative methods or a low rate of success will obviously determine the economics of the method. The cost of rootstocks, mainly grown on the Continent, is steadily rising and the home production of understocks for grafting will become more important.

There are some general rules essential for success. The knife used must be very sharp so that the cut made is a 'once only' straight cut. The faces of the cut surfaces will be thereby better suited to fast callusing and uniting and the tying of stock and scion will be more concerned with keeping the faces together rather than forcibly bringing uneven surfaces into contact. The binding material used can be of raffia, cotton thread or rubber strips. It is usual to use raffia for outdoor work and, as it is tough material, it will have to be cut away after the union is complete. Grafting threads are of several strand thicknesses and the use of particular types will depend on the expected speed of callusing (i.e. the formation of wound tissue, the first indication of a successful union). Obviously the subjects callusing over a long period will require the thicker threads which will not deteriorate as quickly as the thinner ones. There is increasing use of rubber strips which are obtainable in several lengths and thicknesses. These are easy to use and, being in pieces, do not require cutting, thereby obviating an extra hand operation. An additional advantage is that, when the graft has united, the upper loose end of the rubber can be tugged and will unwind instantaneously. In general, all tying materials should be applied with sufficient tautness to keep the cut faces of scion and rootstock close together, yet not so tight as to endanger any plant tissue when the graft begins to expand after callusing.

Where grafting takes place indoors and there is a danger of drying out (i.e. bench grafting with dormant material) or outdoors and it is in addition desired to keep water from entering the wounded surfaces, it is necessary to wax all the external parts at the location of the graft. There are many grades and types of wax seals but basically they should be capable of preventing the entry of water, should remain stable for the desired length of time and, although some waxes are applied at high temperatures, they should not scorch or injure in any way plant material which they cover. The temperature of the wax should never exceed 176° (80°C). The substance can be applied by brush or, in the case of grafting dormant material, the whole scion and graft junction can be submerged momentarily in the warm liquid wax. Plants which are grafted and afterwards placed in closed case (i.e. a deep glass covered frame within the glasshouse) are not treated with wax.

The quality of the rootstocks to be used in grafting is important. This will obviously depend on their culture from the germination of the seed. The root system should be complete and healthy. Generally, for grafting under glass, a pencil-thick stem is suitable and, in the case of conifers and a large range of shrubs, this usually means a two-year-old stock. In other cases rootstocks will require three growing seasons to reach the required thickness. Of equal importance is the condition of the scion material. In all cases, only vigorous material from healthy plants should be used. The scions should as nearly as possible approximate to the rootstock in diameter, so that the cambia will coincide when the faces are being lined up for binding. If plants are suspected of being infected with virus, they should, if possible, be avoided as a source of scionwood. The wood should never be cut during hard frost conditions and, where grafting is planned for the cold months, it is recommended to select mature wood before such conditions and store it at low temperatures. It is always advisable to treat the scionwood with a fungicide prior to storage.

Generally speaking, well-developed one year shoots are used as scionwood for grafting. Excessively thick or thin shoots are not suitable. Above all, the wood should be ripe, especially in the case of summer grafting under glass.

In grafting, the union is usually located 3–4 in. (7.5–10 cm) above the root collar. However, grafting higher up the stem is also practised for slower growing subjects (*Acer pseudoplatanus* **Brilliantissimum**) or for pendulous types (*Betula pendula* **Youngii**).

Methods of grafting are many and varied. Only those types commonly used are mentioned here.

Side graft

This is the simplest form of graft and the one most commonly used. The rootstock is not cut back. Starting 3 in. (7.5 cm) or so above the root collar, a downward slice about 1½ in. (3–4 cm) long is cut at the side of the stem, leaving this slice still attached at the base (Fig. 15) and the scion, having a similar length cut on one side and a shorter cut on the other, is fitted into it. The equal

Fig. 15. Side Graft.

faces are placed together and the shorter cut is covered with the lip of wood attached to the rootstock. *Chamaecyparis, Juniperus, Azalea, Acer palmatum* are amongst subjects grafted in this manner.

The *veneer graft* is another type of side graft, but in this case most of the slice of wood made as a result of the vertical side cut on the stock is removed, leaving a small foot at the base of the cut. This means that the blunt base of the scion will be fitted inside this small foot and as the scion is only cut on one side, the necessity for the removal of the slice will be obvious. Subjects like *Picea* are grafted in this way, as their bark is loosely adhering and, should a second cut be made (as in the case of a *Chamaecyparis* scion), the remaining bark would become dislodged, resulting in the failure of the graft.

Whip graft

This is a common method of grafting. The rootstock top is entirely removed about 3 in. (7.5 cm) above the root collar and a slanted upward cut is made in the stem (Fig. 16). A similar but opposite cut is made in the scion and both faces are matched so that the cambial layers coincide as exactly as possible on

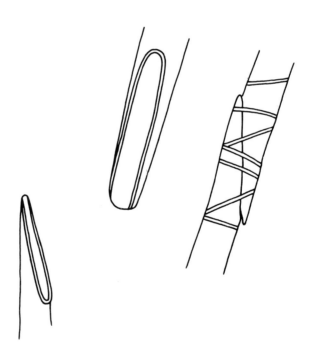

Fig. 16. Whip Graft.

both sides. Thus it is evident that the stock and scion will have to be of similar diameter. After tying with cotton the graft is waxed.

As a variation, matching tongues can be cut on the faces of the original slanted cuts (Fig. 17), when the scion and stock will interlock more securely and increase the possibility of success with more difficult subjects. This graft is known as the 'whip and tongue' method. Both ways are mainly used for grafting with dormant wood.

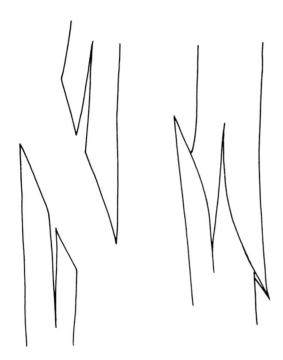

Fig. 17. Whip and Tongue Graft.

Cleft graft

This method of grafting is used when the rootstock is much thicker than the scionwood. The scion is held tightly by the stock as a result of being wedged into the vertically cut stock (Fig. 18). The stock is cut off at the required height and when the scion is fitted, the joint is tightly bound with raffia. This graft is mainly used for subjects that callus slowly.

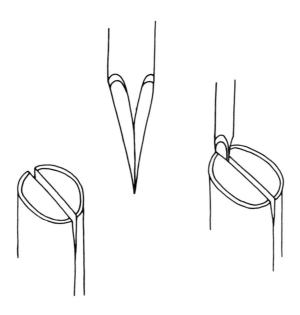

Fig. 18. Cleft Graft

Budding

Budding is really a form of grafting and entails placing a bud beneath the bark of a rootstock so that it comes into contact with the cambium. It is usually carried out in the growing season, especially in July and August. At that time the bark lifts readily and the budwood is sufficiently mature. The location of budding is normally about 2 in. (5 cm) above the ground but in the case of *Rosa*, budding is done at the root collar, which will be at ground level or slightly above, depending on the preparation and planting depth of the stocks. The rootstocks in all cases are well established in the ground and will be stable, facilitating the operation. As with grafting, the location of budding may be 3, 4 or 5 ft (0.9, 1.2 or 1.5 m) up on the stock for some very slow-growing subjects, but more especially for pendulous cultivars.

The budwood must be healthy, well developed and easy to prepare. The ripeness of the wood will vary with genus and species and also with the climatic conditions of the year. Thus the nurseryman's own judgement on suitability will be of importance here. In preparation for a day's budding, the wood should be cut in the morning, slightly dampened and kept in a plastic bag in a shady cool place.

The most common type of budding is where a T-cut is made at the selected place on the stem of the rootstock (Fig. 19). A shield shaped piece of budwood with the bud in a central position is cut from the bud stick, and inserted into the cut after the tip of the vertical cut has been prised open with a budding knife. The ease of dislodging this bark will differ with species. The bud is then

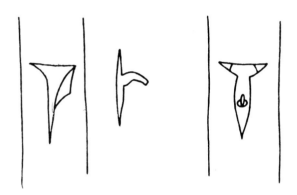

Fig. 19. T-Bud.

pushed down the inside of the bark to the base of the vertical cut. Any budwood over the horizontal cut of the T is trimmed off. The wound must then be tied with damp raffia. This tying operation is very important. The binding should take place from the bottom to the top of the wound as this will ensure that rain will run down the outside of the raffia without seeping into the wound. Binding should be firm and tight. Rubber patches are used for budding roses and are simply stretched over the face of the T-cut and bud and held to the stem by staple attachments.

Another form of budding gaining ground rapidly in commercial establishments is chip budding (Fig. 20). Instead of the usual T-cut, a vertical slice is cut down the stem for 1 ½ in. (3.7 cm) and the piece is removed by a transverse cut close to its base leaving a stub which will hold the bud chip temporarily. A plastic tie binds the bud to the stock.

34

This type of budding is replacing the older T-budding as it can be a faster method and gives better results. The presence of cambial tissue on both bud piece and stock results in quicker and more certain union. There are fewer failures, and the shoot growth in spring is more vigorous and uniform, resulting in a more even stand of young trees. This is important to the nurseryman in view of the relatively high costs involved in establishing the rootstocks, the space occupied by the crop and the high value of the individual trees; he cannot afford to have misses or second grade trees. Chip budding has the

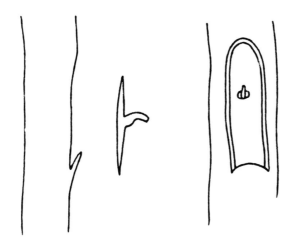

Fig. 20. Chip Bud.

advantage that it is not dependent on the bark lifting easily on the rootstock, but can be carried out from July to September. Genera with which the method has been successful include *Malus, Rosa, Acer, Tilia, Prunus* and *Ulmus*. Tie the chip firmly, without compressing the bud itself.

Under all methods of budding the rootstock top is cut off in February or March just above the bud. By this stage the raffia, plastic, or rubber ties will have rotted or can be removed. During the first season the bud will grow strongly and in the autumn these whips can be lifted and sold as such, or transplanted to grow on for a few years to produce half or full standards as required.

4
Propagating Media

By a propagating medium is meant the substance, be it peat, sand or some other material, into which the unrooted cuttings are inserted. To be suitable for the purpose, the substance must have appropriate physical and chemical properties. These include water and air retentiveness, adequate drainage and freedom from pests and diseases. The acidity or alkalinity (i.e. the pH) of the rooting medium can also greatly influence the successful rooting of cuttings, some genera showing marked preferences. General descriptions of the commonly used media follow, with a brief discussion of the properties of each which are of importance in plant propagation.

Peat

The type most commonly used in horticulture is moss peat, derived mainly from sphagnum moss, and generally harvested from the uppermost layers of basin peatland, i.e. bogs formed in depressions in lowland areas. Moss peat is only slightly decomposed, retaining much of the original structure of the sphagnum moss. This gives it its low density/high bulk ratio, its high absorptive capacity (seven to ten times its own weight of water) and its low pH (3.2–3.8). One of the great advantages of horticultural moss peat is that it is a uniform product, whereas sands and loams vary in physical and chemical properties, even in samples from one locality. It is free of pests and diseases and usually of weeds, though once fertilisers are added, seeds of weeds blown in from adjacent areas can grow with great luxuriance. Cuttings rooted or seedlings grown in peat, or in mixes containing peat, transplant well since the material adheres to the roots and forms a good root ball. Peat is obtainable in several grades. For use in plant propagation the medium grade is preferred.

Peat is easily compressed and is usually purchased in polythene covered bales. The contents must be broken up and well moistened before use, as it is difficult to wet peat afterwards, and if peat or mixtures containing it are allowed to dry out, they can be quite difficult to re-wet. Owing to the remains of the cellular structure of the sphagnum in moss peat, this material has a high capacity to retain air even when very wet. Nevertheless, for many genera of plants the addition of sand makes a better medium for the rooting of cuttings, as discussed below.

Sand

In contrast to prepared and branded peat, sand can vary greatly. It can be
calcareous or non-calcareous, fine or coarse, or a mixture. There can be large

variations even within the same pit. The mineral composition of the sand will depend on the rock from which it has been derived by a process of weathering. Within each naturally deposited sand are several grades, and the fine fractions will determine the water holding capacity of the material.

In general, a non-calcareous sand derived from granite or sandstone is preferred with a good spread of particle sizes (from 0.01 mm to 3.00 mm diameter). The majority of tree and shrub species have given higher rooting percentages in mixes containing non-calcareous sands, others are indifferent and some (members of *Ericaceae*, the heather family) demand an acid rooting medium and, for these, moss peat alone is generally satisfactory. In trials, such diverse subjects as *Elaeagnus pungens* **Maculata**, *Prunus laurocerasus* **Otto Luyken**, *Hebe pinguifolia* **Pagei** *Hypericum* **Hidcote**, *Philadelphus* **Bouquet Blanc**, *Magnolia stellata*, *Prunus incisa*, *Vinca major* **Variegata** and *Ligustrum ovalifolium* **Aureum** have given higher percentages of rooted cuttings when non-calcareous granitic sand was used in a 2 : 1 mix of peat and sand. *Euonymus microphyllus* **Variegatus**, *Forsythia* **Beatrix Farrand**, *Caryopteris* **Heavenly Blue** and *Ulex europaeus* **Plenus** showed no differences in their reactions to the type of sand. Of the species tested only two, *Escallonia macrantha* and *Senecio greyii*, gave more rooted cuttings when calcareous sand was used. There is evidence, therefore, that by using a non-calcareous sand the nurseryman will be using a type that suits a wide range of species. If an inferior sand must be used he may, in many cases, have to put up with lower rooting percentages or slower rooting.

Peat–sand mixes

Apart from the *Ericaceae*, a mix composed of two parts moss peat to one of sand is recommended as a rooting medium for cuttings of most of the subjects in this book. From the remarks on the variability of sands it will be evident why, if several mixtures of peat and sand give little difference in rooting, the mixture containing the highest proportion of peat is preferred. In this way the rooting medium is standardised to a greater extent. Everyone can use a similar peat but one man's sand may be different from the next and, by keeping down the proportion of sand, this source of variability is reduced. In addition, peat is light; more propagating trays can be handled at one time and the weight on the glasshouse staging is lessened. Indeed, from this point of view, peat is preferable as a plunging medium for the trays of cuttings on the bench.

Vermiculite

This material is favoured by many American nurserymen as it is freely available in the USA, is extremely light and sponge-like and can absorb large quantities of water. It contains some magnesium and potassium. Vermiculite is available in many grades and is used for seed germination and the rooting of cuttings. Care should be taken that only a horticultural vermiculite is used as the type used in the building trade is very alkaline and unsuitable for our purposes. Vermiculite should not be compressed when wet as this destroys the porous structure.

37

Perlite

This inert substance is of volcanic origin. Its sterility and lightness makes it useful in plant propagation. It has a high capacity for water retention but, unlike vermiculite, it contains no plant food and cannot hold added nutrients against leaching.

5

Micropropagation

Introduction

Classical methods of plant propagation have been greatly improved with the use of root-inducing growth regulators, with provision of optimal soil and environmental conditions and with increased knowledge of the physiology of root induction, of seed germination and of mother plants. Despite these advances there are many important species where further improvements are highly desirable. Particularly important considerations include increasing rooting percentage and devising techniques for programming production schedules for large-scale market requirements.

In recent years the advantages of clonal propagation under sterile conditions (micropropagation) have been recognised. For the nurseryman this technique offers the following advantages:

(a) it is a rapid method of propagation giving thousands of plantlets in a matter of months.

(b) it is effective for propagation of subjects which are difficult to root by conventional methods e.g. *Daphne, Magnolia*.

(c) it is effective for production of very large quantities of subjects thereby by-passing the need for budding and grafting e.g. roses.

(d) because of the rapidity of production, new cultivars and novel plants can be bulked quickly for widespread release to markets and these can be readily despatched internationally.

(e) healthy material is ensured since soil and other disease organisms are excluded during the propagation cycle.

(f) the method is programmable to meet specific targets of time and of quantity because it is independent of seasonal and climatic conditions.

(g) with some species, plants from micropropagation may exhibit desirable growth forms for a short while e.g. more bushy plants.

(h) this technique is now gaining acceptance, plants are available, and there are many commercial firms already in production (see p. 52).

The nurseryman should also be aware of the limitations and problems of micropropagation and decide if plants from this procedure offer any special advantages for his own conditions. The problems and limitations include the following:

(a) When insufficient precautions are taken the appearance of 'sports' or 'off types' may be increased. These 'sports' or genetic mutants have been reported for fruit species and were found to arise from callus tissue. Precautions to minimise callus production and to propagate only from genetically stable tissue usually avoids this particular problem.

(b) the technique requires familiarity with laboratory and some microbiological procedures. It is also fairly labour intensive. Specialised training, equipment and the need for unfamiliar work practices may deter some nurserymen from investing in the technology.

(c) Methods have been developed for micropropagating many dicotyledonous species. Micropropagation of monocotyledonous species is difficult. With conifers, micropropagation is very difficult and is not yet viable for commercialisation.

Cultures have been initiated from a very large range of dicotyledonous species. In practice, complete systems for production of ornamental dicotyledonous species have been published for a relatively small range. Table 1 summarises results available to date. With other important species such as *Acer, Berberis, Clematis, Cotinus, Hamamelis* and *Viburnum*, studies have already been initiated and are at various stages of completion. In addition, since commercial firms do not normally publish their results it is likely that they have independently developed complete procedures to propagate these and other species. The small range of plants available to date is due to the relatively recent application of the method to nursery stock rather than to any inherent difficulty. Increased demands by nurserymen on micropropagation companies and increased interest by research institutes will undoubtedly vastly increase the species range suitable for micropropagation. An introductory booklet on the subject has been published (Pennel, 1982).

Micropropagation is a specialised means of propagation requiring quite stringent work-practices and some specialised knowledge of plant physiology. Consequently it is best that it should remain in the hands of competent specialists. A list of such commercial laboratories is given on p. 52. Most firms operate on a contract basis and while they may have stocks in hand of the varieties you require, they will also undertake to propagate your own

TABLE 1: NURSERY STOCK SPECIES WITH DEVELOPED
SYSTEMS FOR MICROPROPAGATION

Species	Cultivars(s)	Reference
Alnus glutinosa	—	Garton *et al.* 1981.
Amelanchier alnifolia	—	Harris and Mason 1983.
Arctostaphylos uva ursi	—	Harris and Mason 1983.
Azalea (Exbury)	DH 28, DH 23	Fordham *et al.* 1982.
Betula platyphylia szechuanica	—	Smith and McCown 1983.
Camellia japonica	—	Sanmartin *et al.* 1984.
Castanea sativa	—	Vieitez and Vieitez 1980, Rodriguez 1982.
Chaenomeles japonica	—	Norton and Boe 1982.
Corylus avelliana	Many	Al Kai *et al.* 1984.
Cotoneaster dammeri	—	Norton and Boe 1982.
Crataegus brachyacantha × *mordenensis*	—	Norton and Boe 1982.
Daphne × burkwoodii	—	Cohen and Le Cal 1976
Daphne retusa	—	Constantine *et al.* 1981.
Daphne tangutica	—	Constantine *et al.* 1981
Drimys winteri	—	Jordan and Cortes 1981.
Erica × *darleyensis*	—	Beaujard and Astie 1983.
Eucalyptus nova-anglica		
,, *viminalis*	—	Mehra-Palta 1982.
Fuchsia hybrida	Many	Stevenson and Harris 1980. Kevers *et al.* 1983.
Hydrangea macrophylla	Merveille	Stoltz 1984.
Jasminum officinale		
,, *nudiflorum*	—	Khoder *et al.* 1981.
Jasminum primulinum	—	Scaramuzzi and D'Elia 1984.
Kalmia latifolia	—	Lloyd and McCown 1980.

Lavandula angustifolia		
,, *latifolia*	—	Quazi 1980.
Liquidamber styraciflua	—	Sommer and Caldas 1981.
		Sutter and Barker 1983.
Malus (fruit scions)	Many	Jones *et al.* 1977, 1979.
		Lane and McDougald 1982.
Malus (rootstocks)	Many	James and Thurbon 1979,
		Snir and Erez 1980. Pua *et al.* 1983.
Malus (ornamental crabapple)	Many	Singha 1982. Norton and Boe 1982.
Magnolia soulangiana	—	*Anon 1981.*
Myrtus communis	—	Khosh-Khui *et al.* 1984.
Potentilla fruticosa	Coronation, Triumph, Sutters Gold	Norton and Boe 1982.
Prunus (many fruit species)	—	Tabachnik and Kester 1977.
		Rosati *et al.* 1980.
		Snir 1983.
Prunus cerasifera	atropurpurea	Garland and Stolz 1981.
		Norton and Boe 1982.
Prunus cistena	—	Lane 1979 b.
Pyracantha coccinea	—	Norton and Boe 1982.
Pyrus communis	Bartlet	Lane 1979 a.
Rhododendron (many species)	Many	Anderson 1975. McCown and Lloyd
		1983. Douglas 1984.
Rosa (many species)	Many	Davies 1980. Hasegawa 1980.
		Khosh-Khui and Sink 1982.
Ruscus hypophyllum	—	Ziv 1983.
Sambucus (many species)	—	Hrib *et al.* 1980.
Spiraea bumalda	Anthony Waterer	Lane 1979b.
Vitis vinifera	—	Barlass and Skene 1978.
Weigela hybrids	Many	Duron 1981.
Yucca gloriosa	—	Durmishidze *et al.* 1983.

individual material if desired. Most firms offer a choice of either rooted plants not adapted to soil or rooted plants which are adapted to soil and weaned to glasshouse conditions.

This chapter is aimed at providing nurserymen, students and others interested in the subject with a general account of the technique. The principles involved, equipment needed and procedures for handling of plants and materials are also described.

Principles

As the name suggests micropropagation involves propagating plants from micro-cuttings rather than relatively large conventional cuttings. The type of micro-cuttings or propagules used may differ with the propagation system employed. Three types of multiplication systems have been described:
(a) stimulation of breaking in axillary buds
(b) stimulation of production of adventitious buds and shoots
(c) stimulation of development of somatic embryos i.e. artificial seed.

The first system is most commonly used and is applicable to most species. The propagules used are usually the growing points of shoots. The size of shoot-tip taken is usually 10–20 mm in length. In some cases the smaller meristem tip 0.25–1 mm is used (Fig. 21). By culturing these shoot tips, axillary buds present in the original propagule are stimulated to break and develop into shoots. Buds present in these new shoots may also break giving rise to a clump or mass of shoots (Fig. 22). This system gives the lowest multiplication rates as it is limited by the number of axillary buds originally placed in each 41

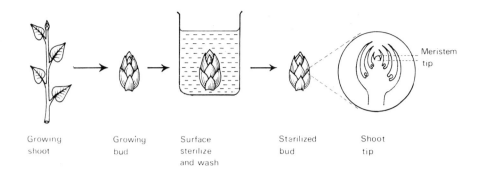

Growing shoot — Growing bud — Surface sterilize and wash — Sterilized bud — Shoot tip — Meristem tip

Fig. 21. Preparing material for culture.

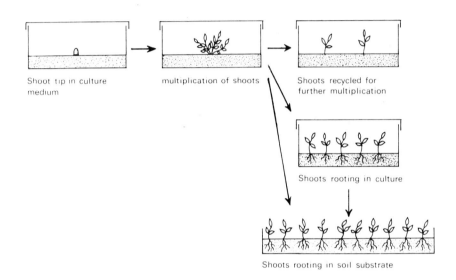

Shoot tip in culture medium — multiplication of shoots — Shoots recycled for further multiplication

Shoots rooting in culture

Shoots rooting in soil substrate

Fig. 22. The micropropagation cycle.

TABLE 2: CONSTITUENTS OF MURASHIGE AND SKOOG (1962) BASAL MEDIUM

Macronutrients	Final Concentration (mg/L)	Vitamins	Final Concentration (Mg/L)
$NH_4 NO_3$	1650.0		
KNO_3	1900.0	Inositol	100.0
$CaCl_2 . 2H_2O$	440.0	Nicotinic acid	0.5
$MgSO_4 . 7H_2O$	370.0	Pyridoxine. HCl	0.5
$KH_2 PO_4$	170.0	Thiamine. HCl	0.1
Micronutrients		*Organic nutrients*	
KI	0.83	Sucrose	30000.0
H_3BO_3	6.2		
$MnSO_4 . 4H_2O$	22.3		
$ZnSO_4 . 7H_2O$	8.6		
$Na_2MoO_4 . 2H_2O$	0.25		
$CuSO_4 . 5H_2O$	0.025		
$CoCl_2 . 6H_2O$	0.025		
EDTA — Ferric Salt	43.0		

culture vessel. With roses we have obtained 8–12 shoots every six weeks per original shoot cultured, Fig. 23.

The second system has a greater potential for multiplication. Here, new shoots are induced to form not only from axillary buds but also from any area of the original shoot cultured. Cells of the petioles and leaf blades may

42

Fig. 23. A culture of rose **Queen Elizabeth**; note presence of many shoots.

therefore become capable of growing and organising themselves into shoots. Many species that respond to breaking of axillary buds also respond to conditions favouring production of adventitious shoots.

The system with greatest potential for high multiplication rates is somatic embryogenesis. With this system the propagules are single cells or groups of cells. With some species these cells can be stimulated to divide continuously and form an embryo similar to the embryo found in the seed of the species. These somatic embryos germinate normally and give rise to a whole plant. The high multiplication potential derives from the fact that a small volume (10 mls) may contain many millions of cells. This system is still at the experimental stage though it has been demonstrated for important subjects such as *Aesculus, Chimonanthus* and *Corylus* (Radojevic, 1980) and for grape, coffee and orange.

The first system outlined above is most commonly used and my further comments will refer mainly to the stimulation of breaking of axillary buds in shoot tips. To ensure growth and development of plants from these tiny propagules such as shoot tips it is essential to supply a balanced supply of nutrients. A typical nutrient medium consists of macronutrients, micronutrients, vitamins and sugar (i.e. Basal Medium, Table 2) together with growth regulators. These rich media are also ideal for rapid growth of bacteria and fungi which are ever-present on the surfaces of plant leaves and buds. The bacteria and fungi must therefore be killed before placing the shoot tip on the culture medium. Once the shoot tip is freed of contaminating organisms it must be maintained in a sterile environment. Sterility maintainance involves sterilising growth media, use of sterile containers and manipulations of shoots in a stream of sterile air. The sterile air is provided by a laminar-flow cabinet.

The shoot tip begins to grow and develop after 3–8 weeks. It is cultured in an environment with controlled temperature (20–25°C) and light, 16 hours fluorescent light, 8 hours dark. Rather than developing into a single plant it is induced to produce shoots from axillary buds (Figs. 22, 23, 24). The multiple shoots are then separated. Some of these shoots are cultured on a medium designed for root induction. Alternatively they may be pre-treated and 43

Fig. 24. A culture of *Rhododendron* **Britannia** with multiple shoots.

inserted for direct rooting in compost. Other shoots are re-cycled i.e. re-cultured on media to produce more shoots (Fig. 22).

Practice

Each stage in practice involves transferring the propagule to new conditions or to fresh medium. For convenience the stages in micropropagation have been designated as follows:

Stage	Process
0	selection of stock plant and propagule
1	establishment of propagule in culture
2	production of multiple shoots
3	production of rooted shoots
4	weaning shoots to soil

In stage 0 one should choose healthy starting material of the best form of the cultivar required. To avoid propagating material carrying viruses one should ideally start with virus-tested stocks. Infected material can, however, be freed of viruses by culturing meristem tips, rather than whole shoot tips (Fig. 21). This consideration may be important with some species e.g. roses and camellias. This technique, however, is a specialised one requiring more exacting nutritional conditions and several analytical methods to confirm the presence or absence of viruses in plants produced. Purchasers of micro-propagated plants should therefore enquire of firms if they provide a virus eradication service as part of their micropropagation operation.

Success in establishing viable cultures may depend on the initial choice of material. The position of the shoot on the stock plant and the time of year at which it is taken are important. We have obtained good results with terminal vegetative buds of rhododendron taken in spring just before they were about to flush. With both floribunda and hybrid tea roses we have used axillary buds successfully throughout the year.

In Stage 1, one aims to achieve the establishment of the shoot tip in a healthy condition in the culture medium. During this stage the shoot tip makes physiological adjustments to the change from growing on the mother plant to growing under 'artificial' conditions. A major adjustment involves the change from conditions in which the shoot would normally photosynthesise actively to one in culture where photosynthesis is relatively insignificant. In culture the major source of energy required for shoot growth is derived from sucrose (sugar) supplied in the culture medium.

The surface tissues of shoots are sterilised before placement in culture. Plants grown in the greenhouse prior to culturing their buds generally are easiest to surface sterilise successfully. A solution of 0.5–1% sodium hypochlorite (laundry bleach) with the addition of a few drops of surfactant per 100 ml of solution is often used. Alternatively a saturated solution of calcium hypochlorite is also satisfactory. Essentially one aims to leave the buds in the solution for sufficient time (10–20 mins) to kill microorganisms but not long enough to damage the plant tissues. Three to five subsequent rinses in sterile water is essential to remove excess chlorine. Initially shoots may be cultured on an enriched medium such as one supplemented with caseine hydrolysate (250 mg/l). On such a medium fungi and bacteria grow rapidly making the detection and discard of contaminated cultures relatively easy. It is essential to select rigorously visually uncontaminated cultures at the end of the first incubation period in stage 1.

As mentioned above survival in stage 1 may depend on considerations in stage 0. The composition of the culture medium also is an important factor in the survival of newly initiated cultures. Generally the presence of growth regulators in low concentrations (half stage 2 level) are beneficial to propagules. Other factors such as the sugar type are important. With malus, sorbitol was superior to sucrose for establishing cultures (Pua and Chong, 1984). The use of a liquid medium rather than an agar-solidified medium can often increase survival rates (Ziv, 1983). The new shoot cultures may benefit from frequent transfers to a fresh medium every 1–4 weeks. The transfers should be undertaken even though the shoots do not appear to be growing or producing secondary shoots. Beneficial effect of frequent transfers during Stage 1 may be due to provision of some limiting nutritional factor in the medium which aids establishment. Alternatively it may prevent the build up of toxic exudates from the propagule.

Stage 2 is very important since the multiplication rate can determine economic success or failure in commercial laboratories. The objective is to maximise output of high quality shoots in each culture cycle (Fig. 22). One aims to produce shoots of uniform size with a good potential for rooting. Shoot productivity is species dependent; thus on a harvest cycle of 3–4 weeks, 300–400 shoots were obtained for *Spiraea bumalda* whereas *Prunus cistena* yielded 35 per culture (Lane, 1979 b).

Determination of the most suitable growth regulators and their concentrations together with the type of basal medium are of major importance in developing media for optimal shoot productivity. The growth regulators have major control over shoot multiplication and development. They may be considered under three headings i.e. auxins, cytokinins and 'other chemicals'. Auxins stimulate cells to divide and expand; they include indoleacetic acid (IAA), indolebutyric acid (IBA), naphthalene-acetic acid (NAA) and 2,4-dichlorophenoxyacetic acid (2,4-D). Cytokinins stimulate cells to divide and to differentiate into shoots; they include kinetin (K), benzyladenine (BA), 45 isopentenyladenine (2iP) and zeatin (Z). The third group of 'other chemicals' includes gibberellins (GA). These stimulate cells present in organs such as stems to elongate and are sometimes used at the end of stage 2 to stimulate shoot elongation prior to rooting.

The choice of auxin and cytokinin and their appropriate concentration requires much systematic experimentation. During the course of building up stock cultures from the original shoot tips one can carry out a preliminary screening of growth regulators. The optimum concentration of growth regulators used can vary between cultivars.

Apart from the type of basal medium and concentration of growth regulators other factors affect the multiplication rate in stage 2. One should identify the best tissue for re-culturing (i.e. subculturing). With some species the basal tissue gives best results; with others the actively growing shoot tips are best. One should investigate the effects of removing the shoot tip to suppress apical dominance in shoot cultures. In addition the size of the subculture tissue and its volume in the container may be important. One must also determine the optimal time interval between subcultures. Other factors such as the use of liquid medium should be studied. With rhododendron cv. **Pink Pearl** we observed a 10-fold increase in shoot production in liquid medium over agar-solidified medium (Douglas, 1984). Use of liquid also offers savings in agar costs and time since it is not necessary to position shoots precisely vertically during subculturing.

For stage 3 one aims to condition the shoot so as to survive the stress that occurs upon transfer to soil. The stresses experienced are low humidity and lack of food supply. In culture the humidity is 100% and the food (minerals, vitamins and carbohydrate) is supplied in a readily available soluble form. Production of roots may be achieved by subculturing shoots to a medium containing auxin only, usually IBA. The basal medium is usually diluted to 0.5 or 0.25 times its normal strength. Alternatively rooting may occur in soil directly (Fig. 22). Direct rooting is gaining favour since roots formed are functional

Fig. 25. Four different cultivars of *Rhododendron* in seed trays. Unrooted shoots were taken from cultures, pretreated and inserted in peat where direct rooting took place.

with viable root hairs. In addition direct rooting avoids breakage of roots which normally occurs with rooted shoots transferred from agar to soil. With several rhododendron cultivars we observed that pretreatment of shoots in solutions of media supplemented with IBA for 10 days stimulated rooting in terms of percentage rooting, root number and speed of rooting (Douglas, 1984). One should systematically determine the optimal auxin and its concentration whether one is rooting in culture or directly in soil.

The number and quality of roots produced in stage 3 affects success in weaning stage 4. During stages 3 and 4 the plant reverts to active photosynthesis for food supply and to providing water via roots. Shoots should be graded at the rooting stage so as to provide a uniform crop for weaning. They should be rinsed so as to remove excess medium which might stimulate the growth of microorganisms. Humidity should be kept high with the use of plastic film to prevent dessication. In addition it may be necessary to provide shading. We have observed that plants grow rapidly after transfer to the greenhouse. For rhododendrons, plants from micropropagation were equivalent in size and development to plants produced from conventional cuttings at the end of the second growing season (Fig. 26).

Fig. 26. A comparison of *Rhododendrons* from micropropagation (left) and conventional cutting (right) at the end of the second growing season.

For plants transferred to soil in autumn or winter it is essential to provide supplementary lighting at least until the plants are established. It is best to control damping-off fungi by cultural practises such as increasing temperature and good hygiene since small plantlets may be susceptible to fungicides supplied at recommended rates.

A brief guide to requirements and procedures

The following is a step by step account of the requirements and procedures used in micropropagation. The equipment given is regarded as the minimum needed for any viable operation. Addresses of suppliers of equipment and reagents are given the appendix at the end of this chapter (p. 52).

Having constructed and equipped a unit the three main procedures used are preparation of (a) culture media, (b) plant material to start a culture and (c) shoots for multiplication, rooting and weaning to soil. In medium preparation the objective is to supply the required nutrients and growth regulators in a balanced form so as to stimulate shoot proliferation. Plant material needs careful preparation so as to decontaminate shoots for their subsequent culture under sterile conditions. During subculturing and rooting the aim is to optimise shoot productivity and procedures for establishing shoots in conventional non-sterile substrates.

Space requirements and equipment

The micropropagation unit should ideally consist of three separate sections the size of which will vary with the scale of the operation.

Section 1 The preparation area

Equipment	Purpose
Sink, worktop and cupboards	Washing, preparing and storage
refrigerator	storing stock solutions and chemicals
unit for deionising or distilling	to produce pure water
autoclave	to sterlise media
balance	for weighing chemicals

Section 2 The transfer area

Equipment	Purpose
Laminar flow cabinet	to produce sterile air
cupboards	to store prepared media and sterile containers
electric panel	to house chokes, starters and fuses for culture room lights and equipment

Section 3 The Culture Room

Equipment	Purpose
Tiered shelving (18″ apart)	to carry cultures
fluorescent lamps	to illuminate cultures (2–3000 lux level)
time switch	to provide 16 hour light period
electric heater with thermostat	to provide heat when required

The three sections should be ideally arranged in a linear design with the preparation area at one end and the culture room at the other. The culture room should be maintained at a constant temperature in the range 20–25°C. Usually heat from lights should provide the required temperature lift in a small unit with supplementary heating from a thermostatically activated electric heater during the dark period. To avoid overheating, the chokes and starters for the lights are housed in the transfer area. With larger culture rooms an air conditioner is required to remove excess heat.

Preparing a culture medium

(a) It is essential to determine if work was previously done and published on micropropagating the species you require (see pp. 40 and 45). Published papers give details of procedures and of the basal and growth regulator constituents of the culture medium to use. Recommendations for any given species and cultivar should be considered only as a guideline; some experimentation to optimise media and conditions are usually required. If information is not available on your subject of choice one must experiment to devise a suitable medium. Most Universities and research institutes will have copies of the journals listed (see References p. 52); if not, copies of the articles you require may be purchased through most libraries.

Additional requirements

plastic storage bottles
beakers and graduated cylinders
glass rods, tinfoil, pipettes
culture medium (pre-constituted)
stock solutions of growth regulators
alkali : solution of sodium hydroxide (0.1 molar)
acid : solution of hydrochloric acid (0.1 molar)
pH meter
agar, sucrose
sterile petri plates and plastic jars.

(b) One may purchase culture media in powdered or liquid form (see appendix, p. 54). Purchased media can be ordered containing all the constituents listed in Table 2, p. 42 or custom made to your specifications. With basal medium (e.g. Table 2) one must add agar and growth regulators to the desired final concentration. Since growth regulators are required in very small amounts (milligrams per litre), stock solutions are first prepared such that each 10 ml contains 1.0 mg of growth regulator. Auxins and gibberellic acid are initially dissolved in ethanol (5–10 ml) and cytokinins in a minimal amount of dilute hot hydrochloric acid before adding gradually by pipette to the stock of water. Preparation is easily accomplished by mixing pre-constituted media with pure water. Before making the solution up to the required volume, the solution pH is adjusted (usually to 5.6–5.8) with acid or alkali and the aid of a pH meter. Media should be continually stirred with glass rods during this step.

(c) The medium is now ready for sterilisation by autoclaving i.e. boiling under pressure. The flasks are covered with aluminium foil and an airspace equivalent in volume to the medium is left above the medium to allow for expansion and boiling. After autoclaving allow the medium to cool (50–60°) within the laminar flow cabinet before pouring it into sterile petri plates or plastic jars. If not used immediately, media should be stored in a cool clean location.

Preparing plant material and starting a culture

(a) Most of the requirements needed for this operation are already given above. If a reference is available on the species of choice one should closely follow the procedures given. A general recommendation follows.

Additional requirements

calcium hypochlorite
filter papers and funnel
glass bottles with metal caps
scalpel handle with blades, forceps
Bunsen gas burner
methylated spirits or industrial alcohol

(b) 1. Using pure water make a solution of calcium hypochlorite (7% w/v) for surface sterlising buds. Weigh out 14 grams of chemical, place in 200 ml of water, stir for 15 mins and then allow to settle for a further 15 mins.
2. Filter the solution by decanting it through a filter paper and into a plastic storage bottle.
3. Prepare sterile water by autoclaving glass bottles which are ⅔ filled with pure water. Leave screw caps loose during autoclaving and tighten when cooled down.
4. Collect shoots into a plastic bag to prevent dessication during transport to the transfer room. Remove the nodes with desired buds and place them in a sterile plastic jar. Cover the nodal segments with the prepared solution of calcium hypochlorite, cap the jar and shake for 10–20 mins to ensure the chemical covers all surfaces of the buds (see p. 45).
5. All subsequent operations including subculturing (p. 52) are performed on the bench of an operating laminar flow cabinet (Fig. 27). After turning on the

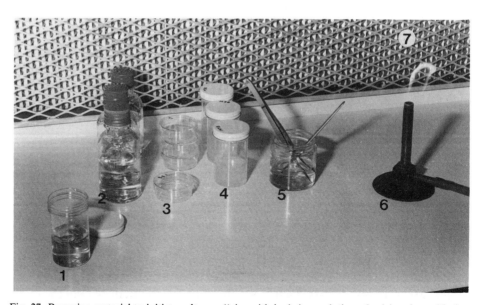

Fig. 27. Preparing material to initiate cultures: 1) jar with buds in a solution of calcium hypochlorite; 2) sterile water for rinsing the surface-sterilised buds; 3) petri plates with culture medium; 4) jars with culture medium; 5) container with alcohol, forceps and scalpel; 6) Bunsen gas burner; 7) laminar flow filter.

fan of the cabinet, swab down its work surfaces with alcohol or methylated
spirits. Immerse the top quarter of scalpels and forceps in a small beaker containing spirits (Fig. 27). Transfer the container with nodal segments to the cabinet and decant off the calcium hypochlorite. Using pure sterile water rinse the segments three times. This procedure should have sterilised the surfaces of the nodal segments.

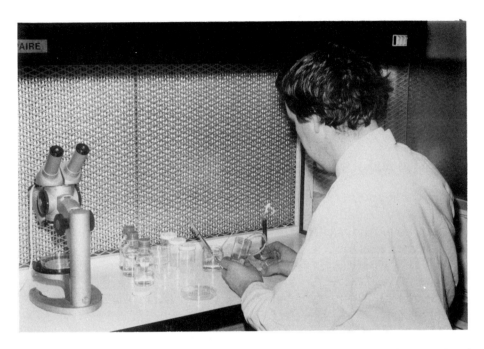

Fig. 28. Operations in a laminar flow cabinet. The operator is working in the cabinet decanting the
solution of calcium hypochlorite from the buds. Note the large petri plate in the foreground to
take the sterilised buds and the microscope for dissecting the shoot tip.

6. Turn on and ignite the Bunsen burner in the cabinet. Remove the scalpel and forceps from their soak solution and shake off excess spirit. Place the instrument tips in the flame to ignite the spirit to ensure sterilisation i.e. flaming. Place a surface sterilised nodal segment in a sterile petri plate in the laminar flow cabinet. By holding the node with a forceps one should remove the outer scales and leaflets of the bud using a scalpel. A dissecting microscope may be required for small buds. After removing several leaflets the shoot tip can be easily cut out and transferred to the prepared medium. It is worth sterilising instruments (by flaming) several times during this operation but be sure to allow them to cool down before touching bud tissue.

7. Once the shoot tip is in the culture jar it should be transferred to the growth room. When starting cultures expect to get a fairly high level of contamination. In our experience up to 90% of new rhododendron cultures may be contaminated whereas less than 20% of rose cultures are contaminated. All cultures should be rigorously checked for the presence of contaminating organisms after 1–2 weeks of culture. Fungi are easy to detect since they usually grow as a fluffy mould over the surface of the shoot tip. Bacteria however appear as a wet droplet at the base of the shoot tip. The droplet may be coloured red or pink but is usually creamy in appearance. Only contamination-free cultures should be transferred to a fresh medium.

Subculturing and rooting

Early growth of the shoot tip can be very slow and may require several transfers to fresh medium to stimulate production of multiple shoots. This process of establishment may take one to several months. Once multiple shoot production begins, one cuts off single shoots or separates the shoot cluster into smaller clusters. These propagules are then transferred to fresh medium and perhaps also to larger sterile containers. The number of shoots obtained per culture vessel is largely dependent on the medium used and the frequency of subculture. (see p. 45.)

For rooting, a fresh medium is specially prepared. With such rooting media, basal medium is usually diluted by a half or quarter normal strength and auxins (p. 46) alone are used as growth regulators. Shoots transferred to such media generally root well within four weeks. They are then transferred to trays of compost and covered to maintain a high humidity until roots and leaves are fully adapted to normal glasshouse conditions (p. 47).

List of some commercial laboratories propagating nursery stock

1. Celler Pflanzen und
   Gewebelabor GmbH,
   Postfach 65, 3100 Celle,
   Fed. Rep. Germany.

2. Delbard International,
   Malicorne 03600,
   Commentry,
   France.

3. Micropropagation Services
   Limited,
   Gotham Moor Farm,
   Gotham,
   Nottingham NG11 0LH,
   England.

4. Microviv,
   14 Blvd. Lavoisier,
   49000 Angers,
   France.

5. Munton and Fison,
   Cedars Factory, Stowmarket,
   Suffolk IP14 2AG,
   England.

6. NeoPlants Limited,
   197 Kirkham Road, Freckleton,
   Preston,
   Lancs PR4 1HU,
   England.

7. Round Pond Nurseries,
   Chobham Place, Chobham,
   Near Woking,
   Surrey GU24 8TW,
   England.

8. Twyford Plant Laboratories,
   Baltonsborough, Glastonbury,
   Somerset BA6 8QC,
   England.

References

Al Kai, H., G. Salesses, A. Mouras (1984). Agronomie., *4* 399–402.
Anderson, W. C. (1975). Proc. Int. Plant. Prop. Soc., 25 129–135.
Anon, 1981. Research Booklet, Long Ashton Research Station p. 1–4.
Barlass, M., K. G. M. Skene (1978). Vitis., *17* 335–340.
Beujard, F. and M. Astie (1983). Can. J. Bot., *61* (12) 3533 — Can. J. Bot., *61* 3533–3535.
Cohen, D. and P. M. Le Cal (1976). Int. Plant Prop. Soc., *26* 330–333.
Constantine, D. R., S. Wiltshire, A. J. Abbott and A. Belcher (1981). Long Ashton Report 1981 pp. 70–72.

Davies, D. R. (1980). Scientia Hort., *13* 385–389.

Douglas, G. C. (1984). Scientia Hortic., *24* 237–247.

Durmishidze, S. V., M. K. Gogobevidze, M. V. Mamaladze (1983). Z. Pflanzenphysiologie, *111* 179–182.

Duron, M. (1981). Agronomie *1* 865–868.

Fordham, I., D. P. Stimart, R. H. Zimmerman (1982). HortScience., *17* 738–739.

Garland P. and L. P. Stoltz (1981). Ann. Bot. *48* (3) 387–389.

Garton, S., M. A. Hosier, P. E. Read, R. S. Farnham (1981). HortScience. *16*, 758–759.

Harris, R. E. and E. D. D. Mason (1983). Can. J. Plant Sci. *63* 311–316.

Hasegawa, P. M. (1980). J. Amer. Soc. Hort. Sci. *105* 216–220.

Hrib, J., H. C. Chatarvedi and J. Dobry (1980). Phytomorphology *30* 266–270.

James, D. J. and I. J. Thurbon (1979). J. Hort. Sci., *54* 309–311.

Jones, O. P., M. E. Hopgood, D. O'Farrell (1977). J. Hort. Sci., *52* 235–238.

Jones, O. P., C. A. Pontikis and M. E. Hopgood, (1979). J. Hort. Sci., *54* 155–158.

Jordan, M., I. Cortes (1981). Plant. Sci. Lett. *23* 177–180.

Khoder, M., P. Villemur, R. Jonard (1981). C. R. Acad. Sci., *293* 343–346.

Khosh-Khui, M., A. Shekafandeh and H. Azarakhsh (1984). Scientia Hortic. *22* 139–146.

Khosh-Khui, N. and K. C. Kink (1982). J. Hort. Sci., *57* 315–319.

Kevers, Cl., M. F. Coumans-Gilles, M. Coumans and Th. Gaspar (1983). Scientia Hortic. *21* 67–71.

Lane, D. W. (1979)a. Plant Sci. Lett. *16*, 337–342.

Lane, D. W. (1979)b. Can. J. Plant. Sci. *59*, 1025–1029.

Lane, W. D. and J. M. McDougald (1982). Can. J. Plant. Sci., *62* 689–694.

Lloyd, G. and B. McCown (1980). Proc. Intern. Plant. Plant. Prop. Soc., *30* 421–427.

McCown, B. H. and G. B. Lloyd (1983). Plant Cell Tissue Organ Culture. *2* 77–85.

Mehra — Palta, A. (1982). Plant Sci. Lett., *26* 1–11.

Murashige, T. and F. Skoog (1962). Physiol. Plant. *15* 743–749.

Norton, M. E. and A. A. Boe (1982). HortScience *17* 190–191.

Pennell, D. (1982) MAFF Booklet No. 2413 pp. 1–47.

Pua, E. C. and C. Chong (1984) Can. J. Bot. *62* 1545–1549.

Pua, E. C., C. Chong, G. L. Rousselle (1983). Can. J. Plant. Sci., *63* 183–188.

Quazi, M. H. (1980). Ann. Bot., *45* 361–362.

Radojevic, L. (1980). Bull. Soc. Bot. Fr., *127*, 99–107.

Rodriguez, R. (1982). HortScience, *17* 888–889.

Rosati, P., G. Marino, and C. Swierczewski (1980). J. Amer. Soc. Hort. Sci., *105* 126–129.

Samartin, A., A. M. Vietez, E. Vietez (1984). HortScience., *19* 225–226.

Scaramuzzi, F. and C. D'Elia (1984). C. R. Acad. Sci., *298* 107–112.

Singha, S. (1982). HortScience, *17* 191–192.

Smith, M. A. L. and B. McCown (1983). Plant Sci. Lett. *28*, 149–156.

Snir, I. (1983) Scientia. Hortic., *19* 85–90.

Snir, I. and A. Erez (1980). HortScience *15* (5) 597–598.

Sommer, H. E. and L. S. Caldas (1981). *In* T. A. Thorpe (ed), Plant tissue culture methods and applications in agriculture p. 349–358. Academic Press, New York.

Stevenson, J. J. and R. E. Harris (1980). Can. J. Bot., *58* 2190–2192.
Stoltz, L. P. (1984). HortScience, *19* 717–719.
Sutter, E., and P. Barker (1983). Proc. Intern. Plant. Prop. Soc., *33* 113–117.
Tabachnik, L. and D. E. Kester (1977). HortScience, *12* 545–547.
Vieitez, A. M. and M. L. Vieitez (1980). J. Hort. Sci., *55* 83–84.
Ziv, M., (1983). Scientia Hortic., *19* 387–394.

Appendix: Some Suppliers of Requirements for Micropropagation*

(a) General requirements

AGB Scientific Ltd., Dublin Industrial Estate, Dublin 11, Ireland.[1, 2, 3, 4]
Astell Hearson, Laboratory Equipment, 172 Brownhill Road, London SE6 2DL, UK.[4]
Babtech Ltd., Coe's Road, Dundalk, Ireland.[1]
Envair (UK)., York Avenue, Broadway Industrial Estate, Haslingden, Rossendale, Lancs BB4 4HX, UK.[1]
Fisons Scientific Apparatus, Bishops Meadow Road, Loughborough, Leics LE11 0RG, UK.[3, 4]
Gallenkamp & Co. Ltd., P.O. Box 290, Technico House, Christopher Street, London EC2P 2ER, UK.[4]
Gelman Ltd., 71 Brownhill Road, Tallaght, Co. Dublin, Ireland. [1, 2, 4]
Hepaire Manufacturing Ltd., Station Road, Thatcham, Newbury, Berks. UK.[1]
Mason Laboratory Suppliers, 29 Parliament Street, Dublin 2, Ireland. [1, 2, 3, 4]
P. J. Brennan & Co. Ltd., 61 Stillorgan Industrial Park, Stillorgan, Co. Dublin, Ireland. [1, 2, 3, 4.]
W. A. Ingle and Co. Laboratory Suppliers, 1 Rockgrove, Little Island, Co. Cork, Ireland. [1, 2, 3.]

*1. Laminar flow cabinets. 2. Water purification. 3. Sterile containers. 4. Laboratory equipment and instruments.

(b) Pre-Constituted tissue culture media

Flow Laboratories Ltd., P.O. Box 17, Second Avenue Industrial Estate, Irvine, Ayrshire, Scotland KA12 8ND.
Gibco Biocult Ltd., 3 Washington Road, Abbotsinch Industrial Estate, Paisley, Scotland PA3 4EP.
Medical Supply Co. Ltd., Unit 9, Santry Industrial Estate, Santry, Dublin 9, Ireland.
Sterilin Ltd., 43–45 Broad Street, Teddington, Middlesex TW11 8QZ, UK.
W. A. Ingle and Co., Laboratory Suppliers, 1 Rockgrove, Little Island, Co. Cork, Ireland.

(c) Chemicals

May and Baker Ltd., Manufacturing Chemists, Cookstown, Tallaght, Co. Dublin, Ireland.
Lennox Chemicals, John F. Kennedy Industrial Estate, Naas Road, Dublin 12, Ireland.
Sigma London Chemical Co. Ltd., Fancy Road, Poole, Dorset BH17 7NF, UK.
BDH Chemicals Ltd., Poole, Dorset BH12 4NN, UK.

6
Composts and Fertilisers

Precision growing should be the aim of the nurseryman today. Enough is said in this book to show how in many directions greater precision can be attained, e.g. by selection of uniform material for cuttings and rooting them by modern methods, by the use of plastic structures and of capillary watering. One of the most important techniques of all is the use of standardised composts.

The John Innes composts

The earliest of these composts were the *John Innes seed and potting composts*. These are based on loam and the scarcity of this material in some areas and the need to sterilise it are drawbacks. The seed compost consists of two parts loam (pH 6.3) to one each of sand and peat. The sand should be coarse, i.e. particles ranging from $\frac{1}{16}$ in. to $\frac{1}{8}$ in. (1.6 mm to 3.2 mm). To each bushel add $1\frac{1}{2}$ oz superphosphate and $\frac{3}{4}$ oz ground limestone or chalk (1.2 kg and 0.58 kg respectively, per cu m). The potting compost is made up of seven parts of loam, three of peat and two of sand, adding $\frac{1}{4}$ lb John Innes Base fertiliser and $\frac{3}{4}$ oz ground limestone or chalk to each bushel of the mix (2.92 kg and 0.58 kg respectively, per cu m). Since a good loam contains sufficient trace elements, the grower does not have to add these.

Loamless composts

A more recent development has been the use of loamless composts based on peat. Some of these, usually formulated with standard type fertilisers, can be purchased ready mixed or with the appropriate nutrients, both major and trace, in a separate package for mixing in by the user. The trace elements may be in fritted form, i.e. combined in a single preparation such as Frit 253A, replacing a long list of chemical compounds. Frits are finely ground man-made silicates with trace elements incorporated. They have the property of readily releasing the trace elements into the soil. The use of frit simplifies mixing, and thorough mixing, always important, is especially so with loamless composts. Peat is so low in plant nutrients that both major and trace elements have to be added and, if not well and thoroughly mixed through the peat, unbalanced nutrition will occur to a greater degree than with loam. Since the latter contains some plant food, it can, to some extent, act as a counter balance against errors.

For large amounts of compost a mechanical mixer must be used. Thorough   55 mixing is aided by mixing the fertilisers with a small amount of the compost before this is mixed through the bulk of the material. For smaller quantities of John Innes composts, spread out the loam a few inches deep on the floor; then spread the peat over it, followed by the sand and lime. The fertilisers should be mixed with a little dry sand and then spread as evenly as possible on top. With a shovel turn over the pile systematically onto an adjacent stretch of clean floor and back again until the lot has been thoroughly mixed three or four times. When using the slow release fertilisers (see below), spread them and the lime over the peat in similar fashion. If the fertilisers are in granular form, see that the grains do not work their way to the bottom of the heap either during mixing or during subsequent handling on the potting bench.

Slow Release Fertilisers

Proprietary slow release fertilisers are a relatively recent arrival on the market. They are of great interest to the raiser of trees and shrubs, particularly when these are container grown. The capillary bed enables one to do away with hand watering, and slow release fertilisers carry labour saving a step further since they reduce or even eliminate supplementary feeding. They help the customer, too, since they should continue to feed the plant after sale.

We have had very satisfactory results in using these slow release fertilisers with moss peat alone. Only occasionally have we considered it desirable to add sand as, for example, with Japanese maples (p. 69). The peat used in loamless composts should be medium grade as, although moss peat has high air capacity, overwatering is more liable to occur with the fine grade. Some growers like to add sand to increase the stability of the containers but we find that this is no problem for low growing plants stood pot thick. Taller plants, (e.g. brooms, climbers) can be supported by stakes at the ends and sides of the beds with a cross mesh of string. Some species only need a retaining line of twine round the perimeter.

Slow release fertiliser may contain nitrogen only. Other types contain N, P and K, with or without trace elements. These give excellent results in loamless composts with the addition of fritted trace elements where necessary. Different formulations are available, some lasting longer than others. We have had very good results with an 8–9 month formulation. In conjunction with the capillary bed system of growing, where leaching is at a minimum, we have not had to give supplementary feeding over one growing season, nor have we noted improved growth from the addition of extra superphosphate. The latter may be necessary where hose or hand watering is practised, since phosphates are leached readily from peat. For all but lime hating subjects, add ground limestone, or chalk, and kieserite, the latter to give magnesium. Suitable quantities per bushel are 7 oz (200 g) ground limestone and 2.8 oz (80 g) kieserite. The various slow release formulations should be added in accordance with the directions of the manufacturers. In particular, note the lower rates and shorter lasting types advised for fertiliser sensitive species.

While loamless composts are a step forward in standardisation, some possible problems should be borne in mind. With a good medium grade moss peat, overwatering should not be a problem with ordinary care owing to the high air retaining capacity of such a peat. On the other hand, it is common experience that, if peat is allowed to dry out, it can be difficult to re-wet. All peat should be well dampened before use. Use of too rich a mix can lead to excess of chemical salts, especially when capillary watering is used. In the shorter days especially, excess nitrogen can build up. For this reason potting on should only be done when roots are in active growth and plants should not be over-potted.

Should the grower wish to make up his own loamless compost, there are several formulae available. One which has given us good results is made up by the addition to moss peat, limed as above, 25 oz (0.7 kg) sulphate of potash, 50 oz (1.4 kg) superphosphate (8%P), 50 oz (1.4 kg) calcium ammonium nitrate and 14 oz (0.4 kg) Frit 253A, all per cu m (27 bushels).

Seedlings are soon pricked off for growing on so the use of slow release fertilisers at sowing would be illogical. For seed sowing, a loamless compost made up to a quarter of the strength recommended above has been found satisfactory. The lime and frit contents should not be reduced.

If, however, slow release fertilisers are not used, vigorously growing species are likely to need *liquid feeding* after three or four months. A liquid feed is also recommended to start off rhododendrons potted early in the year under glass (p. 179). Ericas respond well to liquid feeding throughout (p. 125).

A number of proprietary liquid feeds are on the market, to be diluted and used according to the directions of the manufacturer. We have had good results using a ½% solution of such a concentrate containing 9%N, 9%P, 7%K and trace elements. If a home-made liquid feed is desired, a suitable stock solution can be made up by dissolving 4 lb (1.8 kg) potassium nitrate and 4.4 lb (1.99 kg) ammonium nitrate in 5 gallons (22.7 litres) of water. (These chemicals dissolve more easily in warm water.) If feeding at every watering, dilute 1 : 500 for species of medium vigour in growth, or 1 : 200 for strong growing subjects. For ericaceous plants use only at 1 : 800. If feeding once a week, start at 1 : 200, increasing to 1 : 100 when plants are growing strongly. Do not wet the foliage with the solution and give plain water as needed between feeds. This system relies on sufficient phosphate and trace elements being given in the base, as advised above.

7

The Growing On of Young Nursery Stock

Seedlings which have been raised under glass are generally pricked off into pots. Those sown in frames or seed beds are lined out in the nursery (p. 26). These steps mark the end of the propagating phase and the start of the growing on procedure. Likewise, cuttings weaned from the mist, warm bench and plastic, from the cold frame or from the low tunnel must be grown on efficiently to produce saleable specimens of the desired size and quality.

Today there are facilities available to the nurseryman which enable him to grow on his young plants to saleable size in much shorter time than ever before. These facilities include standardised composts (p. 55), plastic houses and capillary beds. By the combination of these techniques, results that would seem startling to former generations can be achieved by every grower. Indeed, no nurseryman can afford to ignore these up-to-date methods of plant production if his business is to be competitive.

Plastic houses

Though often called tunnels, it is preferable to call them houses to differentiate such structures clearly from the low tunnel of white plastic used for rooting cuttings in the ground during summer (p. 16).

The trade journals carry many advertisements for complete kits for the construction of such houses. Alternatively it is possible to buy the metal separately and cut and shape the pieces oneself. Details for the procedure can be obtained through the advisory services, so it is not proposed to go into details in this book but, instead, to point out the particular value of such a structure to the nurseryman engaged in the production of trees and shrubs.

It is suggested that the minimum size of such a structure that should be considered is 17 ft × 30 ft (5.1 m × 9 m) with a height of 8 ft (2.4 m). Longer houses will be cheaper per square foot but it is useful to have houses that can be moved around for different purposes during the year. For this reason, permanently sited foundation tubes 2 ft (60 cm) long projecting 3 in. (7.5 cm) above the surface are convenient.

Starting at the beginning of the calendar year, the first purpose for which a plastic house can be used is the forcing of mother plants for the production of early cuttings. Genera for which earliness is vital if the young plants are to be strong enough to survive their first winter include Japanese maples, deciduous azaleas and magnolias.

The plastic house is erected over the mother plants in February and is left closed up. Sun heat alone is sufficient to bring on the young shoots. How early they are will depend on the amount of sunshine but a gain of even a few days is sufficient to make a significant difference. Such early cuttings show a tendency to root more easily and, with the proper growing on techniques as described under each genus, will make excellent growth during the summer with few or no losses during their first winter and spring. If cuttings are taken from naturally grown outdoor plants of these genera, there are apt to be heavy losses among the young plants during the winter. This is not due to lack of hardiness but to causes not fully understood but described by such general terms as lack of time to develop into a physiologically fully integrated plant. Often, as for example with climbers and other fast growing subjects, it will be convenient to bring on plants relatively quickly by keeping them in the plastic house during the early part of the season but later it may be desirable to slow down growth before they get too tall. This can be accomplished by moving them to an outdoor bed as they approach the desired dimensions.

Once the cuttings have been harvested, the mother plants are hardened off by giving all the ventilation possible, opening the doors in all suitable weather, and finally, leaving them open day and night. During a spell of calm mild weather the plastic house can be removed finally.

During spring and summer the plastic houses have an important function in hastening the development of potted up seedlings, rooted cuttings and young plants. To develop the full capabilities of this system, the house is placed over a capillary bed, such as described below. The combination of good compost, shelter, high humidity, constant water supply and summer temperatures, leads to very rapid growth indeed. Seedling birches, for example, will reach 8 ft (2.4 m) in one season. Magnolias and azaleas will send out shoots several feet long unless shaped by the appropriate pinching and training to make well shaped bushes.

Instead of keeping plants under plastic for the full season to produce outsize specimens, the structure can be used to hasten the growth of young plants in successive batches. Each batch is removed and hardened off as soon as it attains saleable size to be succeeded by further plants of the same kind, or of other species.

It is frequently asked whether young plants raised in this way lack hardiness. In answer to this it is pointed out that when the nights get cold in autumn it is colder under plastic than under glass and, indeed, colder sometimes than outside. This is because plastic does not trap the heat radiated from objects warmed by the sun and also inflow of air from the surrounding area is impeded. Hence plants under plastic are subjected to a hardening-off process, furthered by cutting off the water to the capillary beds at the end of the season. Experience with a wide range of plants under plastic has not indicated lack of winter hardiness under our conditions. Caution is necessary, however, to keep down *Botrytis*, which can be encouraged by cool moist conditions. Good hygiene is important; remove all fallen foliage and dead tissue. Spray the plants with fungicide as a routine each winter, repeating the treatment if any mould is seen on overwintering plants. Under these conditions plastic houses can be used for the purpose of overwintering container grown hardy nursery stock. Naturally, ventilation should be given on all suitable days to keep down humidity and to avoid any involuntary forcing into growth as the days lengthen.

Capillary Beds

Every nurseryman is familiar with the problem of the watering of trees and shrubs, particularly when container grown. Reliance on the man with the hose so often leads to uneven watering and irregular drying out of the containers. Even when overhead sprinklers are installed, the results may be unsatisfactory as the top growth of well grown specimens of some species tends to channel the water over the sides of the containers, particularly evergreens having a dense habit of growth. Out of doors there is the further source of irregularity caused by wind blow. In any case, the use of sprinklers still entails the personal judgement of the operator. The problem today of *Phytophthora* root rot, a water borne disease, is a very cogent reason for avoiding the presence of free flowing water in the nursery.

Capillary beds can be used both indoors and outside to avoid these problems. Hand watering is done away with, all plants receive a constant supply of moisture and each bed is, in effect, an isolation area for the plants growing on it. Capillary beds can be constructed in several ways. A simple type which has been found cheap to construct and satisfactorily in use is the Kinsealy Capillary Bed (Fig. 29). This consists of a 2 in. (5 cm) deep bed of sand, though the depth is not critical. The dimensions can be conveniently based on the size of the plastic house, e.g. at 30 ft by 17 ft (9 m $\times$ 5.1 m) a house can accommodate one 5 ft (1.5 m) wide centre bed and two 4 ft (1.2 m) wide side beds. The site must be made perfectly level and free from stones. If it is not possible to remove all the stones, a layer of sand or of stone-free soil can be laid down. A channel is made down the middle of the centre bed and along the

Fig. 29. A capillary bed under construction.

edge of each side bed to take a line of 3 in. earthenware tiles laid end to end, deep enough to allow the sand to cover these tiles. Place a frame constructed of 2 in. (5 cm) square timber round the sides of the proposed bed. Line this with a double layer of black polythene and fill in the whole with sand.

An automatically controlled supply of water is arranged from a water tank so sited that the water level in the tiles will be the same as in the tank. Water finds its own level, so when it is siphoned into the end of the tile channel by means of a flexible plastic pipe, the water table will lie just below the level of the sand. As the water evaporates from the wet sand or is taken up by the plants, it is replenished from the tank which is kept full by inflow through a valve controlled by a ball cock.

The term capillary bed should be confined to a structure where the water is automatically maintained at a constant level. In contrast, a sand bed could describe a bed where the sand is kept moist by periodic irrigation as, for example, a pierced pipe lying on the surface and connected to a tap or is watered at intervals from a hose. An advantage of a true capillary bed is that the constant water table reduces the tendency of the plants to root out of the container. If the water table fluctuates, the roots will be prone to go out after moisture when it is low.

Fig. 30. Obsolete cold frames can be easily converted into capillary beds.

The capillary bed can be used either with rigid plastic pots or with plants grown in plastic bags. When using bags, it may be necessary to cut an extra hole at the bottom before they are used. The existing holes punched in the bags are often insufficient and badly sited for ensuring close contact between the compost within and the sand. The surface of the bed should be raked lightly to increase the closeness of contact between sand and compost and should be freshened up in this way between successive batches of plants. It is important when placing the containers on the capillary bed that each be well worked down to ensure full contact with the sand. Then the container grown plants are given a good watering to start off the capillary action. Thereafter it should only be necessary to check over the bed from time to time to ensure that the siphon system is functioning well, that the continuity of the water flow has not been broken and that the capillary stream in the containers is keeping them moist. This stream could be interrupted, for example, by accidental disturbance of the containers. Any pots that have got dry should be well watered to re-establish the capillary action.

This system works well with loamless composts (p. 55) owing to the ready absorption of moisture by peat. Slow release fertilisers (p. 56) are of particular value for it is illogical to set up a capillary watering system and then have to resort to liquid feeding. Indeed, the capillary bed, the peat based compost and the plastic house should be regarded as an integrated system for the production of container grown stock.

It will be realised that containers on a capillary bed are not subject to leaching, as they are when hand watered. This means that over potting or the use of inaccurately prepared composts can lead to injury due to the build up of excess fertiliser salts in the compost. No danger should however, arise if the grower follows the precision growing methods which should be practised by every raiser of plants with the knowledge available today. It is when the individual strays from the beaten track that the difficulties arise. If any plants do not grow as well as they should it is much easier for your adviser to trace the cause of the trouble if you can tell him exactly what system of growing you have followed.

An interesting point in connection with capillary watering is that the movement of nutrients in the compost is upward towards the surface, not downwards and out in the drainage water as with the conventional hose watering. This may lead to a superficial growth of algae on the surface of the compost and, in fact, sometimes one can actually see a deposit of whitish salts left on the surface. These are harmless and if desired can be removed when potting on or removing the plants for sale.

Recently, cloth-like water-absorbent materials have become available for the capillary watering of pot plants under glass. These have not been widely tested yet for use with hardy nursery stock, though they are promising for the purpose. They could be arranged so that one end or side dips into a channel of water.

Sometimes it is asked whether nutrients could be fed through the water system of a capillary bed but this implies a misapprehension of the full functioning of such a system. The objective should be to keep the roots within the container and, if the nutrients are in the compost only, there is no need for roots to seek them outside. From this aspect, too, slow release fertilisers are attractive as the food should be taken up by the plant as it becomes available with minimal seepage to the sand.

Accurate construction, diligent maintenance and above all the provision for adequate and rapid drainage are essentials where capillary beds are the method of irrigation. Water lying on the surface during prolonged periods of rainfall is detrimental to plants (especially those grown in loamless composts) and indicates a poor drainage system. An overflow pipe fixed to the water tank just above the normal level of water in the base of the sand layer will provide adequate back drainage for a bed of two to three metres wide, but in broader beds, additional full length drainage pipes at the same level and running three metres apart into take-away header pipes must be provided.

Vine Weevil in Nurseries

The entire question of pests (and of course diseases) is an extensive one and we do not intend to go into elaborate detail on all the setbacks which nursery stock growers can experience by these agencies. Rather, can we select what has become a notorious pest for nurseries — the vine weevil. This insect can cause major plant losses and serious damage is often done before the symptoms are evident and the infestation detected. The larvae of vine weevil damage roots and de-bark the stem just below soil level resulting in complete collapse of the plant. Adult vine weevils feed on leaves during the summer leaving typically notched edges on them. During the period of summer and early autumn, the adults lay eggs, and larvae which develop from these are fully grown by the following April or May when major damage will have been done.

Apart from regular scrutiny of plants, the purchase of stock from reliable sources and care that easy breeding grounds like old unattended plants are not provided, control of vine weevil has involved the incorporation of aldrin dust in the compost at the rate of 2 lb of 1.25% dust per cubic yard (1.5 kg per m^3). This gave protection for at least a year. However, the EEC derogation for this use of aldrin has recently been withdrawn and the alternative recommendation of gamma HCH incorporation at 1.4 oz active ingredient per cubic yard (30 g per m^3) is less persistent and less effective. There is also evidence that the recommendation of HCH drench at 0.5–1.0 oz active ingredient per 20 gallon water (10–20 g per 100 l) can give less than satisfactory control although the fact that it gives protection for about three months has not been generally appreciated. Adults can be controlled by spraying with gamma HCH at 0.6 oz active ingredient per 20 gallons water (12.59 g per 100 l). Chlorpyrifos at 0.5 oz active ingredient per 20 gallons water (10 g per 100 l) gives good control of vine weevil. It can be used as a drench on conifers but may be phytotoxic on some other species. Parasitic nematodes and entomophagous fungi are being studied in other countries and it appears possible that a biological control of vine weevil will be developed in the near future.

A new proprietory formulation containing micro-encapsulated fonofos is said to give good control

Weed Control

In the production of containerised nursery stock a cultural aspect which often receives too little attention is the control of weeds. Composts for potting will be substantially weed-free, and therefore weed seeds will be mostly distributed by introduction through transplants and in water or by wind. Our most troublesome weeds, especially in containers are:
Cardamine hirsuta (hairy bittercress)
Epilobium spp. (willowherbs)
Marchantia spp. (liverworts)
Poa annua (annual meadow grass)
Senecio vulgaris (groundsel)

Each one produces seed or spores in abundance and distributes them efficiently. All weeds in the nursery, including those at the inside edges of plastic houses, and at headlands and waste patches, must be eliminated.

Chloroxuron at 2 lb active ingredient per acre (2.25 kg per hectare) is recommended for overall application to potted stock, and this will control the most important germinating weeds. However, annual meadow grass is moderately resistant. Foliage should be washed clean of spray immediately afterwards in order to reduce the risk of scorch. Chloroxuron should be applied at two month intervals in dull or wet weather. *Berberis, Buddleia, Hydrangea* and golden-foliaged heathers may be susceptible to scorching.

Simazine 50 w at 1–2 lb active ingredient per acre (1.1–2.2 kg per hectare) can be used on container stock of many species against a wide range of weeds. Compared with chloroxuron this herbicide is more effective against annual meadow grass and less so against willowherbs and liverworts. Application should only be made to weed-free, moist soil surfaces. Some species such as *Senecio greyii*, *Deutzia* × *rosea* and *Weigela florida* **Variegata** are susceptible to damage on some occasions. Small-scale experiments with simazine should be carried out initially before any large-scale spraying is done.

Diphenamid at 4 to 8 lb active ingredient (4.5–9.0 kg per hectare) is effective against many grasses, annual weeds, including hairy bittercress and willowherbs, but mosses and liverworts are resistant. 'Cocktails' of chloroxuron and diphenamid are effective against this latter resistance, in addition to controlling a broad weed seedling spectrum.

Napropamide, applied at 3.6 lb per acre (4.0 kg per hectare) during the dormant season as an overall spray will control most annual weeds like cleavers, meadowgrass and groundsel. The newer herbicide, oxadiazon, though not recommendable as overall spray on many species is nevertheless effective as a directed spray against cleavers, sunspurge, bindweed and knotgrass. This can be applied at 1.8 lb active ingredient per acre (2.0 kg per hectare) during the period January to March before young plant leaves appear, as these are susceptible to damage.

An interesting new herbicide, oxyfluorfen, also for use during the dormant season up to the end of January, is effective against most annual broadleaved weeds. It has some contact action and in our tests, no damage was caused to one year old *Rhododendron*, *Berberis*, *Cotinus*, *Cupressocyparis leylandii*, *Ilex*, *Viburnum* and excellent weed control was obtained from an overall application at 0.4 lb active ingredient per acre (0.5 kg per hectare).

PART TWO
Alphabetical List of Genera

8
Their Propagation and Treatment

Abelia

Abelias are deciduous and evergreen shrubs thriving in sunny positions in any soil. *A. schumannii* (pink) and *A. x grandiflora* (white, tinged pink), low growing shrubs about 4 ft (1.2 m) high, have tubular flowers resembling small weigela flowers. They are appreciated for their long flowering season. *A. floribunda* is strikingly different in appearance, having tubular flowers 1½ in. (3.7 cm) long, rosy red in colour. All are somewhat tender in cold areas, *A. floribunda* being better on a wall in all but the mildest districts.

Propagation Nodal cuttings of the past season's growth 4–8 in. (10–20 cm) long may be inserted in the cold frame in September, after treatment with 0.8% IBA powder. When the cuttings are lifted for lining out in a well prepared bed the following April, 100% rooting may be expected. Alternatively softwood cuttings 2½–3½ in. (6–9 cm) long may be rooted under mist in April–May. Treatment with 0.8% IBA powder gives better developed root systems by lifting time, seven weeks later. Harden off and line out in a cold frame for the rest of the season. By the end of the year the plants should be about 8 in. (20 cm) high. Lift in spring and line out for growing on or containerise for sale in late summer.

Abies

The firs (*Abies*) may be distinguished from the spruces (*Picea*) by their upright, not pendulous, cones. Cedars (*Cedrus*) also have upright cones but have leaves in tufts on spur-like side shoots.

Uses Though many of the firs grow into large trees, they can be enjoyed for several years as young specimens before getting too big for the garden. *A. concolor* and *A. delavayi* are among those suitable for growing in this way. *A. koreana* is outstanding as a tree for small gardens, slow growing and bearing cones when as little as 2 ft (0.6 m) high.

Methods of propagation 1. Seed. 2. Grafting.

Method 1 Home grown trees of some species often produce empty seeds, which is unfortunate, as imported seed does not keep very well, germination falling rapidly after the first year. Order seed early and sow immediately outside in beds or frames. The degree of dormancy is apt to vary, some lots showing more than others, so if germination is poor the first spring, more seedlings may appear the following year. Most species grow slowly in their first year and so should remain in the seed bed for two seasons before being lined out in nursery beds.

Home saved seed may be stored for at least three years at 35°F (1.7°C) if the original moisture content is reduced to 6–8% of that of the fresh seed. This may be done by determining the original moisture content and drying accordingly.

Method 2 This is used for cultivars. The rootstocks used are either the parent species or *Abies alba*. They must be well established in pots before grafting and so are potted in April and plunged with soil just over the rims in outdoor beds for grafting the following February. The potted plants are brought indoors and side grafted by the veneer method (p. 32) with healthy one year old scions. As with *Picea*, one side only of the scion is cut lightly, removing only a sliver of wood. After tying, the grafts are placed in a closed case and allowed as much light as possible without causing scorch. Temperatures in the case are controlled close to 61°F (16°C). After seven or eight weeks, good callusing will have taken place. Harden off gradually and when growth commences, head back the rootstock and plant the grafted plants in well prepared outdoor beds, for growing on to saleable size.

Abutilon

A genus of shrubs hardy only in mild districts, valuable for their long season of flowering. Two species which can be grown out of doors are *A. vitifolium* with mallow-like flowers, mauve or white, and *A. megapotamicum* with tubular flowers of red and yellow.

Uses As specimens in sheltered sunny spots or against walls. *A. vitifolium* reaches 10 ft (3 m) or more and needs plenty of room. *A. megapotamicum* is a more slender shrub up to 6 ft (1.8 m) high.

Methods of propagation 1. Cuttings in the cold frame in September or in the warm bench and plastic in May. 2. Seed.

Method 1 Both species root easily from nodal cuttings. Stock plants may be overwintered in a cool greenhouse in cold areas. If the plants are grown outside, September cuttings are a useful precaution against losses. Pot the cuttings as soon as rooted. Within a year they should be saleable as 1½–2 ft (45–60 cm) high specimens.

Method 2 A. vitifolium sets seed freely. Sow in a warm greenhouse in February. Pot up into 3 in. pots. Subsequent development is rapid, especially if grown under glass or in a plastic house.

Acacia

Acacias, including the mimosa of the florists (*A. dealbata*), are tender plants, though in the mildest localities, as in SW Ireland, some species seed themselves. Seed is, indeed, the best means of propagation. In nature, the hard coated seeds germinate freely after bush fires, hence the advice that imported seeds should have boiling water poured on them, allowing it to cool and leaving the seeds to soak for 24 hours before sowing. Nodal cuttings of the current year's shoots can be struck in July, treating them with 0.8% IBA powder and inserting in two parts moss peat to one of sand in a mist unit. After four weeks, about 80% should have rooted. Pot into 3 in. pots, over-winter under glass and pot on in April into 5 in. pots. By July the plants can be sold as container grown specimens 1–2 ft high (30–60 cm). Acacias transplant badly and so should be planted direct from containers into their permanent sites before they become pot bound.

Acer (Japanese maples)

Japanese maples are small trees or bushes, cultivars of *Acer palmatum* and *A. japonicum*.

Uses *A. palmatum* is highly variable species. Most forms are grown for the gorgeous yellow and red autumn colour of the leaves. **Osakazuki** is one of the best for this purpose; the foliage, green in summer, turns to a flaming scarlet. **Atrosanguineum** is another good form of this type. **Atropurpureum** has coppery coloured foliage all through the season. Very distinct is the **Dissectum** group, having finely cut feathery foliage which, in some forms, turns a good yellow before falling. The cultivars in this group form low mounded specimens unless grafted as standards. **Senkaki** is the Coral Bark Maple, grown for the bright red of the young shoots in winter. The leaves turn yellow in autumn.

The Japanese Maples are not for exposed windy situations. They are at their best when given the shelter of other trees and shrubs.

Methods of propagation 1. Cuttings in mist or in the warm bench and plastic in April. 2. Grafting.

Method 1 The propagation of Japanese Maples from cuttings is not for beginners, though, with sufficient attention to detail, it is not really difficult. The first important point is that, at present, only some cultivars can be recommended as suitable. **Atropurpureum** and **Senkaki** are the best of these, then **Ozakazuki** and **Atrosanguineum**. The dissectums are difficult owing to their lack of vigour, though the purple leaved **Inabashidare** has given promising results. *A. japonicum* **Aureum** roots well but is difficult to grow on. *A.j.* **Vitifolium**, however, responds well.

Efforts, then, should be confined to suitable cultivars, and it is important that the mother plants be true-to-name, vegetatively propagated specimens, not seedlings from the original named cultivars. The second consideration is that the cuttings must be taken early to ensure that the resulting plants develop sufficiently during their first summer. Small weak plants are very difficult to 69 overwinter successfully. Thirdly, grow the plants on in the best conditions possible, under plastic or under glass, to encourage good shoot growth.

The cuttings should be taken in April. To obtain these early cuttings, the mother plants can be brought into an unheated but sunny glasshouse in February or into a plastic structure. The latter is very satisfactory. Sun heat alone is sufficient to bring on shoot growth. The mother plants should be healthy and vigorous so as to give good quality cutting material. Basal or internodal cuttings should be taken as soon as the shoots are 2–3 nodes and about 4 in. (10 cm) long. These will come in successive flushes but the yield per mother plant is not very high. A four-year-old plant can be expected to give about 25 good cuttings. One or two cuttings can be taken from one-year-old plants without spoiling them for sale. More recently, single node cuttings have given very promising results and may be the answer to the problem of obtaining plenty of material. Such cuttings have been very successful with *A. palmatum* **Inabashidare**, **Osakazuki** and *A. japonicum* **Vitifolium**, giving straight stemmed plants 1 ft (30 cm) high by autumn, which overwinter without loss.

The cuttings should be lightly wounded, removing a sliver of bark about ½ in. (1.2 cm) long from the base of the cutting. Treat with 0.8% IBA powder and insert in a compost of two parts moss peat to one of sand. Root in a mist unit, taking care that it is working efficiently. Japanese maple cuttings do not tolerate over-wet conditions. The warm bench and plastic method will give good results, but these thin-leaved cuttings need special care in shading. Given the care, they come out in better condition than from mist.

Up to 100% rooting can be expected in three to five weeks with **Atropurpureum** and **Senkaki**, with slightly lower percentages in other cases. Pot up promptly in 3 in. pots when rooted, and return the pots to the mist bench for a few days to get the plants fully established, but do not leave them a day longer than necessary as they deteriorate if wet for too long.

Japanese maples enjoy life in a plastic house, including the constant moisture of a capillary bed inside such a structure. As a group, they are sensitive to excess fertilisers in the compost, especially under the no-leaching conditions of an indoor capillary bed. The safest compost for potting up and growing on is that based on a proprietary slow release fertiliser. Though these added to moss peat alone have given excellent results, it is recommended that one part of sand be added to two parts of moss peat at least until experience has been gained in raising these maples. Ensure that all composts are thoroughly and properly mixed.

Assuming the cuttings have been potted up in May, root action should be rapid and potting on into 4½ in. pots will be needed in late June or early July. Grow them on in the plastic house but, at the beginning of leaf fall in October, the capillary beds should be run dry for the winter. By this time the plants should be branched specimens 12–15 in. (30–37.5 cm) high or single stems 20–24 in. (50–60 cm) long. Keep the compost only slightly moist over winter.

Ventilate the plastic house on all mild autumn days by leaving the doors open. The plants should be sprayed with a fungicide as a precaution against *Botrytis*, and, for the same reason, all dead leaves should be removed from the house. Should there be any signs of *Botrytis* subsequently, spray again.

The bush plants do not need winter pruning. Cutting back the shoots of Japanese maples does not induce free branching. The single stem specimens, however, should be headed back to about 6–8 in. (15–20 cm). These single

Fig. 31.

Fig. 32.

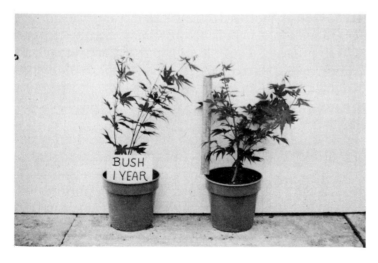

Figs. 31–33. Japanese maples from cuttings. Note light wounding, cuttings rooted in 24 days, and bush specimens a year later.

stems will then give two major branches during the coming season, to be pruned again back to five buds from the base of the new growth the following autumn.

It is important not to re-activate the capillary beds too soon in spring, otherwise the plants will fail to leaf out or will leaf out and collapse, or, at best, make sickly growth. Give the first few waterings by hand and do not start the capillary watering until suitable weather in March, at the earliest, when the plants can be potted on into 6 in. bags. The bush plants can be sold at any time from now on, after hardening off, as container grown plants in leaf. The single stem plants need retention for another season, pruning back as described above during their second winter so that they will be saleable in their third summer.

The raising of Japanese maples has been dealt with in some detail as they are subjects for careful treatment. In summary, the main problem is not so much getting the cuttings rooted as inducing vigorous growth afterwards, avoiding such pitfalls on the way to the point of sale as too rich a compost, too much moisture in winter and, as a further hazard, attacks of vine weevils. If this pest is on the nursery (and it is widespread) the grubs will devour the roots of the maples. Therefore, as a routine, after potting, give a drench of one of the liquid formulations of HCH sold for horticultural purposes.

Method 2 A. Japonicum **Aureum** and the fern-leaved cultivars of *A. palmatum*, though striking readily from cuttings, are troublesome to get through their first winter, owing to the difficulty of producing vigorous growth after rooting. For these, grafting is recommended and this can take place in the winter (February) and in the summer (July). February grafting has the advantage that the plants go straight into the growing season, but it is a more difficult process as the rising sap is liable to flood the cut faces and hinder callusing. For this reason, summer grafting is generally preferred.

The rootstocks may be raised from seed and some cultivars of Japanese maples set plenty of seed in this country. However, it is not ripe until late in the autumn, at or approaching leaf fall. It is best sown in trays of seed compost (p. 55) or in cold frames. Protect from vermin. If the seeds are allowed to dry out, germination may be delayed for a year. For this reason also, purchased seed is often slow and irregular in germinating. It is stated that germination of such seed is improved by placing it in warm water (110°F, 43.3°C) and leaving it to soak for 48 hours before sowing. Seed sown as soon as ripe germinates freely in spring. The following spring, plant out the seedlings 6 in. (15 cm) each way in a sheltered nursery bed. Although a proportion of the seedlings resemble the parent tree, it is not legitimate to give them cultivar names; these names belong only to specimens propagated vegetatively from true-to-name parent trees.

Where winter grafting (February) is to be carried out, the rootstocks should be two years old and about pencil thickness. About one week before grafting, the rootstocks are lifted and potted and stood out in a frost-free place. These plants are not encouraged to start into growth before grafting, because there is the danger of 'bleeding' when the graft cuts are made and this condition renders the cut surfaces more liable to attack from fungi. The rootstock is cut back to about 1 ft (30 cm) and a side graft with a lip is used (p. 31). One or two-year-old scion wood 3 in. (8 cm) long with well developed buds is suitable.

72 The grafted plants are plunged in well dampened peat in a grafting case and

the glass over them must not touch the plants. The bottom temperature should be held at 65°F (18°C) and, after a few days, ventilation should start for two short periods each week. After about four weeks the grafts will grow and hardening off should be effected by reducing the base temperature. At the end of March the grafts should be placed in a cold frame during suitable weather and, at this stage, the remainder of the rootstock stem is cut back and the wound waxed over to avoid any troubles from fungus. At the end of May they are planted out in well protected beds at a spacing of 1 ft square (30 cm × 30 cm). In view of the excellent growth made by Japanese maples inside a plastic house this may well replace outdoor culture of the plants during their first season.

If summer grafting (July) is desired, strong one-year-old rootstocks are potted in the previous April and plunged in soil out of doors. About ten days before grafting, the pots are lifted and brought into a shaded place and the plants are dried off almost to the point of wilting. Small side shoots and most of the leaves of the rootstock are removed and a similar graft to that described for winter grafting is carried out using healthy scionwood of the current season's growth. These grafts can be plunged in damp peat in either a grafting case in a glasshouse or in a cold frame with double glass. Ideally, the bottom temperature should be held at 68°F (20°C) and, by careful manipulation with shading, etc., this can be largely attained in the cold frame at that time of the year. After one week the plants can be ventilated briefly and thereafter given air twice per week. Some three weeks after grafting, callus will form on the cut surfaces and hardening off can start. After a further fortnight, with increasing ventilation, the lights can be removed and the plants protected with lath shading. At the onset of winter the lights should be replaced. As soon as the buds begin to move in the spring, the remaining rootstock stem is cut away and the grafts are planted for two years in the nursery at a distance of 1 ft square (30 cm × 30 cm). During this period, the plants should be sheltered from wind and strong sun. As mentioned above, grafted plants can be grown on on a capillary bed in a plastic house.

Fern leaved or pendulous cultivars are worked on a tall (1 ft or 20 cm) stem.

Acer (other species)

These include the Snake-bark maples (*Acer capillipes*, *A. davidii*, *A. rufinerve* and *A. hersii*) grown for the effect of the bark, striped with white, and for the yellow autumn colour of the foliage. *A. capillipes* has very red young shoots. *A. pennsylvanicum* belongs to this group but is less adaptable, needing an acid soil for best growth. *A. griseum* is grown for the peeling red bark and *A. negundo* principally for the variegated leaves of its cultivar **Variegatum**.

Our native sycamore (*A. pseudoplatanus*) has several important cultivars such as **Brilliantissimum** (pink foliage in spring), **Leopoldii** (variegated yellow and pink), **Worlei** (spring foliage yellow) etc. The Norway Maple (*A. platanoides*) gives us, among other variants, **Crimson King** (purple foliage), **Drummondii** (leaves margined white) and **Schwedleri** (crimson-purple leaves and shoots). The Sugar Maple (*A. saccharum*) is not so successful in Britain and Ireland. It is not to be confused with *A. saccharinum*, the Silver Maple widely planted on the Continent. There are many other species of which descriptions will be found in the standard reference books.

73

Uses For smaller parks and gardens the Snake-bark group, *A. griseum*, and *A. negundo* are recommended. *A. pseudoplatanus* **Brilliantissimum** is so slow in growth that it can also be accommodated. *A. platanoides* **Drummondii** is also quite modest in growth but should be watched for branches with leaves reverting to the normal green foliage. These must be cut out.

The other species and cultivars mentioned above grow large and are more suitable for planting in streets, squares and parks.

Methods of Propagation 1. Seed. 2. Cuttings. 3. Layering. 4. Grafting and budding.

Method 1 Seed, particularly home saved seed, is a satisfactory method of propagation for the species but seed is not produced every year. Since drying out of the seeds will induce dormancy, they should be gathered as soon as they begin to ripen (seen as a yellow-brown colour of the 'keys') and sown without delay. Cut open a few seeds to check that they are viable. *A. griseum* is notorious for generally producing empty seeds. If it is necessary to store the seed for a time, it can be held in polythene bags at 36°F (2.2°C). Successful storage for up to one year has been reported.

For sowing in quantity, the outdoor bed method may be followed (p. 24). The seed is broadcast over the bed, pressed into the soil and the bed surfaced with grit. Germination can be expected about March. In cold districts, frost protection may be necessary, e.g. by spruce boughs placed over the beds. Irrigation in summer is very helpful in encouraging good growth. Line out the following spring.

Small quantities of seed, especially of the rarer species, are better sown in trays under glass. These may be kept in a cold house or frame and brought into a warm house at the initiation of germination, which can be expected in March–April. By pricking off into 3½ in. pots about a fortnight later and placing them on a capillary bed in a plastic house, they will be ready to pot on into 6 in. polythene bags by June. In this way strong growth can be induced in the first year. In late summer the plants will be over 3 ft (0.9 m) high with the coloured bark of the Snake-bark types already showing.

If only dried seed is available it may go through two winters before germinating. Two American species, *A. saccharinum* and *A. rubrum* are exceptional in flowering very early in the year and ripening seed in early summer. Since they scarcely, if ever, produce seed in this country, seed raising would entail the receipt of fresh seed by air from USA for immediate sowing.

Method 2 In view of the uncertainty of seed production, it may be useful to know that some success can result from late struck (September) cuttings of the Snake-bark group. Nodal or basal cuttings 5–10 in. (12.5–25 cm) long are wounded, treated with 0.8% IBA powder and inserted under mist in a medium of two parts moss peat to one of sand. From 50–60% rooting can be expected. The cuttings are left undisturbed in the boxes, to be kept fairly dry over winter in a cold house or frame. Pot up in 4 in. pots in March. By growing on a capillary bed in a plastic house (potting on into a 6 in. bag in June) nice straight stemmed specimens up to 5 ft (1.5 m) can be produced in one year, with five to seven pairs of branches. *A. saccharinum* can be struck from nodal cuttings of the apical 6 in. (15 cm) of the current year's shoots taken in July, treated with 0.8% IBA powder and inserted under mist. Upwards of 60% rooting can be expected in three weeks. After being well hardened off the plants may be lined out in well prepared ground with a spray line for irrigation.

It is worth noting that *A. platanoides* **Crimson King**, often difficult to bud satisfactorily, will root from basal cuttings, not wounded but treated with 0.8% IBA powder, inserted under mist in July. Up to 70% may be expected to root in two months. Containerised and grown on in a plastic house such cuttings make whips up to 6 ft (2 m) high by the end of the following season.

Method 3 *A. cappadocicum* and *A. saccharinum* may be propagated by French layering (p. 28). Established mother plants are cut back hard in early spring to induce strong growth for layering. Lift the rooted layers in autumn and line out. *A. cappadocicum* may also be grown from cuttings as for Japanese maples, and develops well from early cuttings.

Method 4 (i) The grafting of acers can be carried out in February and March or in July and August. Cultivars should only be grafted onto their parent species. For winter grafting (bench), the selected one-year-old rootstocks are established in pots the previous year and, after drying off, are grafted by the whip method (p. 32) in late February or early March. After being tied firmly, the grafts, plunged in moist peat, are placed in a closed case with a base temperature of about 68°F (20°C). The union will develop in about six weeks and, after a suitable hardening-off period, the top growth of the rootstocks is removed. The grafts can be planted out in well prepared ground for growing on to produce a crown. For summer grafting, one-year-old rootstocks, potted in February or March are used. The scions are short shoots of the current season which have completed their growth. A side graft with a lip (p. 31) is used and the graft is plunged in moist peat in a closed case. After five weeks, during which the temperature is maintained at around 73°F (23°C) in the grafting case, the union is secure and, after hardening off, the graft is planted in the cold frame. At this time the stock is headed back and lights are placed on the frames for the winter. In the following spring, the plants are transplanted into outdoor beds and trained to whips and sold as such, or grown on to form a two to four-year-old tree with a crown.

(ii) Though cultivars of these maples are propagated by budding onto the parent species, these are not subjects for the beginner in the art of budding. Careful observance of a number of points is necessary for high percentage success. The buds must be encouraged into growth by restricting the dominance of the rootstock. The first step towards this is when planting the seedling rootstocks, purchased at the 6–10 mm grade. These are headed back to 18 in. (45 cm). They must be planted into ground in good heart to ensure strong growth. Budding should be carried out in June as soon as the bark on the stocks will lift. Use plump buds, avoiding those from sappy, over vigorous shoots. After budding, head back the stock to 14 in. (35 cm) above the bud, a further procedure in reducing dominance of the rootstock. After union has occurred the petioles will become detachable from the buds and practised operators advise that they be knocked off at this stage to prevent them becoming a focus of decay. The following February head back the remainder of the stock to 1 in. (2.5 cm) and stake the young shoot as it develops. It is advisable to seal the wound, e.g. with an anti-canker paint.

75

Actinidia

Actinidias are deciduous climbing plants from China and Japan. The best known species are *A. chinensis*, the Chinese Gooseberry, and *A. kolomikta*. The latter is grown for the pink and white variegation of the leaves. This feature is not apparent on young plants but develops on established plants grown in a sunny position.

Propagation may be effected by taking nodal or basal cuttings of the side shoots in June when they are about 6 in. (15 cm) long. Wound the cuttings, treat them with 0.8% IBA powder and place in a mist unit, in a medium of two parts moss peat to one of sand. In four to five weeks 80% or more of the cuttings should be rooted. Pot up in 4 in. pots. If the rooted cuttings are grown on in a plastic house on a capillary bed, they will be 10–12 in. (25–30 cm) high by autumn. Hold in pots over winter, containerise in April and the plants should be saleable by June–July.

Aesculus

The Horse Chestnut (*Aesculus hippocastanum*), though so familiar, is not a native tree. It comes from Northern Greece and Albania. The red Horse Chestnut (*A x carnea*) is a hybrid of *A. hippocastanum* with *A. pavia*. The pink Indian Horse Chestnut (*A. indica*) deserves to be better known, as it flowers later (June–July). *A. parviflora* is a shrub 8–15 ft (2.4–4.5 m), with white flowers in July–August.

Uses As specimen trees in parks and avenues. *A. parviflora* is fine as a lawn specimen where ample room can be given, as it is broader than high.

Methods of propagation 1. Seed. 2. Budding in July. 3. Root cuttings.

Method 1 Sow in autumn 3 in. (7.5 cm) apart and ½ in. (1.2 cm) deep as soon as ripe. The seed will not keep. Germination occurs in spring. Line out in autumn. *A x carnea* comes true.

Method 2 Budding is carried out in mid July on two-year-old *A. hippocastanum*. Only small side buds of the shoots are used. While the T-cut (p. 34) technique can be used, chip budding gives good results in percentage take and in even growth. When budding care should be taken to ensure that the cut is bound securely after insertion of the buds. The top of the understock is cut away close to the bud in the following February. By the end of the third growing season the plants should be about 5 ft (1.5 m) with six or eight branches to be pruned off, to give a whip.

Method 3 This system is used for *A. parviflora*. In December–January lift the mother plants and remove sections of root about 3 in. (7.5 cm) long, being careful to distinguish between the upper and lower ends (p. 5). Tie in bundles and bury them upside down in sand, out of doors. Line out the right way up in April. By the end of the year the young plants will be 3–4 in. (7.5–10 cm) high.

76

Ailanthus

Ailanthus glandulosa is the Tree of Heaven, notable for the very large pinnate leaves. These may be greatly increased in size by cutting down young trees and training up one of the resultant suckers. The flowers are of no account, those of male trees having an unpleasant scent.

Propagate from female trees by transplanting suckers, or by means of root cuttings (p. 5).

Amelanchier

A genus of deciduous small trees or shrubs, grown for the beauty of the abundant white flowers produced in spring before the leaves. There are a number of species of which *A. canadensis*, *A. x grandiflora* and *A. ovalis* are the best known.

Some species send up suckers which can be lined out. Seed (stratified over winter) and layering are the commonly advised methods of propagation. With *A. canadensis* we have had success with basal softwood cuttings of the current year's growth, taken in May, when four to six leaves were unfolded, the shoots being 3–3½ in. (7.5–8.7 cm) long. Treat with 0.8% IBA powder. After four to five weeks in a mist unit 95% or more should be rooted. Pot up in 3 in. pots and grow on in a plastic house on a capillary bed. By autumn the plants will be about 10 in. (25 cm) high. They can then be lined out or held over and potted on in spring, to be saleable by June. Other species were less successful.

Ampelopsis

See under **Parthenocissus**

Andromeda

Andromeda polifolia, a small shrub with pink flowers, is a rare native of peat bogs. Several cultivars are grown, differing from the type in size and habit. All are suitable for the rock garden or in association with other dwarf shrubs, in moist peaty soil. Cuttings root easily, e.g. basal cuttings of the current season's growth 1½–2½ in. (3.7–6.2 cm) long may be rooted under mist or by the warm bench and plastic method in June. No root promoting substances are needed. Upwards of 80% will root after four weeks, when they may be potted up and grown on on a capillary bed to form small saleable plants with three to four branches in autumn.

Araucaria

Araucaria araucana is the well-known Monkey Puzzle. Seed is produced in this country and may be sown in spring in a cold frame or, with more consistent results, under glass. In the latter case, harden off the seedlings but leave them in the boxes until they are ready to be lined out in a sheltered bed in

77

autumn. Growth in the early years is slow; five years from sowing, the plants will be 2-2½ ft (60-75 cm) high.

Arbutus

The most familiar Arbutus is *A. unedo*, the Strawberry Tree, native of Killarney and the Mediterranean region. The hybrid *A. x andrachnoides* (*A. andrachne x A. unedo*) should be better known on account of its red trunk.

Uses The Strawberry Tree is notable for flowering in autumn and winter, the bell shaped white flowers accompanying the round, rough skinned red fruits of the previous year. Both species grow too large for the small garden but could be used more in parks. Although they belong to the heather family, they are lime tolerant. *Arbutus* can be dismissed as dull shrubs if poorly grown but well treated specimens are handsome.

Methods of propagation 1. Cuttings in the cold frame in November. 2. Cuttings in mist or warm bench and plastic in February. 3. Seed.

Method 1 Basal cuttings are inserted in a compost of two parts moss peat to one of sand after wounding and treatment with 0.8% IBA powder. Lift and pot the following spring or early summer. It is advisable to grow on in containers until finally planted out, as *Arbutus* can transplant badly.

Method 2 Basal cuttings 2-3 in. (5-7.5 cm) long, treated as above, are inserted in a compost of two parts moss peat to one of sand. After eight weeks 80-90% rooting can be expected, when the cuttings are potted up and grown on. By autumn the plants will have made 14-16 in. (35-40 cm) extension growth.

Though *Arbutus* grows to tree-like dimensions, flowering begins early in life, as early as three years from the cutting when well grown.

Method 3 Squash the ripe fruits and mix the seed with sand. Only cover very lightly. The pots or boxes may be kept in a cold frame until germination starts in spring (about April) and then brought into the glasshouse. Prick off the seedlings into 3 in. pots when 1-2 in. (2.5-5 cm) high and grow on under glass or in a plastic house. Development is relatively slow and by autumn the seedlings are still in pots, 4-5 in. (10-12.5 cm) high. They may be lined out in a frame in spring.

Aristotelia

A genus of shrubs from the southern hemisphere, not very important in our gardens as they are tender and the flowers are inconspicuous. *A. peduncularis* roots readily (six weeks) from cuttings taken in May, treated with 0.8% IBA and inserted under mist.

Arundinaria

See under **Bamboo**.

Aucuba

The Spotted Laurel (*Aucuba japonica*) has come to typify the dull Victorian shrubbery. It has paid the penalty of its willingness to put up with the roughest and shadiest corners in the garden and its endurance of smoke and soot. Given a moderately sunny place in reasonable soil, *Aucuba* can be a handsome shrub, especially if male and female plants are grown together to ensure a good crop of the scarlet fruits. The common variegated form is female and was introduced from Japan long before the male forms; hence it is still not widely realised that aucubas can be grown for their berries.

Methods of propagation 1. Cuttings in the open ground, October–November 2. Layering.

Method 1 Basal shoots of the current year's growth 4–6 in. (10–15 cm) long inserted in October and November root freely. The use of rooting powder is unnecessary. They can be lifted the following May or June. Unless the rooted cuttings are given good conditions, growth in the first year may be slow but they should be saleable 1 ft (30 cm) high branched plants at three years old.

Method 2 Though it may seem strange to recommend layering for such an easily rooted plant as *Aucuba*, this method is described by some authorities as productive once the parent plant is well established as a vigorous stool by annual cutting back. The young shoots of the previous season are pegged down, giving each a twist. Shoots for next year's crop are thrown up from the stool. The layered shoots are removed and lined out the following autumn.

Azaleas (Deciduous)

The deciduous hybrid azaleas are of complex ancestry, numerous species being involved in their breeding. The earliest types (1830–1850) were the Ghent hybrids, comparatively tall and late in flowering, e.g. *Coccinea Speciosa*, still one of the best reds. These were followed by the **Mollis** types and further development included the **Knap Hill** and **Exbury** hybrids.

Uses Like Rhododendrons, these subjects make excellent specimen plants, but do not have the all-year-round effect of the former. Their true value is in the magnificence of their flowering, more especially when the flowers arrive before the bright green leaves in spring. In addition to being used as specimen shrubs, their use in mass planting in a thin woodland setting is recommended for their brilliant display in full flower. Some have scented flowers and the leaves of many are brightly coloured in autumn. These subjects will grow well in acid soils only.

Methods of propagation 1. Softwood cuttings in a warm bench and plastic or under mist. 2. Layering. 3. White polythene tunnel (see p. 19).

Method 1 The majority of the **Exbury, Knaphill** and **Mollis** types can be rooted by this method. The mother plants are covered with a polythene house in February and any flower-buds on the plants are removed. During sunny weather the temperature rises high enough in the polythene house for the 79 shoots to reach the four to five leaves unfolded stage by mid to the end of April. The basal cuttings are then removed with a sharp knife or blade. Each is lightly wounded and treated with 0.8% IBA powder and inserted either under mist or in the warm bench with plastic. The propagating medium recommended is moss peat only but successful results can also be achieved with a mixture of two parts of moss peat and one part of a granitic sand.

Hardening-off should start after about eight weeks as by then rooting will be quite advanced. The rooted cuttings should be carefully handled as the root system, although extensive, is only weakly attached to the stem. The plantlets are transferred to a cold frame for growing on in fertilised peat or in peat only, and liquid fed (p. 57). The frames are covered with shaded Dutch lights until the azaleas are well established. The plants are left in the frames for two

Fig. 34. Deciduous azaleas forced in an unheated polythene house provide excellent cuttings.

seasons. At this stage some of these plants can be sold as strong liners and the remainder transplanted to the nursery for growing on.

Method 2 The propagation of deciduous azaleas by layering is still practised by a few nurseries although, understandably, on a small scale in view of the general ease and success of Method 1. Layering is mostly carried out on the **Mollis** and **Knaphill** types which are pruned hard in spring to give strong growth. When the shoots of the current season's growth are firm (July), layering takes place. The leaves and small shoots along the area which is to be pegged down are removed. The soil is firmed around the layer. The following spring the flower-buds are removed from the tips of the layered shoots, and by autumn, the shoots are fully rooted and can be severed from the mother plant to be planted out for another season before sale.

Azaleas (Japanese)

This is a colourful dwarf-growing group of plants, the majority being evergreen in our climate.

Uses Individual specimens or groups are grown for the profusion of their early summer flowering. Their compact habit make them very suitable for small gardens. The period of flowering, depending on cultivar, extends through April and May and flower colour from white through light pink to deep red. Recommended cultivars include **Hino-Crimson** (bright red), **Florida** (brilliant rosy red, double flowers), **Adonis** (pure white), **Vuyk's Scarlet** (deep scarlet) and **Purple Triumph** (deep purple).

Method of propagation Cuttings (warm bench and plastic or mist).

In July semi-ripe 4 in. (10 cm) nodal or internodal cuttings are prepared. After being treated with 0.8% IBA they are inserted in moss peat only and covered with polythene film. Rooting percentages for most cultivars are high (70-90%) after six weeks.

After hardening off, the rooted cuttings are planted into a cold frame in a fertilised peat medium omitting lime (p. 56) at a spacing of 4-5 in. (10-12.5 cm) square. Dutch lights are placed in position and shaded until the plants are well established, after which they are hardened off by increasing the ventilation and finally by removing the lights. Little growth will take place during the remainder of the first season. The plants can be left *in situ* for a further year and a light trimming over during July will ensure the production of a well branched 6-8 in. (15-20 cm) plant in October of the second season. These are suitable as liners and should be grown on for a further season to produce good-sized saleable plants.

Azara

Apart from specialised collections, only two species, *Azara microphylla* and *A. lanceolata*, are commonly seen and these generally only in the milder districts.

Uses A. microphylla is a small-leaved evergreen shrub or small tree, with inconspicuous yellow flowers in February, strongly vanilla scented. The variegated form is more tender. *A. lanceolata* has more conspicuous, though scarcely scented, flowers in April. A bush in good bloom can be reminiscent of an acacia. Azaras are grown as specimens, needing the shelter of a wall in colder districts.

Methods of propagation 1. Hardwood cuttings in the open ground or cold frame in November. 2. Layering.

Method 1 Basal cuttings may be inserted in the open ground in November. Treatment with 0.8% IBA powder has proved beneficial. When lifted a year later upwards of 55% rooting may be expected. In cold districts it would be advisable to use a cold frame and, in any case, the more tender variegated form of *A. microphylla* is safer so propagated.

Method 2 Layering in spring has been recommended as an alternative to cuttings. Branches of the past season's growth are twisted as they are laid in and sand is worked around the base of the branches.

Bamboos (Arundinaria, Phyllostachys and Sasa)

There are numerous species of bamboo. Probably the commonest and hardiest in our gardens are *Arundinaria japonica, A. anceps* and *Sasa palmata*.

Uses A. japonica is useful for shelter, though no bamboo likes extreme exposure. It has the advantage of forming clumps without many underground suckers, in contrast to *A. anceps* and *S. palmata* which are too invasive for restricted areas. *A. nitida* and *A. murielae* are tall growing species, 10 ft (3 m) or more, of particularly graceful arching habit. They look well beside water. All bamboos thrive in moist semi-shaded situations but not in waterlogged ground.

Methods of propagation 1. Division. 2. Rhizome cuttings. 3. Basal cane cuttings.

Method 1 Although established bamboos give the impression of being robust growers, when it comes to dividing and transplanting all precautions must be taken against drying out of the roots. The top growth will wither in any case, so cut down the canes to 1 ft (30 cm) before clumps or portions of clumps are dug up. Lifting bamboos on a large scale is like trying to drive the spade into a tough mat, so it is advantageous to establish mother plants on a peaty or other stone free soil. Even so, a mattock will be a useful implement. As far as possible, and especially with the clump-forming species, the cane stumps should be brought up two or three together, as such small groups establish well and produce new growth from dormant buds. The operation should be done in mild showery weather in April–May. The canes that grow the first year are short and do not elongate thereafter. Further canes spring from below ground each year, each flush out-topping the last until maximum height is reached. The divisions can go straight to their permanent positions or be lined out for one year.

Method 2 Many species of running bamboos (as opposed to clump forming kinds) can be propagated by lifting and cutting the underground rhizomes into sections about 1 ft (30 cm) long, each bearing dormant buds. Lift the roots in early spring, before the end of March, in advance of shoot growth. Discard old rhizomes as the buds have usually died on these. The sections of the selected rhizomes may be planted horizontally in trenches about 5 in. (12.5 cm) deep in well cultivated fertile soil, but scarce or delicate species should be boxed up under glass to be hardened off and planted out with the minimum of disturbance when well established. At no time should the rhizomes be allowed to get at all dry during operations. Keep them covered with wet sacks until planted. Irrigate afterwards if necessary. Leave for two years, then lift and head back, as already described, before planting in their permanent position. Plants in transit should be kept from drying out.

A word of warning is necessary in relation to *A. anceps*. This species does not send out true rhizomes but underground stolons with a bud only at the tip. When the cane has developed from this bud it then throws out roots at the base. This species is unsuitable for propagation as described, since there are no buds between the stolon tip and the parent plant. *A. anceps* can be propagated by division of well established plants which will have buds at the base of the canes, or by basal cane cuttings (below).

82

Method 3 When long established clumps of many species are examined, it will be found that at the base of the canes there may be one or two rings of incipient roots springing from the nodes at or close to ground level. These root initials develop more freely in mild areas of high rainfall. Very often these roots have died off after growing to a length of a few centimetres. All stages may be present from a ring of purple spots (incipient roots) on the youngest canes to rings of dead rootlets on old canes. If canes at the right stage, i.e. with roots just emerging and still alive, are cut out at ground level, shortened and placed in soil in a shaded frame or boxed up under glass, the rootlets will develop and be followed by shoots. This method is not practicable on a large scale, owing to the labour involved in selecting and cutting out only canes in the right condition. After hardening off, the boxed or frame grown plants can be lined out during mild weather in autumn or spring.

Banksia

A genus of Australian trees and shrubs, not hardy enough for outdoor cultivation except in the mildest localitieis. They are allied to *Grevillea*, but carry their flowers in dense cylindrical spikes, variously coloured yellow, green or silver grey.

Uses As specimens in well drained sunny places in the mildest gardens only.

Method of propagation Our limited experience has been confined to *Banksia marginata* which can be rooted quite readily from basal cuttings, inserted in a mist unit in late August. Pot up the rooted cuttings in 3 in. pots and over-winter under glass. In spring pot on. The young plants should go from pots into their permanent positions.

Berberidopsis

Berberidopsis corallina is an evergreen climber capable of reaching 18 ft (5.4 m) with dark green, slightly spiny leaves. The pendant flowers are dark red, on red stalks, and are globose in shape. This species is not hardy in cold districts but in milder areas is a beautiful specimen on a north wall, in a moist, lime-free soil.

Method of propagation Cuttings under mist in July.
   Semi-hard side shoots of the current year, 2–4 in. (5–10 cm) long are treated with 0.8% IBA powder and inserted in a compost of two parts moss peat to one of sand. About 90% rooting may be expected after eight weeks, when the rooted cuttings may be potted up in a loamless compost. Pot on and sell as two- and three-year-old staked, container grown plants.

Berberis (deciduous)

The deciduous barberries are grown for their masses of red berries or for their coloured foliage. The former include *Berberis aggregata* and its hybrids, such

83

as **Barbarossa, Buccaneer** and **Pirate King**. *B. thunbergii* in its typical form has foliage that turns a brilliant red before falling, while the cultivar **Atropurpurea** has leaves that are purple throughout the season. *B x ottawensis* **Superba** is similar in leaf colour but is much larger and more vigorous.

Uses **Barbarossa** and its fellows are worthy of a sunny spot in the garden. Their intense prickliness renders them impervious to marauders in parks and public gardens. *B. thunbergii* **Atropurpurea** makes a striking low hedge some 2½ ft (75 cm) high. The dwarf form **Atropurpurea Nana** can be used in bedding. *B. x ottawensis* **Superba** is more striking where a single specimen of a purple foliaged shrub is required.

Methods of propagation 1. Cuttings in the cold frame or cold frame and plastic in September–October. 2. Cuttings in the cold frame and plastic or under mist in July. 3. Seed. 4. Division.

Method 1 In our experience, while *B. thunbergii* **Atropurpurea**, *B. thunbergii* **Atropurpurea Nana**, *B.* **Kobold** and *B. x ottawensis* **Superba** are easily rooted by this method, the **Barbarossa** types need more care and extra cuttings should be inserted as a precaution. For the easier types, take nodal or heeled cuttings of the past season's growth. *B. x ottawensis* in particular sends up long straight shoots which can be cut into sections four to five nodes long, cutting just above and below a bud. Any side shoots can be used as basal cuttings. After treatment with 0.8% IBA powder, insert in a cold frame of compost two parts moss peat to one of sand. For the aggregata types, take nodal cuttings of the past season's growth about 8 in. (20 cm) long. For dwarf forms, eg. *B. thunbergii* **Kobold** use basal cuttings 2–4 in. (5–10 cm) long. As an added precaution against rotting, add a fungicidal powder to the IBA powder to the extent of 5% by volume. The prickly cuttings are awkward to handle but the leaves and spines must be removed from the lower 1½ in. (3.7 cm) or so of the cutting, which is then wounded. The cold frame should be tight fitting to exclude draughts, even to the extent of bedding down the light onto strips of foam rubber. Space at 1 × 2 in. (2.5 × 5 cm). Harden off and lift the cuttings the following April. Since the rooting compost is very peaty, the cuttings should lift with a good root ball for transplanting to a well prepared nursery bed. This frees the frame for further use. The plants should be saleable as two-year-olds 1 ft (30 cm) high.

Method 2 Two-node cuttings, mallet or heeled as convenient, may be rooted in the cold frame with plastic or under mist. Treat the cuttings with 0.8% IBA powder. After one month 75–90% rooting may be expected, but no shoot growth takes place until the following season. Harden off the rooted cuttings and line out in a sheltered, well prepared bed in spring.

Method 3 Follow the procedure advised for evergreen barberries. Named clones cannot be raised from seed. Seedlings of *B. thunbergii* **Atropurpurea** can be rogued to give a stand of coloured-leaved seedlings.

Method 4 Dwarf tufted forms, e.g. *B buxifolia* **Nana** can be increased by
84 division in autumn.

Berberis (Evergreen)

There are many evergreen barberries. Those more commonly seen include *B. darwinii*. *B. candidula*, *B. linearifolia*, *B. gagnepainii*, *B. x lologensis*, *B. x stenophylla* and *B. verruculosa*. There are several other species that deserve to be better known, such as *B. valdiviana*, notable for the long yellow racemes of blossoms contrasting well with the dark foliage.

Uses As specimens in gardens and for group planting in parks and other open spaces. They are well protected by thorns or prickles and can be used as barrier plants. *B. darwinii* and *B. x stenophylla* are among the most colourful of taller shrubs reaching 10 ft (3 m). *B. linearifolia* and *B. x lologensis* are rather smaller shrubs of the same group. *B. verruculosa* and *B. candidula* are densely prickly evergreen for the middle or front of the border. The latter species has a particularly neat rounded habit of growth. There are dwarf forms of *B. x stenophylla* such as **Corallina Compacta** (1–1½ ft or 30–45 cm) which might be used more often in groups in bedding plant fashion.

Methods of propagation 1. Cuttings in the cold frame in September–early November. 2. Cuttings in mist in July–September. 3. Seed. 4. Grafting.

Method 1 Suitable species include *B. verruculosa*, *B x stenophylla*, its cultivars, and *B. candidula*. Basal, nodal or heeled cuttings 2–5 in. (5–12.5 cm) long, according to species, are treated with 0.8% IBA powder after removal of the leaves and spines from the lower portion with a sharp knife. Mallet cuttings of *B. verruculosa* are convenient to prepare as this species branches freely, though showing no advantage in rooting over basal or heeled cuttings. The rooting medium is two parts moss peat to one of sand. Water in and close the frame tightly. To ensure close fitting, bed the sashes into strips of foam rubber. Should the weather be sunny, shade the frames and renew the shading in spring (February onwards). 95–100% rooting can be expected by April when they are lifted and lined out for growing on.

Method 2 *B x lologensis*, sometimes considered a relatively difficult species to root, and *B. valdiviana* will root 65–80% in 7–10 weeks by this method. Unwounded mallet or basal cuttings are treated with 0.8% IBA powder and inserted into two parts moss peat to one of sand. Late struck (October) cuttings can be left in the boxes until spring. Harden off and line out in frames for one year.

Method 3 Prepare the seed bed the previous autumn so that the final breaking down to a fine surface can be carried out as soon as the seed is ready in early spring. Gather the berries as soon as coloured, crush and mix with twice the volume of sand for stratification over winter. Small quantities may be placed in boxes or pots and placed outside. The pots may be plunged. Larger quantities can be pitted in a cold frame (but see p. 22). Inspect periodically to ensure that mice are not attacking the stratifying seed. As soon as germination begins (as shown by the seedling roots starting to emerge) sow sand and seed thinly together on the prepared bed. Cover with soil or sand to a depth of ½ in. (1.2 cm). It is advisable to sow in drills 5 in. (12.5 cm) apart so that hand weeding can be carried out until the roots are 2 in. (12.5 cm) down into the soil. Then simazine can be applied to maintain a weed free bed. From 3–6 in. (7.5–15 cm) of growth can be expected the first season. Give a top dressing of 85 calcium ammonium nitrate at 4 lb per 100 sq yd (2.1 kg per 100 sq m) in June–July. Line out the seedlings in autumn. A year later the plants can be sold in two grades, 12–15 in. and 15–18 in. high (30–37.5 and 37.5–45 cm).

Transplanting of *B. darwinii* is important in the nursery, otherwise the plants may move badly later.

Method 4 Grafting is sometimes employed for barberries troublesome to propagate from cuttings. We have had success in grafting *B. x lologensis* **Orange Queen** and *B. linearifolia* **Orange King** onto one-year old *B. x ottawensis* raised from cuttings. The rootstocks were side grafted in February after their tops had been removed to leave a stub of a couple of inches. The grafted plants were held in a close case at 15°C until union was complete, and then grown on in a plastic house on a capillary bed. By the end of the season they were saleable branched specimens at 2 ft (60 cm) high.

Betula

Our native birches belong to two species, *Betula verrucosa* and *B. pubescens*. The former is the Silver Birch, whiter in the trunk than the latter and having smooth, shining brown, rather than dark brown twigs. The birches have synonyms which can be pitfalls for the unwary. *B. verrucosa* has been known as *B. pendula*, but to be sure of a true weeping birch one must specify *B. verrucosa* **Youngii**. *B. alba* is another synonym. *B. verrucosa* **Tristis** is a very attractive tall growing cultivar with a white trunk, forming a slender tree with pendulous branches, though it is not weeping in the full sense of the word.

There are a number of exotic birches which deserve to be more widely known. Among these *B. costata* has a smooth creamy bark. *B. albosinensis* var. *septentrionalis* has pink and grey tints to the shining orange brown bark. *B. jacquemontii* has the whitest trunk of all.

Uses As specimen trees, for bark colour and graceful habit. *B. verrucosa* **Youngii** makes an umbrella shaped specimen for smaller gardens. *B. verrucosa* **Tristis** is suitable for landscaping round buildings on account of its tall, relatively narrow habit of growth. Birches associate well with heathers and low growing junipers. The birch is a good roadside tree.

Methods of propagation 1. Seed. 2. Cuttings from May to July or in September, according to species. 3. Grafting.

Method 1 Birches can be grown so quickly from seed that this method should be used whenever possible. Our experience is that the species come quite true from seed. Though hybrids between our native birches do occur, they are stated by leading botanical authorities to be 'probably rare'. Various other hybrids are recorded but, provided the parent trees are reasonably isolated, there does not seem reason to fear uncontrollable hybridisation.

The seed should be gathered in late autumn, when incipient disintegration of the catkins is seen. Scales and seed will be mixed together but it is not practicable to separate them. The mixture should be stored in linen bags, hanging them up in a cold and airy shed open to frost until sowing time in February. If the seed is sown in an outdoor bed, the plants will be only a few inches high by the end of the season. For horticultural purposes it is better to avail of the great response shown to a little warmth, food and shelter. By the system detailed below, specimens 7 ft (2.1 m) high can be produced in seven months.

The seed is sown under glass in February, in a temperature of 60–70°F (15.6°–21.1°C) using trays or boxes of seed compost. Sow thinly, even though the seeds are mixed with the scales of the catkins. Cover the seed lightly and place a sheet of glass over the box. Shade with sheets of newspaper. Provided the seed was sown thinly, the seedlings may be kept in the trays to grow quickly to the second rough leaf stage (this takes about one month) when they are potted up into 3 in. pots, using a loamless compost (pp. 55–6). At all stages in their development, pot on promptly to avoid a check to the seedlings. From the 3 in. pots they can go to 6 in. polythene bags (about May). The plants should be placed on a capillary bed inside a plastic house. In this way the young trees will be encouraged to reach 4 ft (1.2 m) or more high by the end of June. At this stage they can be planted out from the containers into the open ground. Such specimens may not make much more growth during the remainder of the season unless conditions are particularly favourable, e.g. well sheltered fertilised peatland. To grow 7 ft (2.1 m) specimens before October, it is necessary to pot them on further (in July) into a 14 in. bag and keep them on the capillary bed under plastic.

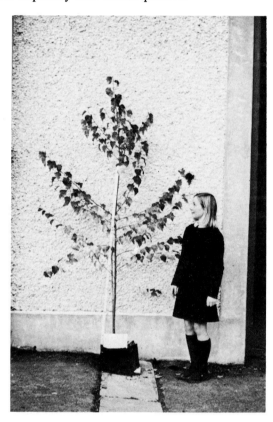

Fig. 35. *Betula* seedlings grow rapidly under plastic.

In our experience *B. jacquemontii*, when grown well, can be expected to show a white trunk three years from the sowing of the seed, as a specimen 2½ in. (6.8 cm) in girth. Other species have not been so quick to assume their characteristic bark colours.

Method 2 It is possible to grow birches from cuttings under mist, though they are not the easiest subjects to root or to grow on successfully, unless attention 87 is given to detail. *B. lutea* has proved the most amenable of the species tried, shoots of the current season's growth rooting readily (75–92%) from mid May to mid July, but even early cuttings of birches do not make extensive growth until the following season. Other species root poorly before September and, even then, a 50% strike can be regarded as good. It is important to take strong cuttings 5–6 in. (12.5–15–cm) long of the current year's growth from vigorous trees. They are wounded and treated with 0.8% IBA powder before being inserted in a compost of two parts moss peat to one of sand in a mist unit. Rooting will occur after one month. The best chance of successful overwintering is to leave the cuttings undisturbed in the box, overwintering them in a cold house, keeping them moderately dry. (*B. lutea*, rooting early, can be potted up as soon as rooted or even successfully established in a cold frame with the protection of lights and shading.) Pot up in 4 in. pots, using a loamless compost just before growth starts in March. When in leaf, place on a capillary bed inside a plastic house. Pot on into 6 in. bags in June. By leaf fall the trees may be expected to reach a height of 5–7 ft (1.5–2.1 m).

Method 3 Grafting is carried out in January and early February. Considerable advance preparations have to be made. Two-year-old seedlings of *B. verrucosa* are used as understocks; they should be 3–5 mm diameter. These are potted up in the autumn into 3–4 in. pots, using a loamless compost. They are plunged out of doors until early January, when they are brought under glass for the preliminary drying off, a process stressed as important by experienced operators. This means that the stock plants should be dry at the root but showing a swelling of the buds indicating that they are right for the grafting operation. Very humid conditions are required, so a polythene tent is arranged over a bench fitted with bottom heat. Set the thermostat at 68°F (20°C). The bench may be filled with sand or peat thoroughly wetted to aid in maintaining the humidity. The scions, selected in November, are of clean straight lengths of the past season's growth, cut to 10–14 in. (25–35 cm). Heel these in under a north facing wall in sand. At grafting time, head the stock back to within 6 in. (15 cm) of the soil. Graft by the side veneer method (p. 32). The cuts on stock and scion should be long (1½ in. or 3.7 cm) with a bud on the opposite side to the cut on the stock. Use rubber ties. Place the grafted plants within the polythene tent and spray them periodically with a fine mist. Keep the house shaded. Under these conditions callusing should be evident in two to three weeks. All this time the grafted plants should be kept in a humid atmosphere but watering should not begin until the tent is removed. This should be done in very easy stages beginning when callusing is obvious and, when completed, there should be a strong union of stock and scion with several inches of new growth. Give water freely, harden off gradually and place the young trees on a capillary bed in a plastic house where subsequent growth will be so strong that the trees may be 6 ft (1.8 m) by July. Then they should be placed outside to be held for sale in autumn, or they may be planted out for growing on.

The American method of grafting on the open bench can be equally successful. The precautions and procedure are as above but, after grafting, the graft unions are coated in paraffin wax. This is accomplished by inverting the grafted stock and dipping it into a container of warm liquified wax covering the scion and graft junction. A stout cardboard disc with a slit in one side is useful for placing over the surface of the pot to prevent loss of soil. After waxing, the pots are stood on a warm bench of moist peat and the humidity of the house kept up by damping down the floor from time to time. This method makes the use of the polythene tent unnecessary. Once the union is complete, cut the ties, harden off the plants and then transfer them to a capillary bed in a plastic house to be grown on as above.

Billardiera

Billardiera longiflora is an evergreen twining climber from Tasmania. The flowers are not very conspicuous, being greenish yellow, but are followed by oblong fruits, bright blue in colour. These make the plant a conspicuous feature in autumn, the fruits being over ½ in. (1.2 cm) long. Since the plant is light in growth and does not exceed 6 ft (1.8 m) in height, it is suitable for training up wire netting on a sunny wall in the milder districts. There is a white fruited form.

Methods of propagation 1. Seed. 2. Cuttings.

Method 1 Each berry contains numerous seeds. Despite the origin of the species, it has been our experience that the seeds only germinate after two winters in a cold frame. On initiation of germination the boxes may be brought into a glasshouse, temperature circa 65°F (18°C), pricked off and grown on under glass or plastic to be sold as pot grown specimens in autumn, 12–18 in. (30–45 cm) high.

Method 2 Basal cuttings of the current year's shoots 4–5 in. (10–12.5 cm) can be rooted under mist in June. Pot up and grow on using a capillary bed in a plastic house.

Buddleia

The well known buddleias are cultivars of *Buddleia davidii*, a native of China. Improved newer forms include **Black Knight** (deep violet), **Royal Red** (red-purple), **White Profusion** (white) and others. *B. globosa* with round ball-like heads of flowers is quite well known. Less often seen are *B. alternifolia*, willow-like in habit with lilac flowers, and *B. colvillei* with tubular, deep rose flowers, tender in cold districts.

Uses B. davidii will grow in any sunny place where a tall shrub up to 10 ft (3 m) is required. They flower in late summer and are well known for attracting Red Admirals, Peacocks, Tortoiseshells and other butterflies. The plants should be cut back very hard each spring. *B. globosa*, also tall, flowers in late spring and early summer and needs plenty of room. *B. colvillei* is best with the shelter of a high wall.

Methods of propagation Buddleias grow so easily from any type of cutting that description seems almost superfluous. (Soft cuttings under mist or warm bench and plastic are recommended for *B. alternifolia*.) However, two economical methods are:
  1. Cuttings in the low tunnel in June.
  2. Cuttings in the open ground in November.

89

Method 1 Nodal cuttings about 4 in. (10 cm) long are inserted. Treatment with rooting powder is not needed. Every cutting should root and, after hardening off and being left *in situ*, should be 3½ ft (1 m) high by autumn. Since growth is so strong do not place the cuttings too close together but give them 3 in. (7.5 cm) each way.

Method 2 In November long shoots of the past season's growth can be sectioned into portions 8–10 in. (20–25 cm) long and are inserted to three quarters of their length in the ground. Lift when rooted in spring and line out for growing on until autumn.

Buxus

The commonly cultivated forms of Box are derived from *Buxus sempervirens*, a native of Europe, N. Africa and W. Asia.

Uses The typical form can grow to 15 ft (4.5 m) or more high and is adaptable to topiary work, including clipped specimens in various shapes for growing in tubs. Box edgings, once so popular, are of the dwarf cultivar **Suffruticosa**. Box is so tolerant of any soil or situation that its value in the garden may be underrated. The variegated form (**Argentea**), for example, can look well clipped low and flat as ground cover at the sides of entrance drives and other semi-formal places.

Methods of propagation 1. Cuttings in the open, September–November. 2. Division.

Method 1 Box comes very readily from cuttings of the past season's growth, 3–6 in. (7.5–15 cm) long inserted in September–November, in the open ground, or in a frame or in cold districts. A suitable compost would be two parts or one part of moss peat to one of sand. The use of rooting powders is not necessary. Line out in spring.

Method 2 Dwarf box can conveniently be multiplied by simple division in spring. Established plants are lifted, pulled apart and re-inserted in rows 8–12 in. (20–30 cm) apart.

Callistemon

A genus of Australian shrubs for sunny positions in mild localities. They are called 'Bottle Brushes' from the cylindrical spikes of flowers, usually red or white. They may be raised from seed, sown under glass or softwood basal cuttings from side shoots about 5 in. (12.5 cm) long may be taken in June. Treat with 0.8% IBA powder and insert under mist. Lift and pot into 3 in. pots after four to five weeks when 90% or more of the cuttings should be rooted. Grow on under glass and re-pot to sell in summer and autumn of the following year.

Callitris

Callitris rhomboidea, the Oyster Bay Pine, is a conifer from Australia with finely divided branchlets, somewhat Cypress-like. It is too tender for any but the mildest localities. Basal cuttings treated with 0.8% IBA powder may be struck under mist in July; though rooting is slow, 60% success may be expected finally, the cuttings tending to root irregularly over a period of months. Further investigation may result in improved techniques.

Calluna

See under **Erica**.

Camellia

A group of evergreen hardy shrubs. The older cultivars are derived from *C. japonica* and have dark, glossy, rounded leaves compared with the pointed leaves of the *C. x williamsii, C. reticulata* and *C. reticulata x saleunensis* types introduced since the beginning of the century.

Uses Though more lime tolerant than rhododendrons, camellias need neutral or acid soil to thrive. Ideally they are shrubs for light woodland but they will thrive in the open if given a north or west aspect. Shelter from the morning sun is desirable to minimise damage to the flower buds after frost. They are excellent shrubs for growing in tubs as they will tolerate being pot bound if watered and fed, e.g. with a proprietary liquid feed. All feeding should stop in August as camellias are sensitive to excess fertiliser salts.

Methods of propagation 1. Single node cuttings under mist or warm bench and plastic in February. 2. Nodal shoot cuttings in late June or early July, under mist or warm bench and plastic.

Method 1 has the advantage of yielding more cuttings for a given amount of material but the resulting plants take a year longer to reach saleable size. The shoots of the past season's growth are cut into sections, each consisting of a single leaf with a bud in the leaf axil. Cut just above and approximately 1 in. (2.5 cm) below this bud. Wound by removing a strip of bark and underlying tissue about 1/5 in. (0.5 cm) long at the base of the cutting on the side opposite to the bud. Treat with 0.8% IBA powder and insert in a medium of peat only. Do not discard the tips of the shoots as they root particularly well; make each into an additional cutting with two leaves. From 45–100% rooting can be expected in ten to twelve weeks. Pot up into 3 in. pots. Camellia cuttings are very sensitive to excess fertilisers in the compost, so caution is needed. Two composts that have given good results are John Innes Base fertiliser at the rate of ¼ lb per bushel of peat (2.9 kg per cu m) or slow release fertilisers used at low rates as recommended by the manufacturer. Where necessary add fritted trace elements to the latter.

By keeping the rooted cuttings continuously under glass or in a plastic house 6–12 in. (15–30 cm) extension growth should be made by autumn. Hold over winter in a cold house. Repot in spring into 5 in. pots and sell in summer and autumn as 12–18 in. (30–45 cm) plants.

Method 2 Nodal cuttings 4 in. (10 cm) long of the current year's growth taken at the end of June are wounded, treated with 0.8% IBA powder and inserted   91 in moss peat. 60–100% rooting can be expected in seven weeks. Pot up in 3 in. pots as described above. Little extension growth is made during the rest of the season. Hold over winter under cover and pot on into 5 in. pots in spring. During the summer 1–2 ft (30–60 cm) extension growth will be made and if unstopped one or two long willowy shoots will result, especially with the Williamsii types. Pinch the leader when 3–4 in. (7.6–10 cm) long. Sell in autumn. The Williamsii types make flower buds while still in the 3 in. pots. Such small plants should be disbudded.

Carmichaelia

These are curious shrubs belonging to the pea family. The branchlets are flattened and carry out the functions of leaves. The small pea shaped flowers are pink or purplish. Plant in a sunny place in well drained soil.

Home or imported seed, sown under glass in February, pricked off in April into 3 in. pots and potted on in June–July will give plants about 1 ft (30 cm) high for sale as container grown plants in autumn.

Carpenteria

There is only one species in this genus, *Carpenteria californica*, a dark leaved evergreen shrub with clusters of white, scented flowers in summer. Surprisingly enough, it is related to the familiar mock orange (*Philadelphus*).

Uses Carpenteria is rather tender and in most districts is best as a bush against a sunny wall. Though it can reach 6 ft (1.8 m), it is more often seen as a medium sized specimen 3–5 ft (1–1.5 m) high.

Method of propagation Hardwood cuttings in April in the warm bench with plastic.

Basal hardwood cuttings 2½–3 in. (6.2–7.5 cm) taken in April have proved much more satisfactory than the softwood cuttings recommended in the literature. They are not wounded but, after treatment with 0.8% IBA rooting powder, are inserted in a compost of two parts moss peat to one of sand under the warm bench and plastic method (p. 13). Pot up into 5 in. pots using a loamless compost (pp. 55–6). It is advisable to pinch the leader as soon as the plants are established, to induce bushy growth. Grow on the plants on a capillary bed in a plastic house, repotting into 5 in. plastic bags towards the end of June. By autumn they should be 7–9 in. (17.5–22.5 cm) high. Overwinter under glass. They can be sold during the second year as container-grown plants.

Though softwood cuttings root well under mist in June, they make negligible growth during the remainder of the season and by autumn are still small plants in 4 in. pots, only 2–3 in. (5–7.5 cm) high.

Propagation of *Carpenteria* by hardwood cuttings as described above has proved so satisfactory that we do not consider the older system of layering a mother plant inside a cold frame to be any longer an attractive method.

Carpinus

The Hornbeam (*Carpinus betulus*) is a tree rather like a smaller beech in general aspect. If used for hedging it holds its dead leaves through the winter in the same manner as the beech. For horticultural purposes, the fastigiate form **Fastigiata** is a useful small tree for roadsides, parks and larger gardens.

Methods of propagation 1. Seed. 2. Cuttings in mist in August. 3. Grafting.

Method 1 Seed should be used only for the typical form. Gather in autumn immediately the seeds are ripe and sow at once in beds in the open ¼ in. deep (0.6–0.7 cm). Germination should occur the following spring. Seed allowed to dry out is less predictable.

Method 2 Cuttings have proved successful with cv. **Fastigiata** and, no doubt, other cultivars would respond. Cuttings taken before August have given poor results but inserted under mist in mid August have rooted 100%. The cuttings should be about 6 in. (15 cm) long. After wounding the cuttings, treat them with 0.8% IBA powder. We have had 100% rooting in six weeks with powder of this strength but in America a 2% IBA powder is recommended. Pot up the rooted cuttings and overwinter in a cold house or frame with temperatures a little above 32°F (0°C). If kept warm successful overwintering is doubtful.

Method 3 The rootstock used is *C. betulus*, and these should be established in pots a year before grafting in February and should be about pencil thickness. The stocks are brought into a warm glasshouse in January and left on the bench until root growth has commenced. At that stage, the stocks are headed back to about 2 in. (5 cm) and the whip graft (p. 32) is used. The scions should be healthy wood of the previous season's growth. Bind the graft securely and place in a closed case with a temperature of 68°F (20°C). Callusing will take place after five or six weeks and hardening off can then proceed by reducing the temperature and increasing ventilation. Plant out in a sheltered, well prepared outdoor bed or frame for one year. It will be necessary to stake the plants in the first year. Transplant to beds and grow on for two years.

Caryopteris

In gardens the most important *Caryopteris* is the hybrid *C. x clandonensis*. This is a low growing shrub 2 ft (60 cm) tall, with grey leaves and masses of blue flowers, valuable for flowering in late summer and autumn. **Ferndown** and **Heavenly Blue** are clones with darker flowers.

Uses Excellent for any spot in full sun in well drained soil, particularly where lime is present. *Caryopteris* could be used more for massed planting in parks and other public places.

Methods of propagation 1. Mist or warm bench and plastic in June. 2. Cuttings in the low tunnel in June.

Method 1 By this method 90–100% rooting of softwood nodal or basal cuttings can be expected in three weeks in a compost of two parts moss peat to 93 one of sand. Treatment with rooting powders is not necessary. The rooted cuttings can be potted, then containerised for sale in flower in autumn.

Method 2 The low tunnel method (p. 16) is so successful that we regard it as the main system. Basal or nodal softwood cuttings of the current season's growth, 3–4 in. (7.5–10 cm) long, without treatment with root promoting preparations, are inserted in June. After three weeks check for rooting and, if ready, harden off gradually. The plants may be containerised or left *in situ*. In either case they will be good flowering plants of saleable size by autumn. Alternatively the cuttings may be inserted in the cold frame and plastic (p. 14) in June to be lifted and potted up as soon as well rooted (about three to four weeks later) into 6 in. bags for sale in autumn.

Cassinia

Cassinia fulvida and *C. vauvilliersii* are evergreen shrubs from New Zealand. Despite their heath-like appearance, they belong to the natural order Compositae (Daisy family).

Uses More interesting than colourful, these shrubs can be used as occasional specimens where an evergreen shrub 4 ft (1.2 m) or so high is required. They will grow in any sunny place, are easily propagated and can be used as space fillers in beds of choicer shrubs.

Method of propagation Cassinias are readily propagated by heel or basal cuttings in a cold frame in autumn. Line out the following spring.

Ceanothus (Evergreen)

For garden purposes ceanothus can be divided into two groups. The evergreen group is usually characterised by smaller leaves and by flowers carried in roundish clusters. Among the numerous species the best known include *C. x veitchianus, C.* **A. T. Johnson,** *C. dentatus, C. thyrsiflorus, C. papillosus* **Roweanus,** etc. They form large rounded bushes up to 12 ft (3.6 m) high when grown in the open garden.

The deciduous group (q.v.) are different in habit and are generally seen as low bushes in gardens, as they are commonly pruned back in spring, to carry elongated panicles of flowers in late summer, as typified by the well known *C.* **Gloire de Versailles.**

Uses The evergreen ceanothus are vigorous growers notable for abundant blue flowers in spring and, with some cultivars, again in autumn. They should be treated as wall shrubs in cold districts. As ceanothus flower freely when young, they can be sold as attractive container-grown specimens in flower, mainly to private gardeners, though they could be used more in parks, particularly near the coast.

Methods of propagation Semi-hard cuttings can be rooted at almost any time during the growing season except when in flower. Four alternative systems

are:

1. Cuttings under mist in March.
2. Cuttings under mist in late summer (July).
3. Cuttings in the low tunnel in June.
4. Cuttings in the cold frame in October.

The warm bench and plastic method is not suitable for the rooting of ceanothus cuttings owing to heavy defoliation and reduced rooting. Under all systems of propagation, the rooted cuttings should be potted promptly, otherwise establishment may be poor. Where ceanothus cuttings are accompanied by those of other species, they need watching as they may be overlooked until large roots have formed. Method 4, for example, can be troublesome owing to root damage if the cuttings are not potted as soon as roots appear.

Ceanothus must be container grown and customers should be advised that they transplant badly once established and so should be planted directly into permanent sites in well drained sunny positions.

The milder winters of our southern and western areas give an advantage over Continental producers. Evergreen ceanothus in general commerce are few despite numerous Awards of Merit. Among those deserving wider cultivation are *C. cyaneus*, *C. thyrsiflorus*, *C. papillosus* **Roweanus**, *C.* **Cascade** and *C.* **Southmead**. *C.* **Burkwoodii** and *C.* **Autumnal Blue** are good late flowering

Fig. 36. March cuttings (left) of *Ceanothus* make saleable plants before winter. Those from July cuttings (right) have to be held over winter.

hybrids uniting the early flowering evergreen section of the genus with the late summer and autumn flowering types.

In all cases treat the cuttings with 0.8% IBA powder. Wounding is unnecessary. A suitable rooting medium is two parts moss peat to one of sand. 70–100% rooting can be expected.

Method 1 This system, though unorthodox, is the quickest, enabling the production of saleable plants in one season, thus eliminating the need to carry young plants through the winter for growing on in the second season. Flower buds may be present on the cuttings but, with proper care, are not detrimental. Pot up the rooted cuttings in 3 in. pots after five to six weeks (May) and place on a capillary bed in a plastic house or glasshouse. Pot on in June (5 in. bags). The plants will be ready for sale from July when they will be 2–3 ft (60–90 cm) high. At this point they can be held on an outdoor capillary bed to avoid significant further growth during the remainder of the season.

Method 2 This is the standard time for taking cuttings. By the beginning of September they should be rooted and potted into 3 in. pots for overwintering in a cold house or frame. They should be potted on in April (5 in. bags) and placed on a capillary bed in a plastic house or greenhouse and will be ready for sale from midsummer.

Method 3 As soon as the cuttings are rooted they should be lifted and potted as in Method 2 and overwintered under cover.

Method 4 Pot up as soon as possible in spring and grow the plants on under cover as above. Saleable from midsummer.

Ceanothus (Deciduous)

These are botanically grouped under the name *C x delilianus*, being hybrids between *C. caeruleus* and *C. americanus*. They are typified by the well known *C.* **Gloire de Versailles**, deservedly the most popular of the group. Others less familiar include **Indigo, Marie Simon, Topaz** and **Henri Desfosse**. Ceanothus are always sold as container grown specimens.

Uses These are valuable shrubs for bringing blue colour into the later summer and autumn garden. All grow to 4–6 ft (1.2–1.8 m) high, with annual pruning. They should be planted in sunny positions. Ceanothus can be sold as container grown plants in flower. The deciduous sorts are more lax and spreading in habit than the evergreen kinds. In colder areas they can be grown as wall shrubs reaching 12 ft (3.6 m) in height.

Methods of propagation 1. Semi-hard nodal cuttings in the low tunnel in June. 2. Cuttings in the cold frame in October.

Method 1 Prune back mother plants hard in April. Take cuttings in June, treat with 0.8% IBA powder (no wound needed) and insert in the low tunnel. These will be 12–15 in. (30–37.5 cm) high by the beginning of October. Lift and pot in 3–4 in. pots. Overwinter in a cold house.

In March head back by one third to encourage branching. In April sell to retailer to grow on, or pot on into 6 in. plastic bags and place on the outdoor capillary bed. After taking cuttings in June for rooting in the low plastic tunnel, sell in September as container grown plants in flower. By this system there is no need to continue to maintain special mother plants or to use mist or bottom heat since each June cutting is taken from the plants that are to be sold in late summer and autumn.

Method 2 Cuttings in a cold frame in October is an alternative but needs preparation of the mother plants by heading back in June (i.e. later than the normal spring pruning). Unpruned plants flower so freely that suitable cuttings are scarce in October. Percentage rooting of such cuttings can be low and, at potting time in spring, there can be further losses from root injury. Take heel or basal cuttings 4–6 in. (10–15 cm) long and treat with 0.8% IBA powder. Wounding is unnecessary. Upwards of 60% rooting can be expected.

Cedrus

There are three cedars in general cultivation, *Cedrus deodara*, with pendulous terminal shoots, *C. atlantica* with ascending branches, at least while young, and *C. libani*, the well-known Cedar or Lebanon, of picturesque spreading habit when mature. The blue form of *C. atlantica* is very popular. The rarely seen weeping form is spectacular.

Uses As specimen trees where there is plenty of space.

Methods of propagation 1. Seed. 2. Grafting.

Method 1 Good seed can sometimes be gathered from home grown trees, particularly of *C. atlantica*. A proportion of that from the blue form will give blue seedlings. When the seeds are ripe, the cones disintegrate on the tree. Cedar seed is oily and so does not keep very well. It should be sown as soon after gathering as possible and, in any case, by early spring. Small quantities may be sown under glass in February and should germinate in 15–20 days.

Method 2 The rootstock used is *C. deodara*. Select the best of pencil-thick two-year old seedlings and pot up in March. Plunge in outdoor beds and lift them during the first two weeks of August. The side shoots of the understock are removed from the bottom 4–5 in. (10–12.5 cm) of the stem. The best scions are of the previous season's growth taken from young trees and removed when the current season's growth is still active. The graft is the side graft with a lip (p. 31). The grafts are placed in an outdoor frame with a cover of thin polythene (100 gauge) and with frame lights placed in position. If available, a closed case in a glasshouse can be used as the plants require as constant a base temperature of 66–68°F (19–20°C) as possible and outdoor temperatures can drop rapidly at the end of September or beginning of October. Callusing will be well advanced after seven to nine weeks. Reduce the temperature and harden off by increasing the ventilation under the plastic. Water once per week and, when conditions are favourable in the middle or at the end of May, plant out the grafts in well prepared beds after first removing the stem of the rootstock above the graft union. The plants will require room when being planted on account of their drooping habit and a spacing of 12 in. (30 cm) square is recommended. Grow on to saleable size, which will be from two to four seasons later.

Celastrus

A genus of vigorous deciduous climbing shrubs of which *Celastrus orbiculatus* is in general cultivation. Provided a hermaphrodite clone is 97 obtained, it is notable for the brilliant display of scarlet seeds within golden yellow lined capsules; otherwise male and female plants have to be planted together. The fruits are not attractive to birds, so they hang on a long time.

Uses A twiner for covering a tall bush, old stump or for growing with support on a wall. It can reach 30 ft (9 m) or more.

Methods of propagation 1. Root cuttings in February in the cold frame. 2. Cuttings under mist in June. 3. Seed.

Method 1 Root cuttings sprout readily and can be taken from plants of known sex. Sections of root 1½–2 in. (4–5 cm) long are shaken up with a fungicide dust. The pieces of root should have a slanting cut at the lower end to ensure that they are set the right way up. Space vertically at 2½–4 in. (6.2–10 cm) in a moist compost of equal parts moss peat and sand with the tops just above the compost. Finish off with a layer of sand to cover the tops to a depth of ½ in. (1.2 cm). Cover with shaded lights and water as needed. When the shoots are well established, harden off and give a liquid feed. By the end of the year, the root cuttings should have produced good branched plants about 2 ft (60 cm) high. They can be sold then or containerised for sale the following spring and summer.

Method 2 Softwood nodal cuttings taken in June and treated with 0.8% IBA root up to 100% in five weeks under mist.

Method 3 Though cleaned or dried seed can be sown in pots or boxes in autumn and brought in on initiation of germination in spring, this method is not recommended as a general practice as the seedlings will be of unknown sex until they reach maturity.

Cephalotaxus

Cephalotaxus is a genus of evergreen conifers, resembling yews but with larger leaves. They are not very exciting shrubs or small trees. Being tolerant of shaded places and not being affected by drip when planted under other trees, they are often confined to such situations, thus being denied a chance of growing into good specimens. They come from China and Japan.

Propagation may be effected from semi-hard heeled cuttings treated with 0.8% IBA powder and inserted under mist in October. Harden off when rooted and line out in cold frames the following March–April. Alternatively, the cuttings may be inserted in a cold frame in October, to be lifted and lined out the following June.

Ceratostigma

Though a small genus, *Ceratostigma* includes an important species, *C. wilmottianum*, a low shrub from China, bearing heads of blue flowers over a long period in summer and autumn. It is a valuable low shrub for the front of the border in a sunny position in any soil. The long flowering season also makes this species attractive as a container grown plant for display in garden centres.

Propagation is easily effected from cuttings. If these are taken early, good plants will be formed by autumn. In colder districts the plant may be cut to ground level, but even where the top growth survives the winter, production of suitable cutting material is often delayed by cool weather in spring. Mother plants may be brought under glass or plastic in February–March or plastic bags (with holes for ventilation) placed over outdoor plants. In this way basal softwood cuttings may be procured 2–3 in. (5–7.5 cm) long at the beginning of May. Root these in the warm bench with plastic or in the cold frame with plastic. No treatment with rooting powders is needed. Up to 100% rooting may be expected in four weeks (six weeks in the cold frame). Pot up in 3½ in. pots. If grown on under glass or plastic, the plants will be 1 ft (30 cm) high with 5–6 branches by August (smaller if rooted in the cold frame). It may be sold as small plants at this stage or potted on into 4½ in. pots to overwinter to be sold as large plants during the following season.

Cercidiphyllum

Cerdiciphyllum japonicum is a Japanese tree of very elegant habit with rounded leaves which often colour well in autumn. Basal cuttings of the young shoots taken in May about 6 in. (15 cm) long will root 55–60% in five weeks using the warm bench and plastic technique. Treat the cuttings with 0.8% IBA and insert in a medium of two parts moss peat to one of sand. Pot up in 3 in. pots and place on a capillary bed in a plastic house. By late summer these plants will be 1 ft (30 cm) high. Hold over winter under glass or in the plastic house and pot on into 4 in. pots in spring to sell as container grown plants, or line out for growing on.

Seedlings raised from imported seed sown in a cold house in March, pricked off into 3 in. pots, potted on into 'Long Toms' and grown on in a plastic house should reach 14–15 in. (35–40 cm) by the end of the season. Layering can also be recommended as a method of propagation.

Cercis

Cercis is a genus of small deciduous trees with pea shaped flowers. Only one species, *C. siliquastrum*, the Judas tree, is commonly seen. As it comes from the Near East it prefers a sunny, warm spot. In May the leafless branches are covered with the rosy-purple flowers.

Imported seed germinates freely. It may be sown in a cold frame in March. By the end of the year the seedlings will be 6–8 in. (15–20 cm) high. In spring they may be containerised or lined out. Specimens should be planted in their final positions while still small, as larger trees transplant badly.

Chaenomeles

The well known Japanese Quinces, once catalogued under *Cydonia*, are now known as *Chaenomeles*. There are many cultivars in varying shades of red and

99

also white. The popular name Japonica is to be deprecated as this simply means Japanese and there are many other plants equally entitled to this adjective. Most of the Japanese Quinces in cultivation come under *C. speciosa* and its hybrid with *C. japonica*, called *C. x superba*.

Uses The Japanese Quinces are very popular for the colourful flowers that come before the leaves in earliest spring. They will grow in any soil and in most situations, though they flower best in full sun. For small gardens *C.* **Simonii** is one of the best, with deep red semi-double flowers, forming a low spreading bush. **Knap Hill Scarlet** is more upright, growing to 5 ft (1.5 m) or more. The leaves are apt to conceal the flowers partially and our personal preference is for **Rowallane** with redder flowers and a spreading habit. *C.* **Nivalis** is a very vigorous white. Japanese Quinces look fine when trained against walls but, for the best effect, should be pruned back hard after flowering to keep them close to the wall.

Methods of propagation 1. Softwood cuttings in June in cold frame and plastic. 2. Layering. 3. Root cuttings. 4. White polythene tunnel (see p. 19).

Method 1 Take basal cuttings of the current year's shoots in June 2½–3 in (6.2–7.5 cm) long, treat with 0.8% IBA powder and insert under plastic in the cold frame, in a compost of two parts moss peat to one of sand. 85–95% rooting can be expected after four weeks. Lift and plant out 5–7 in. (12.5–17.5 cm) each way in a frame of fertilised peat. Replace the lights and keep shaded until well established. Lift early the following spring and line out. By the end of this season the plants should be 1–2 ft (30–60 cm) high.

Method 2 The mother plants should be well established, strongly growing specimens. Initially prune back hard to a stump or stool to encourage the production of strong shoots. Layer these in February–March, pegging them down into the soil some 6 in. (15 cm) from the top. Lift and line out the following spring. Layer half the available mother plants each year.

Method 3 Mother plants may be lifted in January and lengths of root removed. Roots ¼ in. (0.8 cm) diameter are suitable, especially when nearer the crown of the plant. Lengths of root further away do not regenerate shoots so freely. Section the root into pieces 3 in. (7.5 cm) long. Lay horizontally in trays of suitable compost, e.g. equal parts moss peat and sand and cover ½ in. (1.2 cm) deep. Pot up when the shoots are well developed. The young plants may be grown on in containers, or lined out in a frame or in the open ground under good conditions. By the autumn of the third year the plants should be saleable as specimens 2–2¼ ft × 2–2¼ ft (60–70 cm).

    A method described as used in Holland is to cut the roots into ¾–1 in. long pieces (2–2.5 cm). These are sown in drills in an outdoor bed, 1 in. (2.5 cm) deep to give plants for lining out at the end of the first year.

Chamaecyparis

This is one of the most important genera of trees in the garden and landscape, mainly on account of the very numerous forms of Lawson's Cypress (*Chamaecyparis lawsoniana*), some of these arising from the retention of the juvenile foliage indefinitely. *C. pisifera* and *C. obtusa* also provide many garden cultivars. *C. nootkatensis* is mainly remarkable for the weeping cultivar **Pendula**.

Uses For planting in the larger landscape. Blue forms include **Triomphy van Boskoop, Allumii**. Golden forms are **Stewartii** and **Lane**. Green types include **Hollandia** and **Naberi**. **Erecta Viridis** is a well known large fastigiate form. **Drummondii** is similar but more attractive. **Kilmacurragh** is a narrowly columnar green type. For smaller gardens **Blom** and **Columnaris** (both blue), **Fletcheri** and **Ellwoodii** are erect forms.

For the front of the shrub border or the large rock garden **Minima** and many *C. obtusa* and *C. pisifera* cultivars are suitable.

Propagation Before describing the different methods of propagation there are a number of points of a general nature to be discussed briefly. In the first place is the importance of young and vigorously growing mother plants. Older trees of *Chamaecyparis* often make but a small amount of new shoot growth each year, making it difficult to find suitable material to give large uniform cuttings. Experiments have shown no significant difference in rooting conifer cuttings with and without a heel. Time of insertion has an influence on rooting, more particularly with the harder to root cultivars, e.g. in trials using mist over the period from beginning of February to end of March, there was a drop in numbers rooted of **Lutea, Smithii, Versicolor, Stewartii** and **Darleyensis** after the beginning of March but not in such easy cultivars as **Ellwoodii** and **Pottenii**. Propagation before March gave larger plants by November. In trials in Holland, using cold frames from August to March, the best rooting was recorded from cuttings inserted in October.

Conifers are slower to root than many other subjects but here the skilful grower can make up time by good treatment of the rooted cuttings. Hence it is recommended that cuttings be grown on in frames of loamless compost (pp. 55–6). In a general way the standard to be aimed at is the production of a 12 in. (30 cm) plant from a 4 in. (10 cm) cutting within a year and this can be exceeded.

For most cultivars the use of 0.8% IBA powder has given satisfactory rooting of cuttings but a few need special treatment. These include the well known **Triomphe van Boskoop** and **Stewartii**. These require treatment by the dilute soak method (p. 8) or they may be grafted, as mentioned below.

Some of the dwarf and semi-dwarf cultivars have juvenile type foliage, i.e. they have retained their seedling foliage and have never developed the adult form. Well known examples are *C. lawsoniana* **Ellwoodii**, the taller *C.I.* **Pottenii** and *C. pisifera* **Boulevard**. These types are notably easy to root from cuttings. Plants of **Boulevard** are liable to botrytis if crowded in a plastic house.

Methods of propagation 1. Cuttings in the cold frame in October or in February. 2. Cuttings in mist or warm bench and plastic in February. 3. Grafting in March and August. 4. White polythene tunnel in September–November (see p. 19).

Method 1 Semi-hardwood cuttings about 4 in. (10 cm) long are clipped off the parent plant ¼–½ in. (0.6–1.2 cm) from the base of the past season's 101 growth and inserted in a cold frame containing a medium of two parts moss peat to one of sand at 1–1½ × 2½ in. (3 × 6.5 cm) spacing. They are treated with root promoting substance as above. The lights are placed in position and it should not be necessary to shade the glass at this time of year, though it is wise to have slats at hand for emergencies. However, from February onwards a sharp watch should be kept and, as soon as bright sunny days come, the glass should be shaded with one of the proprietary washes sold for the purpose. As the sun increases, follow with slatted shading. In mid May check for rooting in anticipation of lifting the cuttings at the end of the month or early June (July for cuttings inserted in February). Once the cuttings are well rooted they must be hardened off gradually. Finally, plant out in cold frames of fertilised peat fitted with irrigation lines. The shaded lights may be replaced for a few days to assist establishment. By October the plants should be about 12 in. (30 cm) high. They can then be sold as liners or planted out for growing on to be sold one year later 15–18 in. (37.5–45 cm) high, two years later, 18–24 in. (45–60 cm) or as 2–2½ ft (60–75 cm) specimens three years later. They may also be containerised at any stage.

Method 2 Gather the cuttings and treat as described for Method 1, before insertion in two parts moss peat to one of sand in the warm bench, and cover with plastic (p. 13). After 8–11 weeks 70–100% rooting may be expected according to cultivar. Good rooting percentages can be obtained by either system. After hardening off, the plants are lined out in cold frames and grown on as for Method 1.

Method 3 Grafting is used for cultivars which root less freely, e.g. *C. lawsoniana* **Stewartii, Speck, Triomphe van Boskoop, Golden King, Silver Queen**. *C. nootkatensis* **Pendula** can be reluctant to root from cuttings, though we have had 75% success with February cuttings left under mist for fourteen weeks.

Grafting can be carried out in March and August. At both times the rootstock should be about pencil thickness and this usually means the use of a two-year-old seedling of *C. lawsoniana* (*Thuja orientalis* for *C. nootkatensis*). These are cheap and readily obtainable. For March grafting, the rootstocks should be potted during the previous autumn and plunged in a cold frame so that they are well established when brought into a warm glasshouse in the middle of February. The pots are stood on the bench in temperatures of 60°–65°F (15.6°–18°C) so that root action will begin. This can be checked for by knocking one or two plants out of their pots and examining for new extension growth to the roots. This will occur after about three weeks. Scions of the past season's growth, a little stouter than that used for cuttings, are grafted by the side graft method with a lip (p. 31). In this case both sides of the scion are cut and the folded back lip is brought into contact with the outside cut on the scion when the latter is in place. After tying, the grafts are placed in a closed case. Callusing takes place quickly and, after three or four weeks, the plant can be hardened off. Plant into a cold frame (mid April) after first cutting off most of the rootstock stem, but making sure to leave a small amount of stub with a side shoot or two. Protect with shaded lights for a couple of weeks till established. By the end of the year the remaining stem of the rootstock can be cut away and the plants will be ready for lining out at a spacing of 6 × 9 in. (15 × 25 cm), or for container growing.

When August grafting is desired, the rootstock can be potted in the previous March or April. Some days before the grafting, the plants are brought inside so that they will be a little on the dry side before grafting begins. The top growth of the rootstock is trimmed down to 6 in. (15 cm) in height. Graft as in March and, after callusing in the closed case and hardening off, plant out from the pots into a cold frame with the graft union below soil level. Lift in spring, cut the rootstock stem away and plant out in the field for growing on at a spacing of 4–6 in (10–15 cm), or grow on in containers.

Although cuttings of dwarf forms of *C. obtusa* root readily they are often slow to reach saleable size. For example, cuttings of *C.o.* **Pygmaea Aurescens** 9 cm long were only 11 cm tall by 19 cm broad five years later. Similar shoots grafted in April were 15 × 20 cm six months later. Cuttings of the cultivar **Nana Gracilis** reached 12 × 8 cm in eight months compared with 22 × 14 cm after six months for grafted plants. The latter attained 30 × 15 cm two years from grafting.

Grafted plants of **Pygmaea Aurescens** are apt to make lop-sided growth during their first season and need a further year to develop the shape typical of this cultivar. With **Nana Gracilis** there is no such problem.

Chimonanthus

Chimonanthus fragrans, the Winter Sweet, is grown as a wall shrub for the intensely fragrant flowers which appear on the leafless twigs in January and February.

Propagation may be effected by seed sown under glass in February. This seed has to be imported, as plants grown out of doors in our climate do not set seed. Seedlings may be slow to reach the flowering stage. Layering in July–August is the general means of propagation.

Though cuttings can be struck in May–June under mist or in the warm bench with plastic, they are subject to much defoliation and cannot be recommended as a commercial proposition.

Choisya

Choisya ternata, the Mexican Orange, is a low, evergreen shrub (6 ft–1.8 m) with trifoliate leaves which are strongly scented when crushed. The white flowers appear in spring and early summer.

Uses A useful evergreen for sun or semi-shade, indifferent as to soil and generally hardy.

Methods of propagation 1. Cuttings in low tunnel in June. 2. Cuttings in the open ground in October. 3. Cuttings in the cold frame in October.

Though *Choisya* is so easily rooted that 100% take can be expected by all methods, it shows a positive response to treatment with 0.8% IBA powder by quicker and greater development of the roots. In the low tunnel method this is followed by greater shoot growth by autumn. At this time semi-hard nodal cuttings of the current season's shoots will be used, about 4 in. (10 cm) long. These will be approximately 10 in. (25 cm) long by autumn when they can be 103 lifted and lined out for a further year's growth at a spacing of 8 in. × 8 in. (20 cm × 20 cm). By the end of the second year they can be sold as specimens, some 15 in. (37.5 cm) high.

Propagation in the open ground is safe in the milder districts but in cold areas the cold frame should be used as a precaution. The plants so propagated will be smaller by the end of the second year compared with the earlier struck June cuttings.

Cistus

Cistus (Sun Rose) is a genus of slow growing shrubs, usually around 3 ft (90 cm) high, though some can reach twice this height. There are many species and hybrids. Those most frequently seen include *C. corbariensis* (white with a yellow stain in the centre), *C. crispus* (purplish red), *C. x cyprius* (white with a red blotch), *C. ladanifer* (white with a red blotch), *C. populifolius* (white, stained yellow), *C. x purpureus* (reddish purple blotched darker red) and *C.* **Silver Pink** (pink).

Uses The sun roses are shrubs for dry, sunny places in light soil. They are not hardy in severe winters but this disadvantage is mitigated by the ease of propagation.

Method of propagation Though cuttings will root at any time in summer and autumn, nodal cuttings inserted in a cold frame in September–October are convenient, both as an insurance against loss of stock and for potting up in spring, since *Cistus* must be container grown; they do not transplant from the open ground. Nodal or basal cuttings 3–4 in. (7.5–10 cm) are inserted in a sandy compost (2 parts sand to 1 of moss peat). Protect the frame temporarily with sacking should there by a very cold spell. Pot up in spring (3 in. pots) avoiding a rich compost, e.g. by diluting the peat of the standard composts with an equal volume of sand. At this stage the cuttings will be 9–10 in. (22.5–25 cm) high with two to three branches and with flower buds forming. Stand the pots in a sunny place and pot on as required, selling during summer and autumn as flowering specimens.

Clematis

To many people *Clematis* recalls the spectacular large-flowered hybrids and the vigorous *C. montana* but several of the species are important too, such as *C. alpina*, *C. macropetala*, *C. tangutica*, *C. flammula* and the evergreen *C. armandii*.

Uses Well known as climbers, best suited where they can have their roots in shade and their heads in the sun. The non-climbing *C. heracleifolia* and *C. integrifolia* are occasionally seen in large herbaceous borders.

Methods of propagation 1. Softwood cuttings in the warm bench and plastic in April. 2. Semi hardwood cuttings in mist, warm bench and plastic or in cold frame and plastic in June. 3. Grafting. 4. Seed.

104

Method 1 To be successful with the large flowered hybrids, it is advisable to have early cuttings to ensure well established plants before winter. Pot grown mother plants are placed in a plastic house at the beginning of March. Single node cuttings are taken early in April, when the flower buds are well developed but still tight. Take each cutting just above a node. Shorten the internode to 1–2 in. (2.5–5 cm). Treat with 0.8% IBA powder and insert in two parts moss peat to one of sand. The long leaves are awkward to handle, necessitating a little ingenuity in arranging the cuttings. They can, for example, be placed close together with the leaves parallel but the lines of cuttings further apart. It is permissable to shorten the leaves, or to remove one completely. *Clematis* cuttings are susceptible to leaching of the foliage under mist, and, in our experience, come out from under plastic in better condition. Even so, close attention is essential to minimise scorching or decay of the foliage. About 60–70% rooting can be expected on average after four to five weeks. The rooted cuttings need to be accustomed to full air in easy stages before being potted up in 4 × 5 in. 'Long Toms'. Though the leaves on some cuttings may not be in good condition at this stage, this is not so important, provided the buds in their axils are alive and these soon grow out. (The use of two-node cuttings has been advocated in USA as a precaution against 'blindness'.) Stand the pots on the bench in the glass-house until the plants are well established. They may then be transferred to a capillary bed in a plastic house. When the stem has grown to about 12–18 in. it may be cut back to the lowest pair of good buds; this will give a double stemmed plant easier to transport and establish, since a single stem may get kinked. As the shoots grow, stake the stems. By late June or early July the plants will be about 2 ft (60 cm) high. They may then be plunged outside to slow their growth and may be sold in July–August as flowering specimens.

An alternative but troublesome method is to use leaf bud cuttings, splitting a single node cutting through the node, thus making two leaf bud cuttings. To facilitate splitting the node evenly, shorten the internode to ½ in. (1.2 cm). Treat with 0.8% IBA powder and root by the warm bench and plastic method. To accommodate the leaves, the short stem piece may be laid horizontally in the compost with the bud almost covered. After five to seven weeks harden off the cuttings carefully and pot up for growing under glass. The parent shoots are not firm enough for this method until May–June and we find it necessary to carry the plants through the winter to make saleable plants in early summer. **Duchess of Albany, Mrs. Cholmondeley** and **Huldine** do not root so freely with us as do most other cultivars.

Method 2 Semi-hardwood cuttings to be rooted by these systems are recommended for the species clematis, mostly easier to rear from cuttings than are the hybrid types. The cold frame with plastic may be used for the strong growing *C. montana*. Single nodes from the current year's shoots are treated with 0.8% IBA powder. Around 75% rooting can be expected after four to six weeks, when the cuttings are hardened off, lifted, potted into 4 in. × 5 in. 'Long Toms' for growing on on a capillary bed out of doors for the stronger growing species. Stake, and sell at the end of the season.

The cold frame and plastic is successfully used in Holland for the large flowered hybrids from outdoor cuttings in May–June and it may be described here though we have not tried it under our conditions. Internodal cuttings are inserted in the frames in a medium of three parts peat to one part sand, in

105

staggered lines 3 in. (7.5 cm) apart. A close watch is kept for fungal attacks. Ventilate by removing the plastic and inspecting the cuttings twice a week. Rooting starts after about four weeks. The plastic is removed gradually, leaving the shaded lights in position until the shoots appear from the leaf axils. When these are ½–¾ in. (1–2 cm) long, ventilate more freely, hardening off the plants and after two weeks take away the glass altogether. At this stage stake the plants and give them a liquid feed. At leaf fall (end September–October) lift the plants, cut them back to about 6 in. (15 cm) pot them up and plunge the pots in outdoor beds. Leave the stakes in position and tie up the growth in the following season. Sell the plants in autumn.

Method 3 The production of clematis by grafting is an older method and may suit some growers better in that it is carried out under glass in February. The objective is to provide nurse roots, potting up the grafted plants deeply so as to encourage scion rooting. One-or-two-year-old seedlings of **Traveller's Joy** (*C. vitalba*) are used as stocks for the larger-flowered hybrids. The stocks may be bought in or they may be raised from seed sown in outdoor seed beds in February–March. Grafting is carried out on 3 in. (7.5 cm) lengths of root with fibrous roots present and about ⅛ in. (3 mm) diameter. The scions are made by cutting the shoot just above the buds and 1½ in. (3.7 cm) below. Use the cleft graft method (p. 33). Pot up so that the buds are at the soil surface and grow on under glass. Transfer to a polythene house in early May and plants will be saleable as flowering specimens from June onwards.

Method 4 The species may be raised from seed sown under glass in February. The fluffy awns should be gathered as soon as they show signs of parting from the receptacle. Check that good seeds are present as in some seasons the awns may only have vestiges of seeds at the base. Sow in pots or boxes and leave in a cold frame as some species, at least, need exposure to cold. Do not allow the containers to dry out and bring in on initiation of germination. If the seedlings are potted on and kept under glass or plastic they develop quickly and can be 3 ft (0.9 m) or more by late summer.

Clerodendrum

There are many species of *Clerodendrum* but only two are hardy. *C. bungei* is a suckering plant, sending up stems 3–6 ft (0.9–1.8 m) high. Though rather a coarse plant, it is striking in having dark coloured foliage and heads of purple-red flowers in late summer. The stems usually die down to ground level in winter. *C. trichotomum*, usually seen as the var, *fargesii*, is effective where it has room to form a large bush covered with blue berries.

Propagation of *C. bungei* is easy by division in spring. *C. trichotomum* comes very readily from root cuttings. The parent plants may be lifted in December. Sections of root 3 in. (7.5 cm) long, laid horizontally in boxes of sandy peat and kept under glass, can be potted up in 2 in. pots in March. Each root will have sent up several shoots. They can be hardened off and lined out in late April, 8 in. (20 cm) apart. By autumn the plants will be 6 in. (15 cm) high with two to five shoots. They are grown on for a further year for sale.

Clethra

Shrubs or small trees allied to the heath family, demanding an acid soil. They flower in July and August, bearing scented lily-of-the-valley like flowers, but some species are tender. Though the conventional time for taking cuttings of clethras is August, we have had over 60% success with nodal cuttings of *C. alnifolia* **Rosea** placed in the warm bench and plastic in February, after treatment with 0.8% IBA powder.

Clianthus

Clianthus puniceus, the Lobster Claw, so called from the clusters of red, pea-shaped flowers with elongated standard and keel petals, is a New Zealand shrub tender in our climate. It will, however, survive most winters grown against a sunny wall where it usually grows 3–4 ft (1–1.2 m) high.

Method of propagation Easily raised from the seeds, usually produced freely. Sow under glass in February; prick off into 3 in. pots. Pot on as required, harden off and sell as container grown plants in summer and autumn. Add an equal volume of soil to the standard potting composts (pp. 55–7). After hardening off, the plants can be placed on the outdoor capillary bed, but not until the weather is warm. This will hasten development. The plants should be removed after a few weeks as prolonged moist conditions are not favourable to this plant. As an alternative means of propagation semi-hardwood cuttings can be struck in sandy compost under mist in summer.

A spectacular but rarely seen species is *C. dampieri*, from Australia. Seed will germinate readily in a warm greenhouse, but the subsequent culture of the plant is troublesome. It is usually recommended that the seedlings be cleft grafted onto seedlings of *Colutea arborescens*, and placed in a plastic tent until union is complete. Harden off carefully. The seeds of the latter are sown ten days in advance. Plants raised in this way have done better with us than specimens left on their own roots.

Convolvulus

This family of obnoxious weeds includes one sub-shrubby species, *Convolvulus cneorum*, of value in the garden. It forms a low mound of silvery foliage above which appear, from May onwards, the shallow trumpet shaped white flowers, tinged pink.

Uses Not hardy in very cold districts. Plant as a specimen to the front of a sunny border in well drained soils or on a large rock garden.

Methods of propagation 1. Cuttings in the cold frame in September. 2. Cuttings under mist in August.

Method 1 The semi-hardwood cuttings about 4–5 in. (10–12.5 cm) long are treated with 0.8% IBA powder and inserted in the cold frame in a compost of two parts moss peat to one of sand. Lift the following April when around 80% rooting can be expected. Containerise in 6 in. bags. Though not a plant for

107

damp soils, *Convolvulus* will tolerate a capillary bed during the summer months. Sell as containerised plants in late summer and autumn when they should be plants about 7 in. (17.5 cm) across.

Method 2 Soft tip cuttings 1¾–2 in. (4–5 cm) in length will withstand mist conditions long enough to give 90–98% rooting in nine weeks. Treatment with rooting powder is not needed. Pot into 3 in. pots as soon as rooted, overwinter under glass and containerise in spring to grow on as above for sale in summer and autumn.

Cornus

Cornus (Dogwood) is a very diverse genus. For horticultural purposes it may be divided into those species grown for the colour of the bark in winter (sometimes with variegated leaves) and those grown for their flowers.

Uses C. *alba* and C. *stolonifera* are allied species grown for the colour of the stems in winter. Both form a thicket of stems, the latter suckering freely. C. *alba* **Siberica** (the Westonbirt Dogwood) has paler, brighter stems. The bushes should be pruned almost to ground level in March every second year as the young bark has the brightest colour. C. *stolonifera* **Flaviramea** has yellowish green shoots and can be planted as a contrast to the red forms. These are rampant shrubs giving a splendid effect when massed by the waterside. Forms with variegated leaves are C. *alba* **Spaethii** (golden) and C. *a.* **Elegantissima** (white). C. *mas* forms a large shrub or small tree which is covered with yellow flowers in February before the leaves appear. C. *kousa* is one of the most beautiful large shrubs with masses of white flowers in June, generally more successful in our gardens than C. *florida* and C. *nuttallii*. C. *capitata* is easy to grow in the milder areas, is evergreen and has yellow flowers followed by large pulpy crimson fruits. C. *canadensis* is very different from all the foregoing, being a creeping species for acid soils, with white flowers followed by red berries.

Methods of propagation 1. Hardwood cuttings in the open ground in November. 2. Semi-hardwood cuttings in the cold frame in October/ November. 3. Softwood cuttings under mist in June/July. 4. Layering. 5. Seed.

Method 1 Cornus alba and C. *stolonifera* may be struck from nodal or basal cuttings about 8 in. (20 cm) long inserted in the open ground (p. 19) though rooting may only be about 50% and the use of rooting powders does not seem to help. Lift and line out one year later.

Method 2 is suitable for C. *capitata*. Semi hardwood nodal or basal cuttings, treated with 0.8% IBA give good percentage rooting by the following June. Line out in frames of fertilised peat (pp. 56–7) for growing on.

Method 3 The American system of propagating C. *florida* is by cuttings of the current year's growth after flowering, treated by the quick dip method (p. 8) and inserted under mist. In Holland this species and C. *kousa* are rooted at this period also, using 1% IBA powder. Overwintering of the rooted cuttings is precarious. Pot up the rooted cuttings and in autumn keep them at a temperature above freezing but below 45°F (7.2°C). The young plants need 1,000 hours of this treatment. In spring they break dormancy and make good growth.

Method 4 All the shrubby species mentioned may be layered in June–July, pegging the layers down.

Method 5 In this country only *C. capitata* of the large flowered species produces seed frequently. The large red fruits are gathered in autumn, and the seeds cleaned from the fleshy pulp. Store in moist sand and sow under glass in February in trays. The seed will germinate freely in July. Pot up in 3 in. pots the following spring. Harden off when 2 in. (5 cm) high. They may then be lined out in frames of fertilised peat. Seed of other species is uncertain as it has to be imported and may then have varying degrees of dormancy. *C. florida*, for example, germinates best if stratified immediately it is ripe and sown in spring. The most hopeful system is probably to sow immediately the seed is received and keep in a shaded cold frame through one or two winters, examining each spring and summer for germination. As an instance, imported seed of *C. kousa* sown as soon as received in April gave 18% germination by June of the same year. By autumn the seedlings were 6 in. (15 cm) high.

Corokia

A small genus of evergreen shrubs from New Zealand of distinct twiggy habit, particularly *C. cotoneaster*, known as the 'Wire Netting Bush' from the angular, tortuous growth of the branches. The other species in general cultivation. *C. x virgata* is more regular in habit and bears orange berries dotted over the bush. Both species have small star shaped yellow flowers.

Uses Not hardy in very cold districts. These interesting species will eventually reach 8–10 ft (2.4–3 m) high. They are not particular as to soil but should be grown in sunny sheltered places.

Method of propagation Basal cuttings of the past season's growth are taken, treated with 0.8% IBA powder and inserted in a cold frame in September–November. Lift and line out or containerise in spring. *C. cotoneaster* sometimes layers naturally where branches touch the ground.

Coronilla

A genus of shrubs belonging to the pea family (Leguminosae) with clusters of yellow flowers. Only two species are usually seen in gardens — *C. emerus* and *C. glauca*.

Uses *C. emerus* is a 6 ft (1.8 m) shrub, deciduous except in mild winters, that may be grown in any sunny place. The leaves are pinnate and the yellow flowers appear all summer. *C. glauca* is a wall shrub for all but cold districts, valuable for the low walls found in most modern gardens as it only reaches 109 four to five feet. The bush is a sheet of yellow in April but has flowers most times of the year. The glaucous pinnate leaves are attractive.

Methods of propagation 1. Cuttings in the cold frame in October. 2. Cuttings in the low tunnel in June.

Method 1 (*C. emerus*) Semi-hard basal side shoots are inserted in a cold frame in a compost of two parts moss peat to one of sand. It is advisable to put extra sand at the base of the cuttings. Lift and pot in June.

Method 2 This is a convenient way to root *C. glauca*. Semi-hard nodal cuttings 4–5 in. (10–12.5 cm) long are inserted in June. No treatment with rooting powder is needed. Up to 100% rooting may be expected by September–October, when the cuttings may be lifted and potted into 3–4 in. pots for over-wintering in a cold house or frame. This should be done promptly to avoid over-large root systems, as the plants wilt readily and need care in watering until re-established in the pots. Sell in spring as bushy plants in flower.

Corylopsis

A genus of deciduous hardy shrubs appreciated for the pendant racemes of pale yellow flowers. These appear in spring before the leaves and give a pretty effect. The most generally obtainable species are *Corylopsis spicata* and *C. willmottiae*. These grow to 6 ft (1.8 m) or more. The dwarfer *C. pauciflora* does not thrive on alkaline soils.

Uses As specimen shrubs sheltered from cold winds and early frosts which may damage the flowers.

Method of propagation Corylopsis, like its relative *Hamamelis*, is difficult from cuttings, though we have had 50% and upwards success with *C. glabrescens* and *C. sinensis* from basal cuttings of the young shoots inserted under mist in June (*C. pauciflora* under warm bench and plastic). Subsequent growth was good, *C. glabrescens* attaining 5 ft (1.52 m) two years later. If simple layering is practised (p. 27) large well rooted branched specimens can be lifted after leaf fall and lined out for a further year to become fully established. Cuttings can also be propagated in the white polythene tunnel (see p. 19).

Corylus

Corylus avellana, our native Hazel, is seen in gardens in the curious form **Contorta**, in which, as the name implies, the branches are contorted and twisted, giving a bizarre effect, especially in winter. There is also a purple leaved form. The Turkish Hazel (*C. colurna*) is different in habit from the hazel, forming a pyramidal tree with a definite trunk and corrugated bark.
    Simple layering is the generally recommended method of propagation. The contorted hazel can be whip grafted in February or side grafted in August using two-year-old seedlings of the type species, established in pots. The Turkish Hazel also grafts successfully onto the common species.

A small genus of only two species, of which *Cotinus coggygria* and its cultivars are in general cultivation.

Uses C. *coggygria* is known as the Smoke Tree or Wig Tree from the mass of feathery inflorescences which cover the bush in a smoky grey or purplish pink haze. As the shrub forms a rounded bush up to 15 ft (4.5 m), it needs plenty of room. While it is not particular as to soil, too rich a soil will not give such good flowering or autumn colour. The leaves of the type turn good orange and red colours before leaf fall. **Flame** is a cultivar selected for autumn colour. The purple leaved cultivars give a splash of purple colour all through the summer. **Royal Purple** is particularly good.

Methods of propagation 1. Softwood cuttings in June under mist or by the warm bench and plastic method. 2. Layering.

Method 1 2 in. (5 cm) basal cuttings should be taken as soon as the young shoots are this length. They are usually not ready until June as this shrub comes into leaf late. Wounding is not necessary but there is a positive response to treatment with 0.8% IBA powder. Up to 100% rooting can be expected in six weeks. It is important to induce good shoot growth before winter, otherwise plants will be lost during the dormant season. To obtain this, pot up the rooted cuttings into 4 in. pots and keep in a cold house or plastic structure. By autumn the young plants are saleable as liners at 6–10 in. (15–25 cm) high or they may be lined out the following year to grow on to 1½–2 ft (45–60 cm) specimens 1½ years from taking the cutting.

Method 2 Cotinus coggygria responds well to French layering (p. 28), a productive method for this species, as the buds break freely when the shoots are pinned down in spring. Growth from these buds is strong so, by leaf fall, the layered shoots can be sectioned up into well rooted pieces, each with a shoot 1–2 ft (30–60 cm) long. These are lined out 1 ft (30 cm) apart and are headed back to 6 in. (15 cm) since, if left unpruned, leggy plants develop with dieback at the tips.

Cotoneaster (Bush)

This group contains numerous evergreen species, among the best known being C. *bullatus*, C. *conspicuus* **Decorus**, C. *dielsianus*, C. *franchettii*, C. *horizontalis*, C. *lacteus*, C. *microphyllus*, C. *pannosus*, C. *salicifolius*, C. *simonsii*, C. *wardii*, C. *frigidus* and C. *x watereri*.

Uses These cotoneasters are grown for their red berries, as single specimens in gardens or in groups in parks. C. *horizontalis*, well known for its herring bone arrangement of branches, is excellent for growing against a low wall or on sloping banks. C. *microphyllus* is often grown as a trimmed wall shrub. C. *simonsii* and C. *lacteus* are often used for hedging. C. *frigidus* and C. *x watereri* are tall species up to 20 ft (6 m) which can be trained as small trees. 111

Methods of propagation 1. Cuttings in the cold frame in autumn. 2. Cuttings in mist or in cold frame and plastic in June–July. 3. Seed. 4. White polythene tunnel (see p. 19).

Method 1 Suitable, e.g. for *C. microphyllus* and *C. franchettii*. Basal cuttings of the current year's wood, unwounded and treated with 0.8% IBA powder are inserted in October in a compost of two parts moss peat to one part sand. When lifted the following April 45–80% rooting can be expected. Line out and grow on.

Method 2 *C. horizontalis* roots poorly in the low tunnel in June but 90–100% may be obtained under mist or cold frame and plastic at this season. Other species successful under mist are *C. conspicuus*, *C. microphyllus*, *C. frigidus*, *C. franchettii*, *C. dielsianus*, *C. pannosus*, *C. bullatus* and *C. x watereri*. Up to 100% rooting can be expected in five weeks (*C. microphyllus* and *C. conspicuus*) but *C. frigidus*, *C. franchettii*, *C. dielsianus*, *C. bullatus and C. pannosus* are often slow, rooting 60–90% in up to 11 weeks. Firm cuttings of the current season's growth are treated with 0.8% IBA powder, inserted in a medium of two parts moss peat to one of sand. After rooting, harden off and line out in a cold frame to grow on for a further season.

Method 3 Though seed is the most practicable means of raising these cotoneasters in quantity, it is not as simple a matter as might be thought from the frequent appearance of self sown seedlings. Many species have a hard seed coat which needs to be softened by warm moist conditions before the embryo within is subjected to a chilling period. Hence the importance of gathering the seed promptly and treating it immediately. The berries should be macerated by passing them through a household mincer, for instance, and mixing them with an equal volume of sand. They are then stratified in a pit (p. 22) or in plastic bags (p. 23). In this way the seed coat is moistened and softened somewhat during the comparatively mild days of autumn, before being exposed to winter chilling. Even so, germination does not follow automatically during the first spring. Some species, including *C. dielsianus*, *C. frigidus*, *C. franchettii*, *C. lacteus* and *C. wardii* generally give some germination the first year. Others, such as *C. horizontalis* and *C. microphyllus* usually germinate poorly or not at all until the seed has been through two winters. When inspection of the stratified seed shows incipient germination, sow seed and sand together in a frame or outdoor bed. The former has the advantage of easier protection against mice if the seed has to be left a further year. The first flush of seedlings can be lifted in autumn, when they will be up to about 8 in. (20 cm) high and lined out, leaving the seed bed until the following spring to obtain a second flush of seedlings. Of course, the seed can be sown direct in the cold frames after harvest but this means close supervision against vermin and occupation of frame space that, in the meantime, might be useful for other purposes.

Cotoneaster (prostrate)

Evergreen prostrate or semi-prostrate shrubs. Species in general commerce include *C. adpressus*, *C. congestus*, *C. dammeri* **Radicans**, *C. d.* **Skogholm**,

C. **Coral Beauty**, *C. microphyllus* var. *cochleatus, C. salicifolius* **Repens**. *C. buxifolius* var. *vellaeus* should be more widely known.

Uses These are excellent shrubs for ground cover, especially on sloping banks. For large areas the most suitable are the vigorous *C. salicifolius* **Repens**, *C. dammeri* **Radicans**, *C. d.* **Skogholm**. Less vigorous are *C. microphyllus* var. *cochleatus, C.* **Coral Beauty** and *C. buxifolius* var. *vellaeus*. Relatively slow growing but eventually covering several square feet are *C. adpressus* and *C. congestus*. The former has stiff 'herring bone' branches. *C. congestus* will follow the contours of the ground in a neat, small leaved carpet. Not all prostrate cotoneasters berry freely. Those which do include *C.* **Coral Beauty**, *C. buxifolius* var. *vellaeus* and *C. salicifolius* **Autumn Fire** (**Repens** group).

Methods of propagation 1. Cuttings in the cold frame in autumn. 2. Cuttings in the low tunnel in June. 3. Cuttings under mist in June or July.

Method 1 Take nodal cuttings 2–3 in. (5–7.5 cm) long in October, do not wound, treat with 0.8% IBA powder and insert in a medium of two parts moss peat to one of sand. 70–95% should be rooted by the following April. Line out in the open ground. Except for *C. congestus*, the plants will be good saleable specimens 1½–2 ft (45–60 cm) across by October; that is one year from the insertion of the cuttings. *C. congestus* grown on for a second season will be 9–12 in. (22.5–30 cm) across. *C. buxifolius* var. *vellaeus* is also rather slow. The plants will be 6 in. (15 cm) across at one year old but, if kept for a second year, will be 2 ft (60 cm) across with berries.

Method 2 *C.* **Coral Beauty**, and no doubt others, root well under the low tunnel in June. Nodal cuttings, unwounded, treated with 0.8% IBA powder root up to 100% by autumn, when they are bushy plants 1 ft (30 cm) high, not yet showing the trailing habit of this cultivar.

Method 3 While this is a comparatively expensive system to use for cotoneasters, they could be a useful catch crop, especially the slower growing *C. buxifolius* var. *vellaeus* and *C. congestus*, where quicker growth to saleable size is desirable, e.g. 1½–2 in. (3.75–5 cm) cuttings of the latter inserted at the end of June rooted 100% in 16 days and were 9 in. (22.5 cm) across 15 months later.

Crataegus

There are an enormous number of Thorns (*Crataegus*), most of them N. American, but to us *Crataegus* means the Hawthorn (*C. monogyna, C. oxyacantha* and their hybrids). **Paul's Scarlet** is a splendid double red form, **Plena** a good double white.

Uses As specimens in parks, roadsides and gardens.

Methods of propagation 1. Budding. 2. Grafting. 3. Seed.

Method 1 Budding (p. 34) of the appropriate stock (*usually C. monogyna*) is carried out in July or August. The rootstock should be very well established   113 and buds from the middle portion of the cultivar stem are used. The stocks are headed back in the following February and the necessary training of the ensuing shoot will depend on whether it is intended to grow a standard, half-standard or bush.

Method 2 Two- or three-year-old field-established rootstocks are grafted close to the ground with the whip and tongue graft (p. 32), using scion wood of the previous season's growth. Bind and wax. At the end of the season a nice bush liner is produced. Transplant for growing on.

Method 3 Seed is used for raising the species only. The haws are gathered as soon as ripe but have to be exposed to two winter's cold in a stratification pit (p. 22). Early in the second spring inspect frequently and, on initiation of germination, sow seed and sand together on previously prepared seed beds at a depth of about ½ in. (1.2 cm).

Crinodendron

The only species in general cultivation is *Crinodendron hookerianum*, otherwise known as *Tricuspidaria lanceolata*. It is an evergreen from Chile, often seen as a large shrub about 15 ft (4.5 m) high, but capable of reaching almost tree-like dimensions in the mildest districts. The flower buds are visible over winter and in May develop into lantern-like red flowers pendant on long stalks. Though often stated to be a lime hater, we find it quite tolerant of our alkaline loam. *Crinodendron* is not a shrub for cold areas.

Method of propagation Readily struck from basal cuttings about 3 in. (8 cm) long, of the current season's growth, inserted after treatment with 0.8% IBA under mist or warm bench and plastic in June, without wounding. After five weeks 100% rooting may be expected. Pot up the rooted cuttings in a suitable compost (pp. 55–6) and grow on under glass or plastic. Pot on in spring. Alternatively, insert in a cold frame in September and pot when rooted the following spring.

Cryptomeria

Horticulturally the most important form is *Cryptomeria japonica* **Elegans**, widely grown for the bronzy-red colour of the foliage in winter. There are a number of other cultivars, including variegated types and dwarfs, comparatively seldom seen. *C. japonica* itself is a tall tree of columnar habit, capable of reaching 100 ft (30 m).

Uses The cultivar **Elegans**, a juvenile form, is widely planted as a specimen for winter effect. Where there is ample room, it will form a small bushy tree, apt to become top heavy and lean over. This may be corrected by periodic heading back in the early stages. Cryptomerias thrive best in moist soils.

Methods of propagation 1. Cuttings in the cold frame in September. 2. Grafting. 3. Seed.

Method 1 C. japonica and its cultivars are successfully rooted from cuttings taken in September. The type of cutting used is heel or stem up to 3–5 in. (7.5–12.5 cm) long. Wounding and treatment with a dilute steep of 25–100 mg/1 NAA is recommended in Holland for the dwarf types. The cuttings are placed in a cold frame in a medium of two parts peat to one of sand. Lift in late spring and plant into frames of fertilised peat and leave the lights in position until well established. In the autumn lift and plant into nursery beds at a spacing of 10–12 in. (25–30 cm) apart. Grow on for two seasons, when plants of 18–20 in. (45–50 cm) are ready for sale.

Method 2 This system of propagation is seldom used. The rootstocks — C. japonica — are potted in April and plunged out of doors. These are lifted in the following February and brought into the glasshouse and, after the roots have started into growth, are side grafted with a lip (p. 31) and placed in a grafting case in a temperature of 21°C (70°F). After some weeks callusing will be complete and, after hardening off, the stocks are headed back and the plants, knocked from the pots, are lined out in well prepared outdoor beds for growing on. These plants will be saleable after two or three growing seasons.

Method 3 The type species may be raised from seed sown under glass in February. Large quantities may be sown out of doors in March with provision for irrigation in dry weather.

X Cupressocyparis Leylandii

This is a hybrid between *Cupressus macrocarpa* and *Chamaecyparis nootkatensis*. Originally there were several seedlings from this cross and these have been propagated separately from cuttings, thus giving rise to a number of clones. These clones have been given the cultivar names **Green Spire** (Clone 1), **Haggerston Grey** (Clone 2), **Leighton Green** (Clone 11), **Naylor's Blue** (Clone 10) and **Stapehill**.

Uses This, the fastest growing of conifers, forms a columnar tree if allowed to develop naturally, far too big for garden use. However, it stands trimming well and can be used for screens or hedges, being preferable to *Cupressus macrocarpa* for this purpose, as it is hardier and not apt to die in patches.

Methods of propagation 1. Cuttings in mist or by warm bench and plastic in February. 2. Cuttings in cold frame and plastic in October.

Method 1 The selection of cutting material is important whatever method is being followed. Cuttings taken from old trees are much less successful than from younger specimens. If cuttings from young nursery stock are available, they should be used, but, to ensure supplies, mother plants should be set aside. Grown in hedge form, clipped annually (if the collection of cutting material does not complete this process) and top dressed with nitrogenous fertiliser, such plants will retain their juvenility and continue to yield material suitable for use in propagation.

Some investigators have found that some clones (e.g. Clone 2) are easier to root than others. This, however, is not invariably the case. In our experience, in rooting cuttings under mist, Clones 2, 5 and 11 did not differ significantly   115 in percentage rooting, but all were significantly better than Clone 1. In other trials, using cuttings inserted in a cold frame at the end of September, Clone 1 rooted as well as any. It may be that some clones show a wider tolerance of varying conditions, including treatment of the mother plants.

The cuttings should be stem cuttings (p. 4) of the past season's growth, with two of the nodes at the base turning brown. In our experience, leading shoots root just as well as, if not better than, side shoots, though some investigators differ on this point. The cuttings should be about 5 in. (12.5 cm) long. Wounding gives increased percentage rooting. Treat with 0.8% IBA rooting powder. Insert in a substrate of two parts moss peat to one of sand. In our experience, 80–90% rooting can be expected after nine weeks with the normal base temperatures used in the mist unit. As soon as rooted, the cuttings should be weaned from the mist and then potted up in 3½ in. peat pots. Return these to the glasshouse to re-establish and, at the first sign of roots emerging through the peat pots, harden off and plant out into a nursery bed at about 9 × 9 in. (22.5 × 22.5 cm). If desired, they could be containerised into 6 in. polythene bags at this stage and stood on a capillary bed for sale during the summer. Otherwise they may be lifted in autumn from the nursery bed and sold with much of the peat pot and compost still remaining on the root ball, the plants being at least 12 in. (30 cm) high. Any unsold can be left until spring and then containerised for sale as larger specimens during the following season.

Under our conditions cuttings are slower to root and give lower percentages between March and October.

Method 2 Cuttings selected with similar care as for Method 1, wounded and treated with 0.8% IBA powder are inserted in the cold frame with plastic in October. By following this system as advised (p. 14) 80–90% should be rooted by June. They can then be containerised for sale as 12–18 in. (30–45 cm) specimens in autumn. When these young plants are planted out they go ahead rapidly. Plants held too long in containers and allowed to become pot bound are never so satisfactory. For shelter belts, plants grown in peat pots and lifted from the ground have the advantage of being more definitely wind stable after planting.

Cupressus

The genus Cupressus is noted horticulturally for *C. macrocarpa* and its golden forms. Other species occasionally seen include *C. glabra* (usually wrongly called *C. arizonica*), *C. lusitanica* and *C. sempervirens* (Italian Cypress).

Uses As specimen trees. *C. macrocarpa* grows too big for gardens. For hedging it is being replaced by the hardier *x Cupressocyparis leylandii*.

Methods of propagation 1. Seed. 2. Cuttings in mist or warm bench and plastic in February.

Method 1 Sow small lots thinly in boxes under glass in February, larger lots in open beds in a very sheltered spot or in a frame in March–April (pp. 22–5). Germination usually occurs after two to three weeks. Those sown under glass are hardened off when 1 in. (2.5 cm) high in cold frames. When 2 in. (5 cm)

116

high, they are lined out in sheltered beds. Dipping the roots of the seedlings into a puddle of loamy soil and water is recommended. This should be thin enough to coat the roots but not stick them together. Space the seedlings 6 in. (15 cm) apart in rows 1 ft (30 cm) apart. Seedlings raised in open beds are transplanted in spring. *C. macrocarpa* transplants badly and so is often offered as a pot grown plant. Seedlings grown on out of doors should be wrenched each autumn, i.e. the roots under cut with a sharp spade, driving this under the plants from each side so that all the roots are cut and the plants loosened. Firm back the plants afterwards. This encourages the production of a good root ball, especially important with *Cupressus*, as an aid to successful transplanting.

Method 2 The golden forms of *C. macrocarpa* are regarded as difficult to root, a reputation borne out by our limited experience in which only about 25% rooted after ten weeks from insertions under mist and in the warm bench and plastic in February. The cuttings were treated with 0.8% IBA powder but were not wounded. Very good results have been reported elsewhere using material from pot grown specimens described as being in the juvenile state. There are several clones of golden macrocarpa and more work is needed on the comparative rootability of these as well as on such factors as timing, wounding and strength of root promoting substances.

Cytisus

The genus *Cytisus* includes not only the hybrid brooms such as **Lord Lambourne, Dorothy Walpole**, etc., but also many other species. Some of the more widely cultivated of these are mentioned below.

Uses Dwarf species grown in rock gardens include the miniature *C. ardoinii*, *C. x beanii* and *C. x kewensis*. The latter two are large enough for the front of the shrub border. The numerous hybrid brooms are of great value for giving a quick mass of colour in the spring garden. *C. x praecox* **Albus** will start the season with its white flowers (yellow in cv. **Allgold**). *C. nigricans* is interesting as it flowers late (July–August) with long racemes of yellow flowers at the end of the branches. All brooms are useful for dry sunny banks. *Cytisus battandieri* with silvery leaves and heads of yellow flowers in spring is not for cold districts.

Methods of propagation 1. Cuttings in the low tunnel in July. 2. Seed. 3. White polythene tunnel (see p. 19).

Method 1 This method is suitable for hybrid brooms, *C. beanii*, and *C. x kewensis*. Basal cuttings of the current year's growth are taken in July about 3 in. (7.5 cm) long and, after treatment with 0.8% IBA powder, are inserted under the low polythene tunnel. From 40 to 100% rooting can be expected after four weeks, according to cultivar. The cuttings are lifted in autumn and potted up in 4 in. plastic 'Long Tom' pots (i.e. pots 4 in. diameter, 5 in. deep) for overwintering in a cold house or cold frame. If left in the ground until spring the cuttings are liable to be pulled up by the birds or lifted by frost. Though they make little or no top growth before the first winter, growth is resumed strongly the next spring. Pot on into 5 in. polythene bags in April and stand on a capillary bed in the open. By July the plants will be saleable, 1 ft (30 cm) or more in height. The small cuttings of *C. ardoinii* should be rooted under mist.

Method 2 The hybrid brooms will not come true from seed, though an attractive mixture of colours can be raised this way. *C. nigricans* and *C. battandieri* are best grown from seed sown in boxes or pans in spring. A warm house is necessary for the latter and will hasten the growth of *C. nigricans*.

Home saved seed of the latter will germinate 50–60% in seven to ten days if sown under glass in February. About three weeks later the seedlings will be ready to prick off into 4 in. 'Long Toms'. Pinch the seedlings when about 10 in. (25 cm) high to induce bushiness. At this stage it is advisable to move them out of doors to avoid drawn, soft plants. They may be sold as 1 ft (30 cm) high plants in autumn.

Imported plants are often grafted but cuttings raised as above are satisfactory. Brooms could be used as a quick rooting catch crop under mist in July but the low tunnel method is a cheaper system for regular production. A former criticism of plants raised from cuttings was that they may collapse later due to incomplete healing of the base, leaving central pith exposed. Since July cuttings are taken before pith has formed, this problem is avoided. Brooms are sold in containers because established open-ground plants move badly. The plants are not eye catching when out of flower. It would be helpful propaganda to have the stock plants growing in a place where the wide range of colours available would be appreciated by customers.

Daboecia

See under **Erica**.

Dacrydium

These are evergreen conifers from New Zealand and Tasmania. They are frost tender and only thrive in the mildest localities. *D. cupressinum*, particularly beautiful in its pendulous branches and small prickly leaves, was propagated from basal hardwood cuttings, variable in length from 4–6 in. (10–15 cm) treated with 0.8% IBA powder in March. By June 50% rooting was obtained and grown on a capillary bed in a plastic house, the plants were 12 in. (30 cm) high two years from insertion of the cuttings. The plants branched freely and it is necessary to tie up a leader. Similar cuttings inserted in July failed to root.

Danae

Danae racemosa, the Alexandrian Laurel, is an evergreen allied to Butcher's Broom (*Ruscus*). The arching stems, about 2½ ft (75 cm) high, bear shining 'foliage' (not true foliage but flattened stems called cladodes) and are in demand for use in flower arrangements. The plants will grow well in shaded places in any reasonable soil.

118

Method of propagation The most practicable way is by division of the clumps in spring. Seed is rarely produced here but can sometimes be purchased from abroad. It can be sown in a cold frame but may be slow to germinate. The seedlings are slow to reach saleable size.

Daphne

A genus of shrubs for the connoisseur. The best known is *D. mezereum*, deciduous, with purple or white flowers. Other important species, all evergreen, include *D. arbuscula, D. blagayana, D. x burkwoodii, D. cneorum, D. laureola, D. pontica, D. retusa, D. tangutica, D. collina* and the allied *D. sericea*.

Uses All except *D. laureola* are grown for their sweet scent. *D. arbuscula* is a dwarf shrublet for the rock garden. *D. x burkwoodii, D. tangutica* and the slow growing *D. retusa* reach 3 ft (90 cm) and can be used in a shrubbery. *D. collina* (2 ft–60 cm) forms a particularly neat and rounded bush, almost as if it has been trimmed. It may be used in the larger rock garden or as a foreground shrub. *D. cneorum* and *D. blagayana* are trailing species for the rock garden or the edge of a shrub border. *D. laureola* and *D. pontica* are dull green flowered species 3 ft (90 cm) high, not very interesting, though the latter has scented blooms in spring and both will grow in shaded places.

Methods of propagation 1. Cuttings under mist in June–August. 2. Layering. 3. Seed.

Method 1 Daphnes are notoriously fickle subjects to root from cuttings, the results varying considerably between different batches. *D. tangutica* and *D. retusa* are probably the most amenable. Semi-hard basal cuttings treated with 0.8% IBA powder inserted under mist in June–August may be expected to root 60–90%, though seven to eleven weeks may be needed. June–August is also the time for most other species, with similar treatment. *D. cneorum* roots 55–100% after seven weeks. *D. collina* 65% after 14 weeks and *D. blagayana* 50% after five weeks. *D. arbuscula* roots readily from soft cuttings in June, 1–2 in. (2.5–5 cm) long, without treatment with rooting powder. *D. cneorum* also offers prospects of success in a cold frame in September. In limited trials nodal cuttings taken 2–4 in. (5–10 cm) from the tip, so as to cut through semi-hard wood and treated with 0.8% IBA powder rooted 30% by the following April. *D. x burkwoodii* **Somerset** roots best from second flush shoots taken one month after flowering (July).

Method 2 D. blagayana and *D. cneorum* may be layered in June. The former tends to do so naturally but the process must be assisted by covering the bare stems produced by this species with soil. Cut the rooted layers from the parent in autumn but leave till early spring before potting. *D. cneorum* needs the help of peat and sand cultivated into the soil round the parent plant. Pin the young shoots down into this soil so that their bases are 2 in. (5 cm) deep. Lift the following spring and line out to grow on.

Method 3 This is the only practicable way of raising *D. mezereum*. While this species will come from root cuttings, the prevalence of virus diseases makes seed the more desirable method. The parent plants should be selected for colour and freedom of flowering. Since greenfinches devour the seeds greedily while they are still unripe, it is necessary to net the bushes. The seeds should be sown in boxes as soon as they are ripe. Trials have shown that it is not necessary to clean the flesh from the seeds. A problem with *D. mezereum* is that only a proportion, about 15%, of the seeds come up the first spring, the remainder not appearing until a year later. Cleaning, chilling or stratifying the seed has not yet got us over this problem. To maximise germination the first year, it is important to sow the seed immediately it is ripe and leave the boxes in a shady place such as under a north wall. Seedlings should start to appear in February. Sowing in a heated house will inhibit germination but, once the seedlings are above ground, progress will be hastened if the boxes are brought into mild heat (60°F–15.6°C). This will be about mid–March. During mild weather in May, replace the boxes in a shaded spot. In autumn prick out the seedlings into a nursery bed and replace the boxes under the north wall. A second and larger flush of seedlings will appear during the second spring. In all, 70–80% of the seeds sown should germinate. The plants are saleable at 15 in. (37.5 cm) specimens 20 months from germination with one or two branches and with flower buds. At this stage they may be containerised to sell in flower the following spring or they may be grown on for a further year to sell as 24 in. (60 cm) plants. If selling from the open ground, the plants should be lifted with a ball of soil which should be wrapped in sacking immediately. Bare root plants transplant badly unless handled carefully and replanted promptly. They are not suitable for sending long distances.

Daphne cuttings deteriorate rather rapidly under mist, so it is important to remove them promptly when rooted. As they are such high value subjects, they should be potted up and grown to saleable size in containers.

Davidia

The Handkerchief Tree, so called from the large white bracts hanging each side of the inconspicuous globular flower head. The two species, *Davidia involucrata* and *D. vilmoriniana* are horticulturally very similar and are attractive small trees for parks or larger gardens on any soil.

Methods of propagation 1. Seed. 2. Cuttings under mist in June. 3. Layering.

Method 1 The large nut-like seeds are often produced freely. Gather in autumn and stratify in moist peat (p. 23). Though germination may occur in the first spring, two winters' stratification may be needed, especially if the seeds have been allowed to dry, or have not been cleaned of their fleshy covering. Sow in trays under glass as soon as germination is noted or sow individually in 3 in. pots. The seedlings may be potted on and kept on a capillary bed in a plastic house for the first year, and containerised the following spring. If kept under plastic, the young plants will reach 2 ft (60 cm) by autumn. American work indicated that exposure to four or five months of warmth, followed by two to three months cold hastens germination.

Method 2 Basal cuttings of the current year's growth with about four leaves fully developed will root 50% in seven weeks. Wound the cuttings and treat with 0.8% IBA powder before inserting in a medium of two parts moss peat to one of sand under mist. Pot up in 4 in. pots and overwinter under unheated glass or plastic. In April pot on into 6 in. bags and place on a capillary bed in a plastic house. By autumn the young trees should be 2 ft (60 cm) high. Specimens so raised have flowered after seven years. Seedlings take much longer to flower.

Method 3 Simple layering (p. 27) is recommended by some authorities.

Decaisnea

Decaisnea fargesii is a deciduous shrub, eventually 10 ft (3 m) high, with large pinnate leaves and is remarkable for the clusters of dull blue seed pods. Propagation may be effected from home saved seed, though, with us, such seed sown under glass in February has been slow and irregular to germinate. Autumn seed sown could well come more freely. Bring the containers under glass when germination starts. The seedlings will be ready to prick off into 3½ in. pots by May, when they may be transferred to a capillary bed in a plastic house. Pot on into 6 in. bags in June. Such seedlings will be 1 ft (30 cm) high by autumn and can be sold as container grown specimens.

Dendromecon

Dendromecon rigida has poppy-like yellow flowers and a stiff habit of growth, producing long shoots which must be trained against a sunny wall, since it is a tender plant, coming from California. Like its relative, *Romneya*, it may be propagated from root cuttings. Nodal cuttings taken in July are stated to be successful.

Desfontainea

Desfontainea spinosa, a native of Chile, has spiny, holly-like leaves and tubular scarlet flowers in late summer. It is a slow growing shrub, usually seen as specimens up to 5 ft (1.5 m) high but capable of twice that height in favoured localities. Though a native of Chile, *Desfontainea* is hardy in most districts, but thrives best in the western area. It will tolerate a fair amount of lime in the soil.

Propagate by basal cuttings of the current year's shoots in the cold frame in October. When rooted the following spring they may be lined out in a sheltered place for growing on. Containerised specimens flower when quite small.

Deutzia

An important genus of spring flowering shrubs not always seen to best advantage as they will put up with poor conditions and often are not pruned regularly. As soon as the flowers drop, a proportion of the oldest shoots should be pruned back to the point from where a new shoot springs, or else close to ground level.

Uses For planting as single specimens or in groups in any open, sunny place. Most deutzias grow 4–6 ft (1.2–1.8 m) high, but the *Deutzia scabra* group are only for large gardens as they can reach 10 ft (3 m).

Methods of propagation 1. Cuttings in mist in May. 2. Cuttings in the cold frame with plastic in June. 3. Cuttings in the cold frame in October.

Method 1 Nodal or internodal softwood cuttings of the current season's growth, treated with 0.4% IBA powder can be expected to root 100% three weeks after insertion in a substrate of two parts moss peat to one of sand. They can be lined out in further frames and, by the end of the season, should be 1 ft high (30 cm) with two to three shoots. In autumn line out, prune back the shoots by half to two-thirds and grow on for a further season. They can then be sold as small plants 15–24 in. tall (30–60 cm) according to cultivar or, if pruned again and grown on for a third season, as large plants 2–5 ft (0.6–2.5 m) high.

Method 2 Nodal or internodal cuttings of the current year's shoots taken in June root better under our conditions in the cold frame with plastic than if inserted in the low tunnel. Treat with 0.8% IBA powder. Upwards of 85% rooting may be expected and, if the cuttings are left until autumn, especially if given a liquid feed, they should be about 8 in. (20 cm) high with two shoots. They can then be lined out and treated as above.

Method 3 Heeled cuttings of the past season's growth, 4–8 in. (10–20 cm) long, treated with 0.8% IBA powder, are inserted in a cold frame in a compost of two parts moss peat to one of sand. Lift in late spring and transplant to well prepared, irrigated nursery beds. They can be lined out in autumn and pruned as above.

Distylium

Distylium racemosum is an evergreen shrub related to the witch-hazels. It is not an important species on its own merits but recently has been advocated as an understock for *Hamamelis*.

Method of propagation Semi-hard nodal cuttings of the past season's growth, not wounded but treated with 0.8% IBA powder can be inserted under mist or warm bench and plastic in November. They can be hardened off when rooted and potted up the following February. About 85% success can be expected. They can be used for grafting a year later. Alternatively softwood cuttings treated similarly can be inserted in August to give about 60% rooting after seven weeks.

Drimys

Evergreen shrubs from S. America and Australia, not particular in their soil requirements but tender in cold districts.

Uses Drimys winteri is a large shrub or small tree with leathery leaves and clusters of white waxy flowers. It is too large for the small garden, where the slow growing *D. andina* may be tried instead. This will flower when only a few inches high, but is slow to develop into a saleable plant from a cutting, as is *D. colorata* (*Pseudowintera colorata*), grown for the colour of its leaves, blotched red and purple. *D. aromatica* is a low growing shrub with narrow leaves. It has been used as an unusual hedge plant in mild localities.

Method of propagation D. *winteri* will root 100% from softwood basal cuttings taken in April, wounded, treated with 0.8% IBA powder and inserted under mist in two parts moss peat to one of sand for nine weeks. The rooted cuttings are hardened off and planted out in a cold frame of loamless compost (p. 55). Growth is rapid, the plants being 2 ft (0.6 m) high a year later, with three to four branches. With the same treatment *D. andina* rooted 57% from July cuttings, 85% from September cuttings and gave 70% rooted cuttings under warm bench and plastic in February. It seems, therefore, to be propagated over a wide season, corresponding to its long period of flowering. After 2½ years 1 in. (2.5 cm) cuttings of this species developed into plants 1 ft (30 cm) high with six or seven branches. Development is speeded up if the rooted cuttings are potted up in 4 in. pots in April and are placed on a capillary bed in a plastic house. Such plants are 10–12 in. (25–30 cm) high with three to four branches at one year old. *Drimys* is also successful from cold frame cuttings, so it appears to be a genus amenable to different means of propagation, including layering. Old bushes of *D. aromatica* will layer naturally under suitable conditions. *D. colorata* is, in our experience, slow (4 months) to root from cuttings though 85–90% success can be obtained from basal cuttings taken in March, treated with 0.8% IBA powder and inserted under mist. Less mature cuttings taken in July were just as slow.

Elaeagnus

For most nurserymen two species of *Elaeagnus* are important. *E. pungens* **Maculata** is an evergreen grown for the effect of its green and gold variegated leaves. *E. x ebbingei* has silvery undersides to the leaf.

Uses E. *pungens* **Maculata** is grown singly or in groups, mainly for winter effect in gardens and parks and grows 3–5 ft (0.9–1.5 m) high. *E. x ebbingei* is attracting attention as a shrub or hedge for seaside areas as it is wind resistant.

Methods of propagation 1. Cuttings in white polythene tunnel in July (p. 19). 2. Cuttings in mist or warm bench and plastic in February–March.

Method 1 Nodal cuttings 6 in. (15 cm) long from the tips of the current season's shoots are wounded and treated with 0.8% IBA powder before being inserted in a medium of two parts moss peat to one of sand. In two months up to 100% rooting can be expected. Cuttings are potted up in 3 in. (7.5 cm) pots and although they make no further growth in that season, a strong root system develops and plants overwintered under glass retain good leaf colour, starting into growth early in the spring. Containerising at this stage and further culture in a polythene house for the season will result in saleable plants up to 30 cm by autumn.

123

Method 2 Nodal cuttings, 6 in. (15 cm) long from the tips of the past season's growth are wounded, treated with 0.8% IBA powder and inserted in a medium of two parts moss peat to one of sand. Up to 100% rooting can be expected after one month. Though cuttings taken earlier (December–January) will root, they are liable to yellowing and shedding of their leaves after potting up if placed in a cold house. By waiting until February conditions should be better by the time the cuttings have rooted. After hardening off, the rooted cuttings are planted out at 6 × 6 in. (15 × 15 cm) in a cold frame filled with loamless compost (p. 55). The glass and shading are replaced until the plants are well established. On good soils and in sheltered localities they could go into an irrigated nursery bed. With good culture, the cuttings should reach about 7–9 in. (17.5–22.5 cm) in height, with three to four side shoots in that season. Line out on a well prepared sheltered site at 12 × 12 in. (30 × 30 cm) and grow on for a second season for sale as 12–14 in. (30–35 cm) specimens. They may alternatively be containerised after one year to grow on a capillary bed under polythene for the next season and can then be ready for sale as 12–14 in. (30–35 cm) specimens.

Embothrium

Embothrium coccineum is an evergreen or semi-deciduous shrub or small tree from Chile. The scarlet flowers are spectacular in May–June. This species is variable in leaf size and shape, hence such names as *E. longifolium* and *E. lanceolatum*, but botanists regard these as variations of *E. coccineum* as intermediate forms link them with the type. *E. lanceolatum* **Norquinco** form is especially floriferous.

Propagation is by means of suckers, or on a larger scale nodal cuttings of the current year's shoots can be rooted under mist in June. Root cuttings may be raised in a cold frame.

Enkianthus

These shrubs belong to the heather family and need lime free soil. The bell shaped flowers, produced in clusters, are yellow lined red in *E. campanulatus* and *E. chinensis*, white in *E. perulatus* and *E. cernuus* (red in var. rubens). The genus is noted for the rich autumn colour of the foliage.

Method of propagation The fine dust-like seed is ripe in December. Sow thinly under glass in February, scarcely covering the seed. With a temperature of 65–70°F (18.3–21.1°C), good germination can be expected in two to three weeks. The seedlings will be ready for pricking off into 3 in. pots by mid April. If kept under glass (minimum temperature 60°F), development will be rapid and, by mid-June, the plants will be about 5 in. (12.5 cm) high. They may then be potted on into 4 in. pots and, if placed on a capillary bed in a plastic house, will be about 1½ ft (45 cm) high by late summer, branching freely from the base. At this stage, move the plants out to a cold frame or outdoor bed to harden up the soft growth before winter. Cuttings can be rooted in April but are very difficult to overwinter.

Fig. 37. *Enkianthus* 16 in (40 cm) from seed in 5½ months.

Erica (including Calluna and Daboecia)

For convenience the main garden heathers can be grouped as Tree and Bush heaths (*Erica arborea*, *E. australis*, *E. mediterranea*, now called *E. erigena*, and *E. terminalis*); Ling heathers (*Calluna vulgaris* and its many forms); Winter heaths (*E. carnea*); Cornish heaths (*E. vagans*); Bell heathers (*E. cinerea*); Dorset heaths (*E. ciliaris*); Cross-leaved heaths (*E. tetralix*); Connemara heathers (*Daboecia*) and other species not so often seen.

Uses This popular group of plants is in constant demand not only for ground cover but also because by careful choosing of types, an all-year-round flowering sequence can be achieved. These plants require little maintenance and, with new suburban gardens much reduced in size, their role will become more important. The warmth of their colour, especially when planted in drifts in association with dwarf conifers, can present a very pleasing effect. Normally only suitable for acid soil conditions, some, like *Erica carnea*, *E. darleyensis*, *E. mediterranea* and *E. terminalis* and their cultivars, are also tolerant of alkaline soils.

Methods of propagation 1. Cuttings of semi-mature shoots in July–August in the cold frame with plastic. 2. Hardwood cuttings in October in the cold frame with plastic. 3. Hardwood cuttings in February in mist or in the warm bench with plastic. 4. Seed.

125

Method 1 This is the conventional time of year for taking heather cuttings and entails overwintering the young plants and growing them on for a further season before they are large enough for sale.

Stem or basal cuttings of the current season's growth 1–1½ in. (2.5–4 cm) long are inserted in moss peat in the cold frame and covered with light gauge plastic, first stripping the leaves from the basal part of the cuttings. With most types 80–100% rooting can be expected after eight to ten weeks. The rooted cuttings are lifted in autumn or spring and planted into a frame of fertilised peat at a spacing of 4 in. (10 cm) square. Due to the sensitivity of heathers to fertilisers, be careful not to use too rich a mix. Slow release fertilisers at the low rate recommended by the manufacturers for these plants are satisfactory. Alternatively, liquid feeding can be practised, e.g. a fortnightly drench during the growing season of a ½% solution of a 9:9:7 formulation. After planting, place the frame lights in position until the plants are well established. Trim the plant during summer to ensure bushy growth. By the late summer and autumn of the second year they will be specimens about 4 × 6 in. (10 × 15 cm) and may be lifted and sold as flowering plants.

Method 2 Hardwood cuttings 1–1½ in. (2.5–4 cm) long are taken from the tips of the shoots in October. The best material is from young, vigorous plants and, if summer trimming has not prevented flowering, any flower heads may be nipped off. Prepare and insert the cuttings as for Method 1. The plastic sheet is removed in stages in March–April.

The rooted cuttings are lifted in April and planted out into frames of fertilised moss peat as for Method 1 or similar liquid feeds may be given. Shaded frame lights are placed in position until the plants are established and then gradually removed, substituting lath shading for the lights until the plants are well into growth. Water generously. Growth will be vigorous and the plants should be lightly trimmed over twice during June and July to promote bushy growth. By September the plants will reach saleable size, 4–6 in. (10–15 cm) across. Many cultivars will be in flower.

Method 3 This is essentially the same as Method 2. It obviates the need to overwinter small plants but necessitates the provision of bottom heat. The cuttings will be rooted in seven to nine weeks. They are then hardened off in a cold frame before being turned out of the trays and planted out in late April in frames for growing on as under Method 2. The plants reach saleable size in seven to eight months, with flowers in many species.

The systems described above do away with the potting of rooted erica cuttings as is so widely practised. Well grown plants in moss peat form a cohesive root ball. Cut through the layer of peat between the plants from the front of the frame to the back and along its length and lift out each plant with a substantial root block. At this point the plants can be (a) planted directly into their permanent quarters: (b) stood out and loosely bedded by shaking peat through them. In this condition they can be easily lifted and bagged at sale: (c) put in containers for standing out at garden centres.

Method 4 *E. arborea*, often troublesome from cuttings, may be raised from seed, and, indeed, can sow itself in favoured gardens, but other species are not usually raised from seed.

Cultivars of the following species respond well to this system of production: *E. arborea, E. australis, E. carnea, E. ciliaris, E. darleyensis, E. mediterranea, E. terminalis, E. vagans, Calluna vulgaris* and *Daboecia cantabrica*.

Fig. 38. Erica.

Fig. 39. Calluna.

Fig. 40. Daboecia.

Figs. 38–40. Heather cuttings taken in Jan/Feb are saleable flowering plants by autumn of the same year.   127

Escallonia

The escallonias, an evergreen summer-flowering group of plants, are subjects mainly for coastal regions and milder inland areas. Most of them bear red or pink flowers during summer and autumn.

Uses E. macrantha is mainly used for hedging or as a windbreak, responding well to close cutting or shaping. For use as specimen bushes, the most popular cultivars are the Donard range **Donard Brilliance**, **Donard Gem**, **Donard Radiance** and **Donard Seedling**.

Methods of propagation 1. Cuttings in the low tunnel in June–July. 2. Cuttings in the cold frame from July to October. 3. Cuttings in the open ground in October–November.

Method 1 Cuttings, about 5 in. (12.5 cm) long inserted in June and July in the low tunnel give high rooting percentages. These plants, left to grow on until autumn, will be 12 in. (30 cm) high. Transplant to open beds and grow on for a further year.

Method 2 Once shoots of the current season have begun to ripen, they will root quite easily. Nodal, basal or heel type cuttings are used and show improved rooting percentages when treated with 0.8% IBA powder. Insert in a north-facing cold frame in a medium of two parts moss peat to one of sand. Place lights in position. Light gauge polythene stretched over the cuttings is helpful to rooting in July or August but, from then onwards, the plastic covering will not be necessary. Late summer propagated cuttings can be left in the frame until transplanted in October, whilst the later struck cuttings can be left until March when high percentages of them will have rooted and they are then planted into prepared beds in the nursery.

Method 3 Escallonia is easily propagated in October–November in mild localities by using 9–12 in. (22.5–30 cm) hardwood cuttings inserted in open ground to one third of their length, well firmed in. Treatment with rooting powder is not necessary. Rooting will take place during the early spring and, if the cuttings are left undisturbed, they will produce good liners 18 in. (45 cm) high by the following autumn.

Eucalyptus

There are 500 or more species of *Eucalyptus*, mostly native of Australia. Only a few are hardy, even in the milder areas of Great Britain and Ireland, and these include *E. coccifera*, *E. gunnii*, *E. johnstonii*, *E. niphophila*, *E. parvifolia*, *E. pauciflora*, *E. perriniana*, *E. urnigera* and *E. salicifolia*.

Uses For many people eucalyptus is typified by the very large trees, e.g. of *E. gunnii* seen in maritime counties, but there are other methods of growing them besides letting them run up naturally. Coppicing annually in March, i.e. cutting almost to ground level is an effective way of growing many, especially those noted for the glaucous colour of the young foliage, e.g. *E. gunnii*, *E. perriniana* and *E. glaucescens*. *E. niphophila*, the 'Snow Gum' is particularly effective grown as a standard, to show off the white bark and is relatively slow growing. *E. pauciflora* and *E. coccifera* also have attractive bark. *E. johnstonii*, distinct in its apple green foliage, is a useful screening tree. *E. salicifolia* has narrow willow-like leaves. Eucalyptus foliage is in demand for use in floral arrangements.

Method of propagation Eucalyptus must be grown from seed. Home-saved seed from trees of proven hardiness is desirable. Imported seed should, where possible, be from the higher elevations in the natural habitat of the species. Sow under glass in March in temperatures 60–70°F (15.6–21.1°C). To avoid damping off, sow thinly and water the boxes from below by capillarity. Prick off at the second rough leaf stage into peat pots. Continue to water carefully, using a fine rose. About the end of May, when the seedlings are 3–4 in. (7.5–10 cm) high, harden off by transferring to a cold frame. This has a layer of peat at the bottom into which the roots can be allowed to penetrate slightly. Keep the lights on, gradually increasing the ventilation until the plants are completely hardened off. By July they should be 1 ft (30 cm) high, with roots just emerging from the pots into the peat beneath. They should now be planted into their permanent positions. It is necessary to get eucalypts planted while still small if they are to be wind stable. After two or three seasons, the young trees may be headed back. This ensures good anchorage and encourages a bushy, well furnished tree. Occasionally one sees young trees of eucalyptus which have run up in a straggly fashion. These can be cut back to induce branching. Young trees should not be planted where there is overhead shade; they do not like being planted too close to large established trees. Pot bound trees should not be planted as they are hard to keep firm in the ground, hence the recommendation to prick off into peat pots. Staking is advisable for the first two or three years but care should be taken that the fast growing young trees do not become strangled by the ties.

Eucryphia

The Eucryphias are evergreen shrubs or small trees with large white flowers 2–2½ in (5–6.2 cm) across, with a brush of stamens in the centre. As they come from S. America and Australia, they are apt to be injured by cold in inland districts. Acid soil is needed, though *E. cordifolia* and *E. x nymansensis* will tolerate lime. The most important species for the nurseryman are *E. cordifolia*, *E. glutinosa* and their hybrid *E. x nymansensis* (which includes the cultivars **Mount Usher** and **Nymansay**) and *E. lucida*.

Uses Valued as specimens flowering in late summer with attractive foliage all the year.

Method of propagation Nodal or basal cuttings, wounded and treated with 0.8% IBA powder, will root up to 100% in seven weeks if inserted under mist in February–March. Pot up in loamless compost (p. 55) and grow on, preferably under glass or plastic. Semi-hardwood cuttings will also root in late summer. The species can be raised from seed sown under glass in February, pricking off the seedlings into 3 in. pots and growing on under glass or plastic.   129

Euonymus

Euonymus europaeus is our native Spindle Bush, of which **Red Cascade** is a good cultivar notable for the abundance of the rosy red capsules which split open to show the orange seeds within. Other good fruiting species are *E. planipes* and *E. yedoensis*. The foliage of these deciduous kinds colours well in autumn. *E. alatus* is grown particularly for the autumn colour of the leaves.

The evergreen spindles include two kinds of commercial importance with variegated foliage, *E. radicans* **Silver Queen** and *E. japonicus* **Ovatus Aureus**. *E. j.* **Microphyllus Variegatus** is a dwarf, small-leaved form useful for confined spaces.

Uses The deciduous types are planted as specimens for autumn colour of fruit and leaf. The evergreens will grow in shady places even in towns. They are often seen in poor condition due to neglect. *E. japonicus* is sometimes seen as a hedge in cities and on the coast.

Methods of propagation 1. Cuttings in the cold frame, September–October. 2. Cuttings in the low tunnel in June (evergreens). 3. Seed (deciduous species).

Method 1 Basal or nodal cuttings about 4 in. (10 cm) long, treated with 0.8% IBA powder may be inserted in a cold frame in a compost of two parts moss peat to one of sand. Lift and line out in a nursery bed the following spring.

Method 2 While the evergreen types can be propagated by most methods (and can be used as catch crops under glass) this one is convenient. Nodal cuttings about 3–4 in. (7.5–10 cm) long may be used, unwounded and without treatment with rooting powders. When lifted in autumn for lining out 100% rooting can be expected. Grow on for a further year and sell as small liners.

Method 3 Seed is the best method for the deciduous species. Collect the capsules at the first sign of splitting. They may be left in trays to complete the process. Small quantities can be separated out by hand. The orange colour is due to a covering of the seed which can be removed by hand for small quantities. Sow immediately in pots plunged in a cold frame or sow direct in the cold frame or mix with slightly moist sand and stratify (p. 22) until spring, according to the quantity being handled. Those in pots can be pricked off at the second rough leaf stage, hardened off and planted out. The stratified seed can be sown in an outdoor bed, to be left for one or two seasons before lining out 6 in. (15 cm) each way.

Exochorda

A small genus of shrubs from Asia, allied to spiraeas and valued for their abundant white flowers in May. Since they grow large, about 12 ft (3.6 m), they need plenty of room. *E. racemosa* is not recommended for lime soils. Our experience has been with *E. giraldii var. wilsonii* which tolerates lime and can be recommended for its large flowers. Basal softwood cuttings about 3 in. (7.5 cm) long, taken late in April, wounded and treated with 0.8% IBA powder, root 80–90% in six weeks under mist. They can then be potted up in 3 in. pots and held in a plastic house over winter and lined out in spring. Little shoot growth is made in the year of rooting, 1 ft (30 cm) in the second year, followed by vigorous growth in the third year.

Fabiana

Fabiana imbricata is so heath-like in growth that it is a surprise to learn that it belongs to the potato family. It can reach 6 ft (1.8 m) in height but there is a prostrate form. The tubular flowers are white or mauve. It is a shrub for a sunny place but not for districts with cold winters.

Propagation may be effected from nodal cuttings 2–3 in. (5–7.5 cm) long, of the tops of the shoots in April. Treat with 0.8% IBA powder and insert in mist or in the warm bench and plastic. Upwards of 60% of the cuttings will be rooted in 5–6 weeks when they may be potted up in 3 in. pots and grown on under glass or plastic. By the end of the year the plants will be about 6 in. (15 cm) high. Overwinter under glass or plastic and pot on in spring for sale in summer and autumn as container grown plants.

Cuttings may also be struck in a cold frame in October to be lifted and potted in spring.

Fagus

The beeches of horticultural importance are forms of the Common Beech (*Fagus sylvatica*).

Uses The Purple Beech, of which **Riversii** is a good vegetatively propagated clone, is popular for landscaping on a large scale. The Fern-leaved Beech (**Asplenifolia**) is a beautiful tree for the same purpose. Two contrasting forms are **Pendula** (weeping) and the Dawyck Beech. The latter is a fastigiate form that might be planted when space is restricted.

Beech is popular as a hedging plant owing to its habit of retaining the dead, russet coloured leaves through the winter.

Methods of propagation 1. Seed. 2. Grafting.

Method 1 The Common Beech bears heavy crops of seed only at irregular intervals, generally every five to seven years, with lighter crops in between. In view of this, Danish findings that beech seed can be stored for one year (not longer) in sealed containers at 34–36°F (1–2°C) are of interest. The ripe nuts may be collected in autumn and should not be allowed to dry out. They may be sown fresh or stored in moist peat until sown in January–February. At all times the seed, whether sown or in store, must be protected against rodents. Sow to a depth of ½ in. (1.2 cm) and shield from frost with rolls of laths or with wire netting covered with brushwood supported 15 in. (37.5 cm) above the soil. Remove this protection by June. Line out in the second autumn. Beech should be sown on slightly alkaline soil. The young plants should be transplanted regularly to prevent the formation of tap roots.

Method 2 The most popular ornamental beeches are cultivars of *F. sylvatica*, and this species, used as the rootstock, must be very well established in pots before successful grafting can be carried out. Pencil thick stocks are used and 131 should be potted for up to one year before being grafted in February or March. Older stocks with well-developed root systems can also be used. The rootstocks should be well dried off before being side-grafted (p. 31) with selected one year old scionwood, which should be dipped in a fungicide once the grafting cuts are made. After tying, place the grafts in a closed case with a bottom temperature of 60–65°F (16.6–18.3°C). After about six weeks the graft will be united and hardening off can commence. The grafts are then transferred to cooler conditions (cold frame) and the rootstock is cut off from above the graft joint. Plant out in May in favourable weather conditions for growing on.

These subjects can also be field grafted in April using the cleft graft technique (p. 33). The stocks should be established in the ground for two years and in the February before grafting, the stems are trimmed down to about 6 in. (15 cm). At the beginning to the middle of April grafting is carried out with selected two-year-old scionwood. Remove the buds from the scions, otherwise these will grow out and desiccate the scion before union has taken place. Growth will come late in the season from very small buds present below those removed. After tying, the graft is waxed. Select and stake the strongest shoot. The plants can be sold as whips after two seasons, or grown on for further development.

Forsythia

The forsythias are deservedly popular for their early flowering, making a brilliant display, and for their ease of cultivation (including propagation).

Uses One of the brightest and earliest of spring shrubs for gardens and parks.

Methods of propagation 1. Cuttings in the low tunnel or in the cold frame and plastic in June. 2. Cuttings in the cold frame or open ground in November– December.

Method 1 Forsythia cuttings can be struck under almost any system, the low tunnel in June being a cheap and convenient method. Nodal or basal cuttings of the current year's growth about 4 in. (10 cm) long root up to 100% without need for treatment with rooting powders. Such cuttings reach about 12 in. (30 cm) in length by autumn when they can be lined and pruned back in spring to 5 in. (12.5 cm) to give good bushy plants at the end of that growing season.

Method 2 Basal cuttings of the past season's growth can be inserted in the cold frame or open ground and lifted for lining out in the following autumn. Prune the plants in spring to encourage basal breaks.

Fothergilla

Fothergilla, a small genus of shrubs from N. America, is allied to *Hamamelis*. The white flowers, appearing before the leaves, have no petals but give an effect of spikes of flowers due to the conspicuous stamens.

As with *Hamamelis*, propagation is not simple. Layering of the current year's shoots in August is commonly recommended. We have had success

with basal cuttings of the young shoots of *F. major* under mist in June, 70%
rooting in two parts moss peat to one of sand, and 94% in moss peat alone.
The use of IBA did not increase the numbers rooted. Wounding was not tried,
but may be helpful. The young plants were potted up in 4 in. pots and when
established were transferred to a capillary bed in a plastic house. They were
6–8 in. (15–20 cm) high by autumn and developed into well branched saleable
shrubs of 30–40 cm by the end of the following season.

Fraxinus

The common Ash (*Fraxinus excelsior*) is well-known for its weeping form
(**Pendula**). *F. ornus*, the Manna Ash, is grown as a medium sized flowering
tree with panicles of whitish flowers in May.

Methods of propagation 1. Seed. 2. Grafting.

Method 1 Gather the seed as soon as it is ripe (September–October) and sow
immediately in outdoor beds (pp. 23–5), so that it will undergo the necessary
cold period to germinate in spring. The soil for ash should be alkaline rather
than acid (pH 6 or more). Protect against frost as described under *Fagus*. Line
out in autumn.

Method 2 The rootstock used is *F. excelsior*. Two- or three-year-old field
established seedlings are grafted from the beginning to the middle of April,
after the rootstock has been cut back to 6 in. (15 cm). The cleft method of
grafting (p. 33) is used. After binding, the graft is waxed and the young
growth is staked to produce a straight stem and also to prevent dislodgement
of the graft in the early part of the summer. Sell as a whip or grow on for
further development. The pendulous variety is grafted at from 6–8 ft
(1.8–2.4 m) high on the rootstock.

Ash can also be chip budded (p. 34). Two-year-old seedling rootstocks are
planted in March and budding is carried out in August. After cutting back
the rootstock in February, the bud develops strongly in the following season.
Sell as a whip or grow on for further development.

Fuchsia

Fuchsia magellanica and *F.* **Riccartonii** are the hardiest fuchsias and have run
wild in mild districts, e.g. in the West of Ireland. The florists' fuchsias are
hybrids from a number of species and are hardier than commonly supposed,
often springing up again from the roots when cut down by frost.

Method of propagation This is simple. Cuttings will root under any method.
Those rooted early in the year under mist, warm bench and plastic or under
the low tunnel in June have the rest of the season to develop. Cuttings taken
at the end of the summer can be overwintered in frames or under glass.   133

Garrya

Garrya elliptica is an evergreen shrub of which the male form is valued for its 6 in. (15 cm) long, greyish green catkins abundantly borne in January–February.

Uses In addition to flowering at a useful time of year, this shrub will grow in any soil, thriving even on north or east facing walls.

Methods of propagation 1. Outdoor cuttings in October. 2. Cold frame cuttings in November. 3. Hardwood cuttings under mist or by warm bench and plastic in February.

Methods 1 and 2 Basal or nodal cuttings of side shoots, 6–8 in. (15–20 cm) long are inserted in the open ground or in the frame in cold areas. Treatment with rooting powders is not needed. Outdoor cuttings, when lifted a year later, should be rooted 80–90%. Pot up and sell the following autumn as 10 in. (25 cm) plants. Cuttings in the cold frame may be lifted for potting in late spring.

Method 3 Hardwood basal cuttings 4–5 in. (10–12.5 cm) long may be rooted under mist or by the warm bench and plastic method. Insert in February using two parts moss peat to one of sand. Treat with 0.8% IBA powder but wounding is not necessary. About 80% rooting may be expected after five weeks, when the cuttings may be potted up. If grown on a capillary bed in a plastic house, they may reach 1 ft (30 cm) by the end of the year.

It may be noted that we had 82% rooting in eight weeks from single node cuttings taken from long shoots on a hard pruned bush. They were inserted in the warm bench and plastic in December.

Genista

A genus of yellow-flowered shrubs allied to the brooms (*Cytisus*) ranging in size from prostrate shrubs for the rock garden to species attaining 20 ft (6 m).

Uses Low growing species suitable for ground cover or sunny banks include *G. pilosa, G. saggitalis* and *G. tinctoria* **Plena**. *G. lydia* has been used also but in some places is apt to die off suddenly in patches. *G. hispanica* forms a low mound concealed under a mass of brilliant yellow flowers in May–June. The prickly habit is often useful as a deterrent to trespassing humans or animals. The Mount Etna Broom (*G. aetnensis*) reaches 15 ft (3.5 m) or more, with rush-like branches, and makes an interesting specimen plant. It flowers when quite small.

Methods of propagation 1. Seed. 2. Cuttings in the low tunnel in June. 3. Cuttings in the cold frame in October.

Method 1 Where seed is available, this is the best method of propagation and is the only practicable way for *G. aetnensis*. The seed should be gathered when the pods are ripe, as shown by a change in colour to black, but before they split open. The ripening process may be completed in trays on the potting shed bench. Store the seed until February, when it should be sown thinly in boxes under glass. Pot up the seedlings when 2 in. (5 cm) high into 3 in. pots, harden off and grow on in a cold frame. Growth may be hastened by placing the seedlings on a capillary bed in a plastic house until early June, when the plants will be about 9 in. (22.5 cm) high. Transfer them to an outdoor capillary bed or frame to avoid excessively soft growth. The young plants may need staking for a time to ensure upright growth.

Method 2 This gives good results with *G. hispanica*, and probably with other species. Basal cuttings 2½ in. (6.2 cm) long, not treated with rooting powder nor wounded, root 90–95% in 8–9 weeks, when they should be potted into 3 in. pots for overwintering in a cold frame or plastic house. If placed on a capillary bed in spring and potted on in May, they will be about 5 in. (12.5 cm) across by autumn. The young plants grow well on the capillary bed although this species is associated with drier conditions.

Method 3 This is the older method. Basal cuttings of the current season's growth inserted in autumn can be lifted and potted the following spring and grown on on a capillary bed either under plastic or outside.

Ginkgo

Ginkgo biloba is the Maidenhair Tree, so called from the leaves resembling in shape the fronds of the Maidenhair Fern. It is a deciduous tree capable of attaining 100 ft (30 m). The leaves turn a good yellow before falling.

The Ginkgo may be raised from imported seeds. These are large and nut-like. If sown under glass in February, minimum temperature 65°F (18.3°C), germination is quick (17–20 days). The seedlings will be ready for pricking off into 4 × 5 in. 'Long Toms' in two or three weeks. In late May they may be transferred to a capillary bed in a plastic house. In July shoot growth pauses but is resumed and, by the end of the year, the young plants will be 12–15 in. (30–37.5 cm) high. They may then be sold as small plants or lined out for further growth, though containerisation has the advantage of minimising transplanting check apt to occur with open grown plants of this species.

While seed is to be generally recommended basal cuttings can be struck under mist in August. No root promoting substances are needed.

Gleditsia

Trees grown for their attractive acacia-like foliage, the flowers being of no account. They may be raised from seed, and though liable to die-back of the tips when young, they grow out of this in later life. The most important cultivar is *G. triacanthos* **Sunburst** with golden foliage. This is propagated by being side-grafted under glass in January, onto one-year-old seedlings with tops removed leaving a 5 cm stub. After dipping the grafted plants into wax they can be stood on the open bench in a cold glasshouse. Later if grown on a capillary bed in a plastic house, they are capable of reaching 30 in. (75 cm) by the end of their first season.

Grevillea

A genus of evergreen Australian shrubs with dark needle-shaped foliage and tubular red or yellow flowers curling back at the mouth to show the protruding styles.

Uses As specimens or in groups, for gardens in the milder areas. Though grevilleas are stated to be lime haters, the red flowered *G. rosmarinifolia* does well on our limy soil. *G. alpina* is a dwarf species suitable for a sheltered rock garden.

Method of propagation Grevilleas root readily from nodal or basal cuttings of semi-hardwood side shoots taken in the March–May period. Wounding is not necessary. Treatment with 0.8% IBA increased the percentage rooting, which can be up to 100% in as short a period as 15 days in a mist unit. Insert in a medium of two parts peat to one of sand. Pot up when rooted and grow on under glass or plastic. By late summer a 4 in. (10 cm) cutting of *G. rosmarinifolia* should be about 1 ft (30 cm) high. The smaller species give cuttings about 2 in. (5 cm) long and plants about 5 in. (12.5 cm) high develop in the first season.

Griselinia

The New Zealand species, *Griselinia littoralis* is used as a hedging plant, except in cold districts. It will grow well even in difficult situations such as under trees, and is valued for the shining, light green colour of the foliage. Griselinia can also be used for screens (10–15 ft or 3–4.5 m) as it will not get out of hand if trimmed occasionally.

Griselinia is easily propagated from nodal cuttings in the open ground in October–November as for *Escallonia* (p. 128). The use of rooting powders is not necessary. In cold districts use a cold frame. The cuttings can be lifted and lined out the following May.

Halesia

Halesias, known as the Snowdrop Trees, are very beautiful plants from N. America. In May the leafless branches carry white pendant snowdrop-like flowers. *H. carolina* and the larger flowered *H. monticola* are the best species.

Uses As specimen trees for lime free soils.

Methods of propagation 1. Seed. 2. Layering. 3. Cuttings under mist in May.

Method 1 Seeds are produced on home grown trees but their germination is complicated by dormancy and to germinate the first year the seed needs warm temperatures followed by cold. American recommendations are to sow the seeds in autumn under glass, giving a temperature of 59–75°F (15–24°C) for two or three months. Then expose to 33–40°F (0.6–4.4°C) for another two to three months (e.g. by placing the boxes outside, in January). Bring in on initiation of germination. Seedlings can flower when only about 4 ft (1.2 cm) high.

Method 2 Simple layering may be practised in spring (p. 27) and as the mother plants should be layered only every second year, plant sufficient to allow for layering alternate plants.

Method 3 Softwood basal cuttings, treated with 0.8% IBA powder, may be inserted under mist in May. Up to 100% success may be expected, though rooting may be slow.

Hamamelis

The Witch Hazels are deciduous shrubs valued for their spidery yellow scented flowers, but *H. japonica*, a larger growing species, is also highly prized. Both these have good named varieties and hybrids between them have given new colour forms such as *Jelena* (Copper-orange). *H. vernalis* and *H. virginiana* are mainly of interest as understocks.

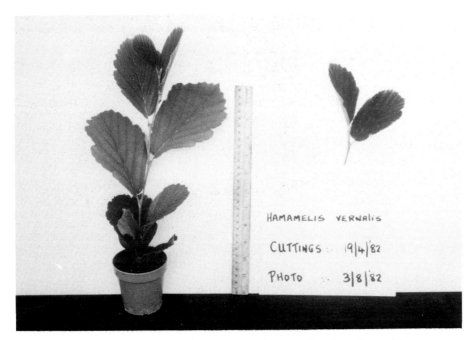

Fig. 41. Cuttings of rootstock *H. vernalis* are propagated from early softwood material.

Uses As specimens in the winter garden. Flowering twigs of *H. mollis* can be brought indoors for their scent.

Methods of propagation 1. Grafting. 2. Layering. 3. Seed. 4. Cuttings in the mist in May.

Method 1 The commonly used understock is *H. virginiana*, but we obtain excellent results with *H. vernalis*, as described below. *Distylium racemosum* has been used also, but with us growth of scions on this understock has been slow.

Bought in seedlings of *H. virginiana* are potted in April in 4 in. 'Long Toms' for grafting in August, when they are brought indoors from their plunge beds and dried off. Their bases are cleaned of side shoots and leaves and they are cut back to 9–12 in. (22.5–30 cm). Strong shoots of the current season's wood are used as scion material, the soft growing tips being removed. 137

Fig. 42. *H. mollis* and cultivars are side-grafted onto *H. vernalis* in August. The rootstock is cut back in the following spring.

Fig. 43. *H. mollis* 1 m high from a graft (*H. vernalis*) after two seasons growth.

After being side-grafted (p. 31) the grafts are placed in a closed case in a glasshouse or under close fitting double glass in a cold frame. When callusing has occurred, the plants can be hardened off slowly and carefully and, after being knocked from their pots, are planted in a cold frame with the graft union above the ground. Whilst establishing in the frame, the lights and shading slats are left in position and then removed as normal hardening off continues. The plants are protected against winter frosts by replacing the lights and in cold areas covering the frames with reed mats. In the following spring, the rootstock is cut back to the graft joint and the plants are lifted and planted out in the nursery for two or more years.

Home grown seedlings of *H. virginiana* can be raised as described under Method 3. Prick off the seedlings into 3 in. pots, and grow them on under glass to reach 6 in. (15 cm) height by the end of the season. The following spring pot on into 4 in. 'Long Toms', keep them under glass and graft as above during the following August, when they should be of pencil thickness.

Method 2 Layering is not a very productive method but may be used where only small numbers are required. In early spring, after bending down shoots of the previous year's wood, a tongue is cut on that part of the stem which will be underground, as such a wound will hasten rooting out (p. 26). The upper part of the shoot is tied firmly to a cane. Cut away the rooted plants the following spring and line out to grow on.

Method 3 *H. mollis* frequently sets seed in cultivation. This seed ripens in late autumn. The capsules should be harvested promptly as soon as they show signs of opening, as the seeds are ejected. Place them in trays on a greenhouse shelf to complete ripening but sow immediately in pots or trays (p. 25) before drying out occurs. Seed treated this way may give some germination in the first spring. One case is reported from USA where seed sown almost green

germinated 90% the following spring, but generally the seeds have to go
through two winters. It is stated that dormancy can be broken by first keeping
the trays in warm conditions 68°F (20°C) for nine weeks and then exposing
to 41°F (5°C) for 14 weeks. Seedlings can grow to 10 in. (25 cm) in one year.
Unfortunately seedlings cannot be relied on to produce good forms. A common fault of plants raised from seed is that they often retain their dead foliage
into the flowering season, thus spoiling the floral display.

Method 4 We have been very successful in raising *H. virginiana* and *H. vernalis* from cuttings for use as understocks. The latter species, in particular has
given very satisfactory results, and subsequent growth of scions of *H. mollis*
has been good. The cuttings should be taken as early as possible, when the
new shoots are 6–7.5 cm (2½–3 in.) long. With us this is in May, and since
H. vernalis comes into growth sooner than *H. virginiana*, cuttings of this
species have a head start and subsequent growth is stronger. If mother plants
can be accommodated in a cold house, the cuttings will be even earlier. With
good treatment some of the cuttings may even be large enough to graft in
August of the same year, though most will need a further season's growth.

Basal cuttings, treated with 0.8% IBA powder, give 70–75% rooting in 6–8
weeks, under mist or warm bench and plastic, in a medium of moss peat or
two parts moss peat to one of sand. The potting compost is the standard peat-
based mix with slow release fertiliser, but diluted by adding one part of sand
to three of peat. At the end of July move the plants on from the 3 in. pots
to 4 in. 'Long Toms', using the same compost and hold until grafted in August
a year later i.e. fifteen months from the time of taking the cuttings. Overwintering is critical. Good plants should be some 30 cm (12 in.) high. Overwinter them under glass, keeping them dry. Graft the following July–August.

Though the rooting of cuttings of *H. mollis* can be successful to the extent
of 80–90% from 4 in. (10 cm) cuttings in May, overwintering losses are
usually so high (50%) that at present propagation of this species from cuttings
cannot be regarded as a commercial proposition. After early efforts at growing on the cuttings in fertilised peat we have had better results from potting
them up in 3 in. pots of unlimed peat and giving one or two liquid feeds of
1% 9.9.7. formulation. Further investigations are required to determine the
conditions for successful overwintering of this species.

Hebe

Included here are many species formerly called *Veronica*. Many dwarf hebes
make attractive ground cover plants, some having the typical opposite
leathery leaves in four rows but others are cypress-like in their closely adpressed
foliage. The taller shrubby species are mostly hybrids of *H. speciosa*.

Uses For ground cover *Hebe pinguifolia* **Pagei** (prostrate with glaucous
foliage and white flowers in May), *H. edinensis* (18 in. (45 cm) with bright
green leaves), *H. cupressoides* (3 ft (0.93 m), heath like) and *H. parvifolia* (3 ft
(0.9 m), late flowering). These should only be planted in sunny well drained
situations. The tall hybrids are suitable for coastal situations but succumb to
frosts inland. *H. hectori*, a curious hardy shrub with whipcord-like stems, is
suitable for the rock garden.

139

Method of propagation Hebes root easily from basal, nodal or internodal semi-hardwood cuttings in a cold frame in autumn. In very mild districts they can be rooted in the open. Line out in spring.

Hedera

Our native ivy (*Hedera helix*) has given numerous cultivars, both plain and variegated, including various dwarf non-climbing kinds like **Conglomerata**. The Canary ivy (*H. canariensis*) and *H. colchica* are large leaved species, also with variegated forms.

Uses As ground cover, wall climbers and the dwarf forms for the rock garden.

Methods of propagation 1. Cuttings in the cold frame in October–November. 2. Cuttings in mist or warm bench and plastic in July. 3. Cuttings in the cold frame and plastic or low tunnel in June–July.

Ivies may be propagated easily by most methods, bottom heat being used (Method 2) where quick rooting is desired. For the cold frame, use nodal or internodal cuttings 5 in. (12.5 cm) long of the past season's growth or for the July cuttings, nodal cuttings 3–4 in. (7.5–10 cm) long of semi-hard shoots. The use of 0.8% IBA powder is not necessary. The cold frame cuttings are lifted and potted the following April. Cuttings being propagated by the other systems can be lifted after six weeks.

Cuttings from the arborescent (non-climbing) shoots will also root, though not so easily, e.g. in a low tunnel, arborescent branches of 'Goldheart' rooted 40% as against 77% for normal shoots. Continental experience indicates good results with wounded cuttings dipped momentarily into a strong (2500 ppm) solution of IBA. The cuttings were inserted in the warm bench and plastic in September.

Hippophae

The most common type, *H. rhamnoides*, is a fairly familiar plant used extensively in coastal areas, being an excellent subject for wind resistance. It grows in most soil types, has attractive silvery foliage, and produces orange berries on the female plants.

Method of propagation Raising from seed is a successful means of propagation. The seed is gathered when ripe and sown in outdoor beds. The seed is covered thinly and, in spring, germination is rapid. The plants are lined out at the end of the growing season.

If only small numbers of plants are required, sow the seed in boxes outdoors and, in early spring, when germination starts, bring the boxes into a glasshouse and prick off the seedlings into 3 in. pots. If grown under glass or plastic, the plants will reach 1½ ft (45 cm) by autumn. At this stage the male plants are identifiable by the swollen buds in the leaf axils. Female plants do not have these prominent buds but can be recognised by their smooth stems. Plant both sexes for good berrying.

Hoheria

A genus of shrubs or small trees from New Zealand, giving a somewhat cherry-like effect in late summer by their masses of white flowers. Unfortunately, they are not hardy everywhere, the evergreen species in particular needing shelter. Of these **Glory of Amlwch** is one of the best. The deciduous *H. lyallii* is more generally hardy. Cuttings may be rooted in a shaded cold frame in August. Pot up and over winter under glass in cold districts. Self sown seedlings appear in gardens in mild areas.

Hydrangea

In addition to the well known hortensias and lacecaps, the species *H. paniculata*, *H. sargentiana* and *H. villosa* are appreciated in gardens, the latter two preferring semi-shade. All dislike drought. *H. petiolaris* is a climber with heads of small greenish white flowers surrounded by white florets.

Method of propagation The hortensias and lacecaps can be rooted easily from cuttings by several methods. The cold frame and plastic or low tunnel in June are cheap systems. Nodal or internodal cuttings are taken from the apical portion of the current year's growth about 3½ in. (8.7 cm) long. Treatment with rooting powders is not necessary. 100% rooting may be expected after three weeks and the cuttings can be left to grow on when propagated in the low tunnel. Cuttings propagated in the cold frame should be lined out. Water freely. The specialist will operate more intensive propagation systems. One method is to keep mother plants in boxes in cold frames. In December–January they are cut down hard and transferred to a warm house. Successive batches of cuttings can be rooted by the warm bench and plastic method or under mist. After each batch of cuttings has been hardened off, they can be lined out in nursery beds, to be watered freely whenever the weather is dry. Later batches of cuttings can be taken from open air plants in April–May. About a fortnight after planting out, the cuttings should be ready for their first stopping. A second stopping is given in July. Well grown early struck cuttings should make good plants by the end of the summer.

The species do not strike so readily from cuttings but when attempted, use of semi-mature shoots in July is usually recommended. With *H. petiolaris*, however, up to 100% success can be obtained with basal softwood cuttings taken in late April. At this stage flower buds will be visible. Non-flowering shoots are selected. These are tripartite, the central shoot being 2½–3 in. (6.2–7.5 cm) long, the side shoots 1–1½ in. (2.5–3.7 cm). Both types may be utilised. Treat with 0.8% IBA powder and insert under mist or in the warm bench with plastic. After six weeks the cuttings should be ready for lifting and potting into 3½ in. pots. Place them on a capillary bed in a plastic house for growing on. By mid-August they should be about 8 in. (20 cm) long. At this stage they may be sold as small plants for growing on, or transferred to a cold frame for potting on in spring to be sold as large plants in summer. We have had similar results with cuttings of *H. integerrima* (also a climber) taken in June.

Hydrangea species may be raised from seed sown under glass in February.

Hypericum

Hypericum (Saint John's Wort) is a very large genus ranging from annuals through herbaceous, perennial, and dwarf shrubby species, to medium sized shrubs.

141

Uses Many of the dwarf species such as *H. coris, H. empetrifolium* and *H. reptans* are valued for sunny places on the rock garden. Medium sized species in general commerce include *H.* **Hidcote,** *H. forrestii* and the more tender *H.* **Rowallane.** All are good for summer and autumn flowering in sunny shrubberies. *H. calycinum* **(Rose of Sharon)** is a good ground cover plant for rougher places. It is improved by occasional mowing down in early spring.

Method of propagation H. calycinum can conveniently be struck from softwood cuttings in April about 2 in. (5 cm) in length cut nodally or internodally close to soil level. Previous mowing down of an established stand of the plant stimulates plentiful growth of suitable propagation material. The cuttings will root easily in the warm bench with plastic, and the use of rooting powder, though not essential, hastens rooting. After hardening off, cuttings are lined out in the open ground and will produce nice compact bushy plants by autumn.

As an alternative approach, the softwood cuttings can be allowed to come up on the mother plants and then be cut off below ground level with a few roots already developed — a process aided by top dressing with soil or peat. These rooted pieces can be lined out and watered until well established.

Propagation by division is also practised but is a less efficient system than the above, owing to the long straggly underground stolons.

The taller shrubby species come easily from cuttings by several methods, e.g. in the cold frame in November, to be lifted and lined out in spring or from softwood cuttings in June inserted in the cold frame with plastic or under the low tunnel. Stem cuttings (p. 4) 3–4 in. (7.5–10 cm) long are taken. The tips are pinched out to prevent flowering. No rooting powder is necessary. From 70–100% rooting can be expected after four to six weeks. By autumn the plants should be about 1 ft (30 cm) high or more with five or six shoots.

Ilex (Holly)

The most familiar hollies in Europe are those derived from *Ilex aquifolium,* the common wild holly, though some like **Golden King** and **J. C. van Tol** are said to be hybrids (*I. x altaclarensis*) between the Common Holly and the Azorean Holly, *I. perado.*

Uses Hollies are valuable for most situations, sunny or shady, and for most soils. They will grow well in town gardens. Good specimens in the open look very fine, particularly the variegated kinds. Male and female flowers are borne on separate plants. **J. C. van Tol** and **Pyramidalis** are free-berrying clones. **Golden King** is female, **Silver Queen** male, despite the names. The common holly makes a good, stockproof, hedge. Well-grown, young hollies can put on 1 ft (30 cm) of growth a year.

Methods of propagation 1. Cuttings under mist from August–February. 2. Cuttings in the cold frame and plastic in August–October. 3. Budding. 4. Seed. 5. White polythene tunnel (see p. 19).

Method 1 Though cuttings can be inserted under mist at any time from August to February, the period August to October is more economical in that it avoids the use of bottom heat during the coldest months of the year. The cuttings, 3–4 in. (7.5–10 cm) long, should be taken from bushes making good annual growth. These may be young plants in the nursery, or older bushes that have been trimmed back regularly for cutting production. Take nodal cuttings, cut off the basal pair of leaves, wound the bases of the stems and treat with 0.8% IBA powder. Insert in a medium of two parts moss peat to one of sand. After six to seven weeks up to 95% rooting may be expected. After hardening off, the boxes of rooted cuttings may be held in a cold house or frame. In spring, line out in frames of compost or irrigated nursery beds 5 in. (12.5 cm) apart. By the following autumn, they should have made 6–9 in. (15–22.5 cm) of growth and are transplanted into the field 18 in. (45 cm) apart. The plants are usually sold when 15–18 in. (37.5–45 cm) high, 1½–2 ft (45–60 cm) or 2–2½ ft (60–75 cm) high.

Method 2 Cuttings, as described above, are taken in August–October. After wounding and treating with 0.8% IBA powder, insert in a medium of two parts moss peat to one of sand. By the following May, 90% or more of the cuttings will have rooted. After hardening off, the cuttings may be lifted for growing on in a nursery bed.

Method 3 Sometimes hollies are budded, using vigorous, three-year-old seedlings of *Ilex aquifolium*. The operation can be carried out in April–May or in August–September, inserting the buds into two-year-old wood. Head back the stocks gradually as the shoot develops from the bud. Sometimes standards are produced by budding onto straight stemmed seedling stocks over 4 ft (1.2 cm) high. Trim off side shoots to within 8 in. (20 cm) of the top. Insert three buds to give a good head. Remove the crown when the buds grow out. Grow on for two seasons in good fertile soil, and ensure successful transplanting by under cutting the rootstocks in the season prior to moving and cutting round them during the growing on years.

Method 4 Gather the seed when ripe in autumn. It needs stratification for two winters, i.e. until sown early in the spring of the second year. This process can be carried out as described under *Crataegus*. The seedbed should be in a moist shaded place. Even with this treatment, holly seed is slow and erratic in coming up and it may be necessary to retain the seedbed for two or three years to obtain sufficient seedlings.

Indigofera

The only species in general cultivation is *Indigofera gerardiana*, a branching shrub about 3 ft (0.9 m) high with pinnate leaves and racemes of small purplish-rose flowers. It is a very pretty shrub for a place in full sun and is valued for flowering in summer and autumn. The bush may be cut to ground level by a hard winter but will spring again from the root.

Method of propagation Nodal cuttings 3–3½ in. (7.5–9 cm) long, treated with 0.8% IBA powder may be inserted in the cold frame with plastic in July. When lifted in September for potting up in 3 in. pots, 80% or more may be expected to have rooted. Overwinter in a cold house, keeping the pots on the dry side. Spray with a fungicide as a precaution against botrytis. Pot on in spring into 4 in. pots, trimming back the shoots to 3 in. (7.5 cm). Place on an outdoor capillary bed, pot on into 5 in. pots as soon as needed and sell in flower in summer and autumn.

143

Itea

Itea ilicifolia is an evergreen shrub up to 8 ft (2.4 m) high, rather holly-like in leaf. It is grown for the remarkable long racemes of greenish white flowers in late summer. *Itea* is not particular as to soil but in cold districts needs the protection of a wall.

Method of propagation Easy from basal cuttings of the past summer's growth, 6–9 in. (15–22.5 cm) long taken in September. Wounding increases the percentage 'take'. Treat with 0.8% IBA powder and insert in a cold frame. When lifted the following April 80–90% rooting can be expected. The young plants may be lined out in the open for growing on or containerised.

Jasminum

The best known species are *J. nudiflorum*, the yellow Winter Jasmine, and the white *J. officinale* with sweet scented flowers.

Uses J. nudiflorum is one of the best known of winter flowering shrubs and is very effective when trained against walls, even those with a north aspect. After planting, the leading shoots should be trained fanwise against the wall. The pendant laterals from these are pruned back hard in spring immediately after flowering. If neglected, the bush forms a tangle. *J. officinale* is allowed to grow naturally, being kept within bounds by cutting out the oldest wood in summer. This species requires a south wall, especially in cold districts.

Methods of propagation 1. Hardwood cuttings in November out of doors or in a cold frame. 2. Semi-hard shoots of the current year may be rooted by several methods during the summer.

Method 1 Stem or heel cuttings up to 8 in. (20 cm) long are selected from stout shoots of the past season's growth. No treatment with root promoting substances is necessary. Upwards of 65% should have rooted when lifted for lining out in April in the open ground 10 in. (25 cm) apart. They may be sold at the end of the year as 1 ft (30 cm) specimens, generally with four shoots.

Method 2 Basal shoots of the current season, 3–4 in. (7.5–10 cm) long will root 90–100%. Spare space in the mist unit or in the warm bench with plastic could be used but the cheaper low tunnel or cold frame and plastic systems would be the main propagation methods. No treatment with root promoting substances is needed to give 90–100% rooting. Such cuttings will develop into 6 in. (15 cm) liners to be planted out for one year to grow into saleable specimens.

Jugeans

Jugeans regia is the well known Walnut. Several other species are native of N. America and Asia but of these only the Black Walnut is occasionally seen in Britain. Nowadays only large parks are likely to have room for these big trees.

Method of propagation is by seed, of which good crops are borne irregularly. The seed will germinate in the first spring. American sources describe autumn sowing but, as the seeds are very attractive to rodents, spring sowing reduces the period of danger. This, however, entails careful storage in slightly moist peat. The seeds and peat could well be kept in plastic bags but beware of moulds developing if the peat is too moist. Inspect periodically and, as soon as germination starts, the nuts may be sown in prepared beds in the open. Walnuts are susceptible to frost damage (even as mature trees) so protect the beds if frost threatens, e.g. by means of spruce branches or bracken. Line out in the autumn in a sheltered area of the nursery, but not one exposed to spring frosts.

Juniperus

There are numerous juniper species growing wild in the Northern Hemisphere, from USA and Mexico through Europe to China and Japan. In addition, there are numerous cultivars, those most commonly grown coming under *Juniperus chinensis*, *J. communis*, *J. horizontalis*, *J. x media*, *J. sabina*, *J. squamata*, *J. virginiana* and *J. recurva*.

Uses Junipers vary in habit of growth from prostrate forms like *J. communis* **Repanda** through spreading types like *J. x media* **Pfitzeriana Aurea** to upright kinds such as *J. squamata* **Meyeri**. Hence they can be used in many ways, as ground cover or as specimen plants. Junipers associate well with modern architecture in beds round buildings or in courtyards. In addition, there are the fastigiate forms available in a range of sizes from the dwarf *J. communis* **Compressa**, so valued in the rock garden, through the medium sizes *J. c.* **Hibernica** 9 ft (2.7 cm) to the taller *J. virginiana* **Skyrocket** 15 ft (4.5 m). These can be used to striking effect as focal points in landscape design. In contrast to these is the weeping *J. recurva* var. *coxii*. As well as contrasting in shape, junipers vary in colour — green, golden yellow, blue and variegated. Junipers associate well with heathers but, unlike most of the latter, thrive in limy soils. They should not be planted in shade.

Methods of propagation 1. Cuttings in the cold frame and plastic in April. 2. Cuttings in the mist in April. 3. Cuttings in the cold frame in October. 4. White polythene tunnel (see p. 19).

Method 1 This, in our experience, has been a very satisfactory method. 65–100% rooting has been achieved in eight to 12 weeks with cultivars of *J. chinensis*, *J. communis*, *J. horizontalis*, *J. sabina* and *J. squamata*. No doubt others would respond well also. Cuttings are taken close to the base of the past year's growth with sharp secateurs. Trials have shown that cuttings obtained in this way root better than those taken with a heel of older wood. The cuttings are not wounded but are treated with 0.8% IBA powder before insertion in the frame in a medium of two parts peat to one of sand. After rooting and hardening off they are lifted and lined out in a frame of loamless compost and, after a further season, field lined for growing on.

Method 2 This is an alternative to Method 1 but has no particular advantage, in our experience, other than a rooting period shorter by one or two weeks. It is useful to know that vacant space in the mist bench could be utilised in this way. The cuttings are prepared and treated as above. After hardening off, about June, they are planted out in a frame or loamless compost.

Method 3 is a slow method, since the cuttings occupy the frame from October to the following June. Prepare and treat the cuttings as described for Method 1. 145

Lift the cuttings in June and transplant to a frame of fertilised peat (pp. 55–7) at a spacing of 6 in. (15 cm) each way giving the protection of shaded lights until well established. The plants will be left *in situ* until October. They may then be transplanted to grow on for one to two years before sale.

Some junipers, notably *J. squamata* **Meyeri**, tend to form lop-sided plants during their early years, making it advisable to pinch the growing tip of the main stem at the beginning of the second season.

Kalmia

Kalmias are low to medium sized evergreen shrubs from N. America, with clusters of rosy red flowers at the end of the shoots in summer. They thrive in peaty, moist, lime-free soil, under conditions appreciated by choicer rhododendrons. The species generally offered are *Kalmia angustifolia, K. latifolia* and the smaller *K. polifolia*.

Uses As specimens in gardens where uncommon shrubs are appreciated.

Methods of propagation 1. Seed. 2. Cuttings in January or August. 3. Layering in August.

Method 1 The fine, dust-like seed is sown under glass in February and is barely covered. When the seedlings are ½ in. (1–1.5 cm) high, prick off into boxes of loamless compost (p. 55). Grown on in a shaded glasshouse until the plants reach 2 in. (5 cm), when they may be hardened off and planted into frames of loamless compost (p. 55). Replace the lights and shade heavily until autumn. Remove or reduce the shading and keep the lights on until the following spring. Irrigate and shade as necessary through the following season. The plants can then be lined out for further growth. Dutch experience indicates that the growth of Kalmia can be hastened by artificially extended daylength during the seedling stages.

Method 2 In America *K. latifolia*, usually regarded as difficult, is successfully rooted from hardwood cuttings taken in January, 3–4 in. (7.5–10 cm) long, double wounded and inserted in a 50:50 moss peat:perlite medium. Mist is used but perhaps (like rhododendrons) the warm bench and plastic would give good results under conditions here. Rooting is slow, up to 50–55%. Harden off and grow on in cold frames. *K. polifolia* may be rooted from semi-hardwood cuttings of the current season taken in August, treated with 0.8% IBA powder and inserted in a shaded cold frame.

Method 3 Layering is an older method useful in nurseries where Kalmias thrive and where large numbers are not required. Rooting is slow, the layers having to be left for 1½–2 years before being detached for growing on. The process is assisted by working extra peat and sand around the plants before layering and by cutting a tongue of bark on the part to be covered, or by twisting the branch.

Kerria

There is only one species of Kerria, *K. japonica*. The double form is common in gardens and suckers freely, forming thickets of stout stems 8 ft (2.4 m) high or more. The flowers are orange and appear in spring. The single form is much more delicate in growth, forming a bush of interlacing twigs, usually only up to 4 ft (1.2 m) or so high. The variegated form is less vigorous.

Uses The double form is useful for the rougher corners of the shrubbery. The single forms are less aggressive and more suitable as neighbours for choicer shrubs.

Methods of propagation 1. Division. 2. Hardwood cuttings in the open. 3. Cuttings in cold frame and plastic or in the low tunnel in June–July.

Method 1 Simple division is a convenient way of multiplication, in view of the suckering habit of *Kerria*, especially the double form. Lift clumps in March, grade the divisions and line out for growing on.

Method 2 Stout stem or basal cuttings of the past season's growth, 8 in (20 cm) long are inserted in October–November in the open ground (p. 19). No wounding or root promoting substance is necessary. When lifted the following autumn 95–100% should be rooted. Line out for a further year.

Method 3 *Kerria* will propagate readily by most methods and while the above are probably the cheapest, it may sometimes be convenient to insert a batch when laying down a tunnel, or in the cold frame with plastic. No rooting powder is needed. Insert 4 in. (10 cm) cuttings. Line out when rooted or in autumn, for growing on.

Koelreuteria

Koelreuteria paniculata is a deciduous tree 30 ft (9 m) or more high with feathery leaves 6–18 in. (15–45 cm) long. It bears racemes of yellow flowers but needs a hot summer to flower well.

Uses An interesting tree for parks or large gardens in districts with warm summers.

Methods of propagation 1. Seed. 2. Root cuttings.

Method 1 Seed is seldom ripened in this country. Purchased seed which arrives in spring may have developed a degree of dormancy causing it to germinate rather poorly. Seed stratified over winter in moist peat or sand would probably germinate better. Sow the large seeds under glass in February in pots or boxes. Germination takes place in about 20 days, the seedlings reaching the second rough leaf stage approximately 15–20 days later. Prick off into 3 in. pots. After a further two to three weeks they will be 2–2¾ in. (5–7 cm) high and ready for potting on into 6 in. polythene bags. If placed on a capillary bed inside a plastic house the plants will be 2–2½ ft (60–75 cm) by autumn and may be sold as container grown plants. If the young plants are held over the winter it is advisable not to keep them under plastic as early growth may be induced only to be frosted.

Method 2 Root cuttings are mentioned by several authorities, but only as
secondary to seed raising. Our own experience bears out that it is an unsatisfactory method, pieces of root being reluctant to throw shoots.

Kolkwitzia

Kolkwitzia amabilis is a twiggy deciduous shrub usually seen about 6 ft
(1.8 m) high but capable of reaching twice that height. The small, pink and
yellow bell-shaped flowers appear in May and June. Only good free-flowering
forms should be propagated.

Uses As a specimen in sunny shrub borders.

Methods of propagation 1. Cuttings in mist in April–May. 2. Cuttings in
June in the low plastic tunnel. 3. Cuttings in the cold frame in August. 4.
White polythene tunnel (p. 19).

Method 1 Kolkwitzia comes into growth early, so basal softwood cuttings can
be ready at the end of April or at the beginning of May, when they should
be about 4 in. (10 cm) long. Treat with 0.8% IBA powder, do not wound and
insert the cuttings in two parts moss peat to one of sand under mist. 80%
rooting can be expected after four weeks. Line out in a cold frame, covering
with shaded lights until the plants are well established. Transplant to outdoor
beds in October and grow on for a further year.

Method 2 Nodal semi-hardwood cuttings about 4 in. (10 cm) long (discarding
the tips) are inserted in June after treatment with 0.8% IBA powder. The
plants are lifted in October, when 75–80% should be rooted and are lined out
in a well prepared bed or in a frame 6 in. (15 cm) apart for growing on for
a further season.

Method 3 Nodal cuttings consisting of 6 in. (15 cm) lengths of stem of the
current season's growth may be inserted in a cold frame in August to give 55%
or more rooted by autumn.

Laburnum

The common Laburnum (*L. anagyroides*) is surpassed by the later flowering
Scotch Laburnum (*L. alpinum*) and by the hybrid between them (*L. x
watereri*). **Vossii** is the best form of this hybrid, having very long racemes.

Uses A small tree for specimen planting, especially valuable for giving an
effect quickly.

Methods of propagation 1. Grafting. 2. Budding. 3. Cuttings in the open
ground in February. 4. Seed.

Method 1 Bench graft in February, using seedlings of common laburnum as
understocks. Stock and scion should be the same diameter. Join by the whip
graft method (p. 32). After binding and waxing with low temperature grafting

wax, heel the plants either in an outhouse or in a frame until spring. When growth starts, plant out in the field. Stake during summer and autumn, training to half or full standards as required.

Method 2 Two year seedlings of the common laburnum (6–10 mm) diameter are planted 3 ft (0.9 m) apart in November and T-budded the following July. Head the rootstocks back in spring. The buds can make shoots 6 ft (1.8 m) high in the first year.

Method 3 Heel cuttings of the past season's growth, 6–9 in. (15–22.5 cm) wounded and treated with 0.8% IBA are lined out in February in the open ground 4 in. (10 cm) apart with extra sand at the base of the cuttings. Not much growth is made in the first season. Transplant in autumn and, during the next season, train a single shoot to form a half or full standard.

Method 4 Seed should only be used for raising the common and Scotch laburnums, not the hybrids. Gather the seed in autumn, shell out of the pods and store dry until spring, when it may be sown in the open in drills ½ in. (1.2 cm) deep on a prepared seed bed. Line out in autumn.

Laurus

Laurus nobilis is the Sweet Bay used in cooking. In gardens it is grown as a clipped specimen in tubs and as shelter screens and hedges in mild districts.

Method of propagation Basal hardwood cuttings of the past season's growth 5–6 in. (12.5–15 cm) long, respond to treatment with 0.8% IBA powder. They may be inserted in October in a cold frame or in an outdoor bed in milder districts. Wounding is not necessary. Cold frame cuttings may be lifted in May–June; those out of doors are left until autumn. Upwards of 80% rooting may be expected. Line out and grow on for two seasons. Cuttings inserted in November–January in the warm bench and plastic root quickly e.g. in 50 days. No root promoting substance is needed.

Lavandula

Although commonly listed under such names as *Lavandula spica*, *L. vera* or *L. officinalis*, the familiar garden lavenders are hybrids from *L. angustifolia* crossed with *L. latifolia*. A few other species are occasionally seen in gardens, including *L. stoechas* with purple bracts, the woolly *L. lanata* and *L. dentata* with serrated green leaves.

Uses Long cultivated for oil of lavender, the lavenders are appreciated as shrubs for sunny dry borders and as low hedges. Sizes range from the tall **Grappenhall** (3 ft or 0.9 m) to the dwarfer **Hidcote** and **Munstead** (10–15 in. or 25–37.5 m).

Methods of propagation 1. Cuttings in the low tunnel or cold frame and plastic in June. 2. Cuttings in the cold frame in September–October. 3. White polythene tunnel (see p. 19).

149

Method 1 Semi-hard heel cuttings of the current season's growth, 2–3 in. (5–7.5 cm) long, are inserted in June removing any flower buds. No wound or root promoting substance is needed. After four weeks 100% rooting should have occurred. The cold frame cuttings are lifted and lined out. Those in the tunnel make better plants, being left to grow on undisturbed until autumn or spring. By this stage they are good liners. By the following autumn they will have developed into bushy plants 9–12 in. (22.5–30 cm) high.

Method 2 Semi-hardwood cuttings, 2–3 in. (5–7.5 cm) long from the second flush of growth are inserted in September–October. No treatment with rooting powder is needed. Lift and line out in April.

Lavatera

Most of the mallows (*Lavatera*) are annual, biennial or perennial herbaceous plants but the sub-shrubby *L. olbia* is valued in sunny borders where it reaches up to 6 ft (1.8 m), bearing a long succession of pink or reddish pink flowers 4 in. (10 cm) across. A good form should be selected.

Uses As a specimen in sunny spots. Associates well with Spanish Broom (*Spartium*). Prune almost to ground level each spring.

Method of propagation By means of semi-hardwood basal cuttings in a shaded cold frame in June–July or nodal cuttings in the open ground in September–October, in each case 5 in. (12.5 cm) long. Use a cold frame in cold districts. The rooting medium is two parts of peat to one of sand and the use of rooting powders is unnecessary.

Leptospermum

The species of importance in our gardens is *Leptospermum scoparium*, an evergreen up to 15 ft (4.5 m) or more, with heath-like foliage. The single and double red forms are spectacular in late spring or early summer. Unfortunately, leptospermums are not hardy in colder areas. They require acid or neutral soil.

Method of propagation Basal cuttings of the current year's shoots, 2–3 in. (5–7.5 cm) long, wounded and treated with 0.8% IBA powder will root 90–100% after five weeks under mist or warm bench and plastic in July. They may be lifted and potted or lined out in a cold frame of fertilised peat at 4 × 3 in. (10 × 7.5 cm) for a further season. Alternatively, basal cuttings may be inserted in a cold frame in October–November, to be lifted in spring for potting or lining out.

In gardens in the mild South-West leptospermums seed themselves. Seed may be sown under glass in February. If the seed is from red flowered specimens the seedlings with dark foliage are the most likely to give good colour forms.

Leucothoe

A small genus of evergreens for lime-free soils. *L. fontanesiana* (*L. catesbaei*), the only one generally met with, is useful as ground cover. Though producing an abundance of white flowers along the branches, these are somewhat hidden by the arching habit of growth.

Method of propagation is by seed sown under glass in February, by semi-hardwood basal cuttings in mist or warm bench and plastic in August, or by layering.

Leycesteria

Leycesteria formosa is a rather coarse growing shrub remarkable for its hanging clusters of reddish purple berries. These are eaten by pheasants, so the plant is sometimes used in coverts.

Method of propagation is by seed, which germinates freely when sown fresh in autumn direct in a cold frame, or stored in damp peat or sand for sowing thinly in boxes under glass in February. Harden off the latter in late spring and line out.

Ligustrum

The parent of our garden privet is *Ligustrum ovalifolium*. The wild privet sometimes seen in roadside hedges is *L. vulgare*.

Though tolerant of almost any soil or situation, privet, especially the golden forms, will respond to favourable conditions. If exposed to hardship it will drop many leaves in winter. Though easily propagated, cuttings of Golden Privet are often left to starve and stunt whereas, with good soil conditions and adequate shelter, cuttings will respond well and first class bushes will result.

Methods of propagation 1. Cuttings in June in a cold frame with plastic. 2. Cuttings in July in shaded cold frame without plastic. 3. Cuttings in the open ground in October. 4. Mist in April–May.

Method 1 Softwood nodal cuttings 4–5 in. (10–12.5 cm) of the current season's growth are inserted in two parts peat to one of sand in a cold frame with plastic. No treatment with root promoting substance is necessary. Up to 100% root after six weeks. Lift and line out in well prepared outdoor beds at 9 in. (23 cm) each way. Irrigate in dry weather. Little extra growth is made before the end of that year. In spring top dress with calcium ammonium nitrate at 1½ oz per sq yd (50 g per sq m). By the end of the second season these plants can be sold as good liners, 12–14 in. (30–35 cm) high, with three or four branches. If left for a further season, they will make good material up to 3 ft (0.9 m) high with 10–14 branches.

Method 2 Cuttings treated similarly may be inserted in a shaded cold frame, preferably north facing, in July. Keep carefully watered. Up to 100% rooting will have occurred 12 weeks later. Plant out in spring and irrigate as needed.   151

By autumn these will be 9–13 in. (22.5–32.5 cm) high with two to four branches, for sale as liners or for growing on.

Method 3 Nodal cuttings of stout shoots of the past season's growth are taken in October, 12–15 in. (30–37.5 cm) long. The soft tips are removed. Treatment with 0.8% IBA powder is helpful and the cuttings are inserted in the open ground. One year later 80–95% of the cuttings should have rooted, but little shoot growth is made. If transplanted carefully to 12 in. (30 cm) each way into good soil and adequate shelter, they make saleable bushes by the end of the second year.

Method 4 Though mist propagation is a relatively expensive method, it may be convenient to insert nodal cuttings 3–4 in. (7.5–10 cm) long in April–May. While cuttings can be inserted earlier, the material is apt to be partially defoliated and to give poor results if the weather has been harsh. Use a medium of two parts moss peat to one of sand. Rooting powders are not needed. About 80% of the cuttings should root in three weeks. Plant out in good soil in a sheltered situation. By autumn they should be good liners 1 ft (30 cm) high.

Lippia

Lippia citriodora is the Lemon-scented Verbena, appreciated for its very aromatic foliage. The flowers are insignificant. *Lippia* is tender and needs to be grown against a sunny wall. Even there it is usually cut to ground level by winter frost.

Basal or nodal softwood cuttings, about 4 in. (10 cm) long, untreated with root promoting substances, root easily in May in the warm bench with plastic or under mist. From 70–100% rooting may be expected after four to six weeks. Pot up in 3 in. pots for growing on under glass or plastic, pinching the tips to induce bushy growth. The plants will be about 1 ft (30 cm) high by late summer. They may be sold as small plants at this stage or potted on for overwintering under glass.

Liquidambar

The Sweet Gum (*Liquidambar styraciflua*) is a spectacular tree in the eastern states of USA when aflame with its crimson autumn foliage.

Uses A large tree, best on moist neutral or acid soils. Seedlings should be selected for good autumn colour.

Methods of propagation 1. Seed. 2. Layering.

Method 1 Seed has to be imported and, if sown fresh, there are prospects of

good germination in the first spring, provided the seeds are left outside and brought in when growth starts. Alternatively they may be stratified in moist peat. Usually, however, the seed has to be exposed to two winters before it comes up. Prick off the seedlings into 3 in. pots and harden off before either growing on in a plastic house on a capillary bed or lining out in a cold frame. Protect young plants from spring frosts.

Method 2 Layering is mentioned by some authorities as an alternative and would ensure propagation of selected forms true to type.

Liriodendron

The Tulip Tree (*Liriodendron tulipifera*) is a large tree with curiously truncated leaves which turn a good yellow before falling. It grows too large for all except large gardens and parks.

Method of propagation From imported seed which is best sown fresh in autumn or stratified in moist peat. Even then germination may be poor in the first spring. Bring the boxes into heat on initiation of germination and prick off the seedlings into 3 in. pots. Pot on, harden off and grow on in a plastic house on a capillary bed, or line out closely in a well prepared sheltered nursery bed. Open ground plants transplant badly unless moved each year.

Lithospermum

Lithospermums are low-growing shrubs with beautiful blue flowers. *L. diffusum* forms wide mats and, though often seen on rock gardens, could be used on sunny banks as ground cover, provided the soil is lime free. *L. rosmarinifolium* is spectacular, especially as it flowers in winter, but is only for the foot of a south wall in warm districts. *L. x intermedium* (often called *Moltkia x intermedia*) can be allowed to grow into a broad dome 18 in. (45 cm) high in the front of a sunny border. The latter two species tolerate lime.

Cuttings of all species can be rooted in a shaded cold frame in July, avoiding too much moisture. Lift and pot when rooted.

Lonicera (bush)

There are many non-climbing species of *Lonicera* but few are of any importance in our gardens. Among the deciduous or semi-deciduous kinds *L. fragrantissima* and the similar *L. standishii* are quite well known for their small white, very fragrant flowers in winter time. *L. syringantha* is a spring flowering species with deliciously scented lilac flowers. *L. tatarica* is grown for the pink colour of its flowers. Some good forms are available with redder flowers.

L. nitida is the well known evergreen hedging species, very neat when well kept but needing to be clipped very often. *L. pileata*, not a particularly interesting semi-evergreen, finds use as ground cover.

Methods of propagation 1. Cuttings in the cold frame in October or in the open ground in November. 2. Cuttings in the low tunnel or cold frame with plastic in June–July.

153

Method 1 Almost any type of cutting of *L. nitida* and *L. pileata* will root. Conveniently 8–10 in. (20–25 cm) stem cuttings may be set in the open ground with extra sand along the base of the cuttings. Lift in spring and line out about 6–8 in. (15–20 cm) apart. Trim during the growing season and sell in autumn. Basal or nodal cuttings of the other shrubby species may be treated similarly but should be propagated in cold frames in cold districts.

Method 2 Basal or nodal cuttings about 4 in. (10 cm) long of the current season's growth of the deciduous types may be inserted in the low tunnel or cold frame with plastic in June–July. Lift in autumn and line out for a further season's growth.

Lonicera (Climbing)

Our native honeysuckle (*Lonicera periclymenum*) is represented in gardens by the cultivars **Belgica** ('Early Dutch') and **Serotina** ('Late Dutch'). Other climbers in common cultivation include *L. japonica*, *L. j.* **Aureo-reticulata** with variegated leaves. *L. sempervirens*, *L. tragophylla* and *L. x telleman-niana*, grown for their showy flowers, have no scent.

Uses For training over pergolas or up small trees or posts, or as wall shrubs.

Methods of propagation 1. Cuttings in the low tunnel in June. 2. Cuttings in the cold frame in October.

Method 1 This works well with the cultivars of *L. periclymenum* and, no doubt, with other species and is a convenient way of producing flowering specimens for sale in spring nine or ten months later. Single nodes from stout wood of the current year are treated with 0.8% IBA powder. When lifted at the end of the season 60–75% should have rooted. Pot up in 3½ in. pots and overwinter in a cold glasshouse or plastic house. Growth starts early and, by the end of April, the plants can be sold 20 in. (50 cm) high, with four or five trusses of bloom. The tunnel has the advantage over the cold frame and plastic in that the cuttings can be left to be dealt with as convenient in late autumn or early winter. Where no house space can be spared, leave the cuttings until spring, when they are potted, staked and sold in summer and autumn.

Method 2 Basal or nodal cuttings of the past summer's growth about 5 in. (12.5 cm) long treated with 0.8% IBA powder are inserted in two parts moss peat to one of sand, in October. Lift and pot up in 3 in. pots in spring and place on an outdoor or indoor capillary bed for growing on. Sell in summer and autumn.

Magnolia

This genus of plants is especially beautiful in its flower display. There are evergreen and deciduous sorts, the most commonly seen of the latter being *M. wilsonii*, *M. kobus*, *M. x soulangeana* and *M. stellata*. The most common evergreen type is *M. grandiflora* which has very large shiny leaves and exceptionally large fragrant flowers.

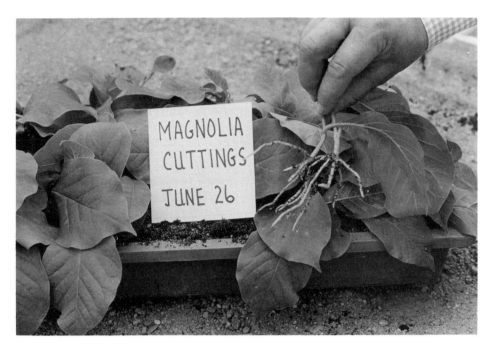

Fig. 44. Well rooted cuttings of *M. soulangeana* **Amabilis** from early softwood material.

Uses Best as specimen trees and shrubs. As many flower early, they need protection from winds and frosts. *M. stellata* is unsurpassed for the small garden and many *M. x soulangeana* forms are striking subjects for specimen planting. An acid soil is not a prerequisite for magnolias as the majority of them do well in a lime soil.

Methods of propagation 1. Cuttings in mist or warm bench and plastic in April–July. 2. Layering. 3. Seed.

Method 1 Many magnolias can be propagated from cuttings provided these cuttings are taken as early as possible. Forcing the mother plants by covering with a polythene house in February gives a supply of suitable cutting material from early April. The stock plants should be pruned hard to produce long annual shoots. These are tipped slightly in February to encourage the production of side shoots for cuttings. As soon as the latter have been removed, prune the mother shoot back to the base to ensure the development of a succession of shoots. These, in turn, will furnish cuttings the following spring. The cuttings are taken with a very sharp knife or blade through the junction of shoot and woody stem to which it is attached.

In the case of *M. x soulangeana* and its cultivars, it is essential to have at least two well developed disease-free leaves on the cuttings which should have a stem length of 3–4 in. (7.5–10 cm). A light wound at the base is necessary and the cuttings are placed in a warm bench after treatment with 0.8% IBA powder. A suitable rooting medium is two parts of moss peat to one of sand. The cuttings will root equally well under mist or under an 80–100 gauge polythene sheet, sealed at its edges and carefully managed (p. 13). High rooting percentages can be expected, especially with *M. stellata* (90–100%) in about eight weeks and, after hardening off, the rooted cuttings can be either planted in a frame and covered with Dutch lights, or containerised.

In high fertility conditions in the frame or in containers (especially where the plants are grown under polythene on a capillary bed), growth in the first   155 season can be up to 1 ft (30 cm) high. In spring of the following year, the young plants should be pruned back lightly and will be saleable plants of 2½–3 ft (75–90 cm) at the end of the second season. *M. stellata* does not require pruning as it has naturally branched growth. The magnolia is a good example of successful propagation from cuttings by the use of recent developments, including the use of plastic structures for obtaining early cuttings (p. 58) and for growing on rapidly in conjunction with loamless composts (p. 55) and capillary watering (p. 60).

Method 2 Layering has long been a standard method of propagation. The stock plants must be grown in good sheltered conditions and the soil in good fertility for the annual production of suitable layering material. Layering of shoots can be carried out in spring or in August. In the former case, shoots of the previous season's growth should be tongued and pegged into place and the soil well firmed in the manner of the customary simple layer. In the spring following, the layered shoot can be severed from the base of the stock plant and the new plants are lifted in the following November to be lined out in the nursery for growing on.

Layering in August in contrast involves the use of current season's wood. The leaves of the shoots are removed from the portion of the plant which will be under the ground. The shoots are pegged as before and the surrounding soil firmed and well watered. In this system of layering, rooting will take up to two years and the plants, at that stage, should be severed from the mother plant. After lifting, the plants can be field lined for growing on.

Method 3 This is not a commonly used method of propagation for most species. The seed should be sown in September and, as so few (*M. wilsonii* and *M. sinensis*) set seed in our climate, there is the added difficulty of obtaining fresh seed at sowing time. However, if seed of *M. wilsonii* and *M. sinensis* is sown in mild localities in September (open ground), germination will take place in the spring following and the seedlings will grow to 3 in. (7.5 cm) in the first season. These plants should be lifted in the autumn and lined out for growing on.

In colder localities and because of the value of the crop, the seed should be stored in slightly moist sand until it is sown in boxes in a glasshouse during February. When the seedlings can be conveniently handled, they should be potted or planted into a prepared cold frame for growing on for one season. They may then be lined out in the field or containerised.

Mahonia

Mahonias, allied to barberries, are distinguished from the latter by their pinnate leaves and thornless stems. All are evergreen with yellow flowers. The commercially important species are *M. aquifolium*, *M. bealei*, *M. japonica* and, to a lesser extent, *M. lomariifolia*, together with some cultivars and hybrids of these species.

Uses The Mahonias will grow in any good soil and in sun or shade. *M. aquifolium* is a useful ground cover shrub of medium height 2–3 ft (0.6–0.9 m). *M.* **Aldenhamensis** is a form of hybrid from it with better heads of flower. *M. bealei*, *M. japonica* and *M. lomariifolia* are grown as specimen

156

shrubs up to 8 ft (2.4 m), the first two valued for the lily-of-the-valley-like scent of the flowers. All three flower in winter. **Charity** and **Winter Sun** are hybrids of this group.

Methods of propagation 1. Cuttings in mist or warm bench with plastic in February. 2. Cuttings in mist in September–October. 3. Seed.

Method 1 This is suitable for *M. japonica*, *M. bealii*, **Charity** and **Winter Sun**. One-node cuttings, consisting of a single leaf and a piece of the stem, about 1 in. (2.5 cm) long, are made from shoots of the past season. Wounding is not necessary. Treatment with rooting powder is not advised as its use so close to a bud tends to delay shoot growth from the bud. Push the stems into the surface of the rooting medium up to the base of the leaf. Owing to the large size of the latter, it may be shortened to two pairs of leaflets for convenience. The rooting medium may be moss peat only, the addition of sand not, in our experience, being an advantage. Up to 100% rooting can be expected after nine to ten weeks. After hardening off the rooted cuttings, plant them out in a frame of a good compost, e.g. of fertilised peat. By the autumn plants 3 in. (7.5 cm) high can be expected. These can then be lined out to be sold a year later, 8 in. (20 cm) high with two to three branches. Rooted cuttings kept in a plastic house did not develop more quickly. A similar procedure can be followed under the warm bench and plastic system, though rooting may be reduced by about 10%.

Fig. 45. Rooted leaf bud cutting of *Mahonia*.

Method 2 is applicable to the *M. aquifolium* group. Basal cuttings of the current year's growth, after wounding and treatment with 0.8% IBA powder, are inserted in a compost of two parts moss peat to one of sand in mist in September. Up to 90% rooting may be expected after four weeks. After hardening off, the cuttings may be left undisturbed in the trays and held in a cold house or frame until the spring, or they can be lined out immediately in a frame of good compost. They may be sold a year later as 6 in. (15 cm) branched plants.

Method 3 Seed of *M. aquifolium* and its allies may be gathered and sown as soon as ripe in late August. Crush the berries and mix with sand to facilitate sowing. Germination is good the first spring, so sow immediately in a cold frame or open bed. 100 berries should give 50–60 seedlings. These will be up to 3 in. (7.5 cm) high by the following autumn, when they should be lifted, graded and lined out to grow on for a further year.

Seed of *M. japonica*, ripe in July, can be sown immediately in a cold frame or in boxes in a cold frame. Keep the frame shaded and watered. Germination will start in autumn and, though the seedlings will only be in the cotyledon stage, they are hardy and can be left to overwinter. Prick off into frames in spring.

Malus

A few of the wild species of *Malus* are appreciated in our gardens but most of the ornamental crabs grown today are hybrids.

Uses Some are grown for the profusion of their blossom which may be pink, e.g. (*M. floribunda*), white (e.g. **John Downie**) or wine red (e.g. **Profusion**). Fruiting crabs include **John Downie** (orange-red), **Golden Hornet** (yellow) and many others. Some have purple-tinted foliage such as **Lemoinei** and **Profusion**. All are grown as specimen trees in our gardens. Species which do not fruit freely or have small fruits are useful as street trees, e.g. *M. tschonoskii* and *M. toringoides*.

Methods of propagation 1. Budding. 2. Grafting.

Ornamental crabs have long been budded or grafted on to seedling crab rootstocks owing to virus infection of clonal rootstocks, but now we have virus-free rootstocks and scion material. The use of virus infected material can frequently result in the complete failure of the plants due to the presence of one or more lethal strains of virus. Once the virus free material has been obtained, it should be worked on to the clonal rootstocks MM 111, MM 106 and M 26, as these are free of virus.

Method 1 Established two-year-old stocks are budded during the summer as low down on the stem as possible. Well developed buds are used from the central portion of healthy shoots and, after insertion in the T-cut (p. 34), are firmly bound with raffia. The training up of the shoot which arises from the bud, after the cutting back of the stock in February, will depend on requirements (i.e. standards, half-standards, etc.). Growth of up to 3½ ft (1.05 m) can be expected in the first growing season.

Method 2 Bench grafting can be carried out in February. This can be convenient where bench grafting is routine under the management scheme for that time of year. The bare rooted stock and scion must be of the same diameter and the whip graft (p. 32) is used. The graft is waxed and heeled in in an outside shaded frame until the buds begin to move. The graft is then planted in nursery beds for growing on.

Grafting by the same method can also be done in April where field established stocks are used. This is a convenient system where small numbers only are required.

Metasequoia

The Dawn Redwood (*Metasequoia glyptostroboides*) has attained wide popularity in a short time, aided by the glamour surrounding the story of how this tree, once thought to be extinct, was discovered in a remote part of China. It is an attractive conifer in its own right, with feathery foliage which turns pinkish brown before falling in autumn. *Metasequoia* thrives best in a deep, moderately moist soil.

Method of propagation Cuttings in mist or in the cold frame in February. Heeled hardwood cuttings of one- or two-year-old wood, 3–5 in. (7.5–12.5 cm) will root 60–80% in 10 to 12 weeks propagated in mist in February, using a medium of two parts moss peat to one of sand. In Holland the cold frame is used and it is shaded until shoot growth has started. Those from the mist are hardened off, lined out in a cold frame, using shaded lights until they are well established. Field plant in autumn.

Rooted cuttings in the cold frame are left *in situ* until autumn. Sell as three-year-old plants 2 ft (0.6 m) high.

Mutisia

Mutisias are climbers from South America, clinging by leaf tendrils. They require a warm sheltered spot in well drained soil. The hardiest species are *M. ilicifolia* (mauve or pink) and *M. oligodon* (pink), both with large daisy-like flowers. Both are beautiful but are best grown through a low shrub as they are apt to become untidy with withered leaves at the base. Basal cuttings of the current season's growth, treated with 0.8% IBA powder, may be rooted under mist during July–September. Pot up in 3 in. pots for overwintering under glass, and containerise in spring.

Myrtus

Myrtus communis is the common Myrtle, associated with wedding bouquets. *M. luma* grows into a small tree and should be kept to a single stem to show off the cinnamon coloured bark. *M. ugni* is low growing with mahogany red berries. *M. bullata* is a medium sized shrub remarkable for the reddish brown puckered leaves. All are evergreens for the mildest localities only, though *M. communis* will survive in many gardens at the foot of a south wall.

Method of propagation Basal cuttings of the current year's shoots may be taken in November and struck in a cold frame. Protect the frames in severe weather. Lift and line out or pot in spring. Nodal cuttings of the rarer species may be struck under mist in July, though rooting may be slow. Pot up and 159 grow on under glass. *Myrtus bullata* treated this way can be 2 ft (60 cm) high at one year old. *M. luma* seeds itself freely in gardens in the south and south west.

Nandina

Nandina domestica, the Sacred Bamboo, is not a bamboo at all, but is related to the barberries. It is grown in gardens in mild districts for its bamboo-like habit and for the effect of the divided leaves, red tinted in spring. Single node cuttings, taken in July, rooted 50–55% in six weeks, by the warm bench and plastic method. The rooting medium was two parts moss peat to one of sand. Treatment with 0.8% IBA powder did not increase the number of rooted cuttings. Such cuttings, potted up in 3 in. pots made small, well rooted plants by autumn, ready for re-potting in spring for growing on under glass.

Basal or nodal cuttings of the past season's growth are stated to be successful if inserted in a cold frame in November–December.

Nothofagus

Nothofagus (Southern Beech) are trees and shrubs related to our own Beech. The species of main horticultural interest are evergreen trees (except *N. antarctica*) with attractive bark, small leaves and elegant habit.

Uses Nothofagus are fast growing trees needing plenty of room. They should be planted more often in parks and open spaces, except where the soil is very alkaline. We find *N. antarctica* to be tolerant of alkaline loam soil. *N. procera* and *N. obliqua* are promising as forestry trees. *Nothofagus* are not suitable for exposed sites.

Methods of propagation 1. Seed. 2. Cuttings under mist in July–August. 3. Layering.

Method 1 Seed is scarce and percentage germination is low. If it is available, home saved seed is recommended. Sow under glass as soon as received. Prick off into 3 in. pots for growing on, hardening off and planting out when 5–6 in. (12.5–15 cm) high. They may be expected to reach 2 ft (60 cm) by the end of the second year.

Method 2 Cuttings in July–August are sometimes recommended for *N. dombeyi* and *N. procera* but, in our experience, rooting percentages are low. The use of 0.8% IBA powder is slightly advantageous. Harden off the rooted cuttings and line them out in a cold frame for one year, after which they can be field lined.

Method 3 Cut back established young trees to form long shoots which are layered in autumn as described for simple layering (p. 27). Lift and line out one year later.

Olearia

A large genus of evergreen shrubs from Australia and New Zealand and, therefore, not hardy in cold districts. They are of great value in windswept areas near the coast.

Uses The holly-like *Olearia macrodonta* is a useful hedge plant in the coastal counties, resistant to grazing by livestock. *O. forsteri* with wavy lighter green leaves can be used for hedging also. *O. traversii* is particularly useful for poor sandy soils. It grows quickly and reaches 20 ft (6 m) if untrimmed. *O. gunniana*, a medium sized shrub with small soft leaves is outstandingly floriferous whether in the white, blue or pink form.

Methods of propagation 1. Cuttings in open ground or in a cold frame in October. 2. Cuttings under mist in May.

Method 1 Heeled cuttings of side shoots 6–8 in. (15–20 cm) long can be inserted in an outdoor bed or, in colder districts, a cold frame. Treatment with rooting powders is not necessary. By the beginning of May 90–100% should be well rooted, when they can be lined out and grown on for sale in autumn.

Method 2 The softer *O. stellulata* can be rooted from heeled cuttings of side shoots 2–3 in. (5–7.5 cm) inserted under mist in May. Treat with 0.8% IBA powder. 100% rooting can be expected after five weeks, when the cuttings can be potted up for growing on.

Osmanthus

A genus of several holly-like shrubs with one outstanding species, *Osmanthum delavayi* which eventually reaches 6 ft (1.8 m). In April it is covered with small tubular, scented flowers. Even young specimens flower freely.

Uses As specimens in the shrub border, in any place, in any soil.

Method of propagation Stocky side shoots of the current year, 3–4 in. (7.5–10 cm) long are treated with 0.8% IBA powder before insertion under mist or warm bench and plastic in August. Wounding is not needed. Long whippy shoots should not be used. From 50–70% should be rooted after six weeks. Harden off and overwinter in the boxes until spring. Containerise or line out in a cold frame for growing on. Propagation from cuttings in the cold frame has not been successful under our conditions.

Pachysandra

A small genus of low growing evergreen shrubs. *Pachysandra terminalis* is widely used in USA as ground cover and is sometimes used for this purpose here. This otherwise rather uninteresting plant will grow in dense shade under trees. Stocks may be increased by splitting up the plants in spring. Propagate from cuttings in July in mist or in the cold frame.

161

Paeonia

A few species of paeony qualify as shrubs by the perennial nature of their overground stems. These include *Paeonia lutea*, *P. delavayi* and *P. potaninii*. The hybrid tree paeonies with enormous double yellow, red, white, pink or violet flowers are derived from *P. suffruticosa* and *P. suffruticosa x P. lutea*.

Uses As specimens in the large herbaceous border or among shrubs in good alkaline soil. Do not plant in shaded conditions or where they will suffer any competition from other plants.

Methods of propagation 1. Seed. 2. Grafting.

Method 1 is only used for the true species. Sow as soon as ripe in a cold frame or in pots to be brought in on the initiation of germination. Prick off the latter into 3½ in. pots to be hardened off and lined out. Those in the cold frame can be lined out in autumn. Sometimes, particularly with seed that has been dried, roots appear the first year, but shoots not until the second year.

Method 2 The garden hybrids will not come true from seed. The roots of *P. lactiflora* and *P. officinalis* are used as understocks. Grafting is carried out in August, using pieces of root about 4 in. (10 cm) long and ½ in. (1.2 cm) thick. The scion is about 1½ in. (3.7 cm) long, consisting of one leaf having in its axil a vegetative (non-flowering) bud. A 2 in. (5 cm) slit is made at the top of the piece of root and the scion, cut to a wedge shape at the base, is pushed in. Immediately place in a 1:1 sand-peat mixture in a closed shaded frame on the glasshouse bench, planting so that the union is covered, and leave until well callused. Harden off by admitting air gradually. By autumn they should be ready for potting into 3 in. pots. Plunge the pots in a cold frame for the winter. Spray with a fungicide as a precaution against botrytis. Next season plant out in cold frames as soon as the pots become filled with roots. From this stage onwards deep planting should be practised to encourage scion rooting.

Paulownia

These big trees, surprisingly enough, belong to the foxglove family (*Scrophulariaceae*). The panicles of heliotrope coloured flowers are formed the previous autumn and so may be frosted before they can open in May. Alternatively, *Paulownia* may be grown for its huge leaves, the size intensified by cutting the young tree down to the ground each spring and reducing the suckers which come up, to one. The best known species is *P. tomentosa*.

Method of propagation The very light fluffy seed (imported) germinates freely and should be sown very thinly under glass in March. If so sown, it can be pricked off directly into 3 in. pots five weeks later. By the end of April the seedlings will be about 1½ in. (3.7 cm) high but as much as 5 in. (12.5 cm) across on account of the large, hollyhock-like leaves. Pot on into 6 in. plastic bags. They may then be transferred to a capillary bed in a plastic house. Development continues rapidly and, by mid-June, the plants will be 2 ft (60 cm) high. At this stage it is advisable to place them on an outdoor capillary bed to avoid having lush, over-soft plants. If the seedlings are placed outside at the end of April, growth will be much slower, giving plants only about 5 in. (12.5 cm) by autumn.

Parrotia

Parrotia persica, a relative of the witch hazels, has flowers with red stamens but no petals, appearing before the leaves. *Parrotia*, however, is grown mainly for the autumn colour of its foliage. As it eventually grows into a large shrub or even tree, plenty of room is needed. Propagate by layering (p. 27) from established stool beds.

Parthenocissus (including *Ampelopsis* and *Vitis*)

Parthenocissus, *Ampelopsis* and *Vitis* have been changed around to a confusing extent. The **Virginia Creeper**, for example, has been called *Vitis inconstans* and *Ampelopsis veitchii*. At present it is *Parthenocissus tricuspidata* **Veitchii**. *Ampelopsis* and *Vitis* have twining tendrils but *Parthenocissus* clings by sticky pads.

Uses Virginia Creeper is well known for its autumn colour. *P. henryana* (*V. henryana*) has beautiful silvery veins to the leaves. *V. coignetiae* needs a support for its tendrils to cling to when grown on walls but can be allowed to ramble up a tree or large bush. The large leaves turn to spectacular shades of crimson in autumn.

Methods of propagation 1. Cuttings under mist or in the warm bench with plastic, July–September. 2. Cuttings and layering (*V. coignetiae*).

Method 1 Softwood cuttings 3–4 in. (7.5–10 cm) long, having at least four leaves to ensure the presence of viable axillary buds, are treated with 0.8% IBA powder before insertion under mist or in the warm bench and plastic; the rooting medium is one part moss peat to one of sand. After four weeks 100% rooting can be expected. Pot up in 3 in. pots and grow on, staking the plants and potting on as required.

Method 2 *V. coignetiae* is often considered to be difficult from cuttings and although layering in spring is recommended, we have had 80% success from softwood cuttings under mist in May. The unwounded cuttings treated with 0.8% IBA rooted in seven weeks.

Passiflora

Passiflora caerulea, the Blue Passion Flower, is hardy on a sunny wall in mild localities. Nodal cuttings strike easily, e.g. by the warm bench and plastic method in July. Up to 100% rooting may be expected in three to four weeks, in two parts moss peat to one of sand. The use of root promoting substances is unnecessary. The rooted cuttings grow rampantly when potted up and kept under glass or in the plastic house.

Pernettya

Pernettyas are low growing evergreen shrubs for non-calcareous soils. The important species horticulturally is *P. mucronata*, especially the named 163 cultivars, which give wonderful displays of red, pink or purple berries. They fruit best in full sun. To ensure good crops, plant in groups and include a known male plant.

Uses Planted for ground cover and as specimens for the long lasting berries.

Method of propagation Division of well established plants in early spring may be a convenient way of increase. Line out in beds of peaty soil. Basal cuttings may also be rooted in the cold frame and plastic in June–July, using peat alone as a rooting medium.

Phellodendron

Phellodendrons are deciduous trees from Asia with large pinnate leaves and inconspicuous flowers. The tree attracts attention when the clusters of fruit are present, hanging on after the leaves have fallen. These fruits are round, soft and black, the size of large peas.

Method of propagation P. chinense, and probably other species, can be raised from home-saved seed. The seeds, sown in boxes in November, start to germinate in April. If brought under glass at this stage, they are ready to prick off into 3 in. pots a month later. In June they can be potted on into 6 in. bags and, if grown on in a plastic house on a capillary bed, development is rapid. The plants will be 2 ft (60 cm) high by August. At this stage they can be moved to an outdoor capillary bed for sale as container grown plants or lined out for growing on.

Philadelphus

Philadelphus, called Mock Orange from the scent of the flowers, is a large genus of deciduous shrubs with tall growing species 10 ft (3 m) or more high, down to low kinds 3 ft (1 m) or so in height.

Uses For planting as specimens or in groups on any soil. Valued for the abundance of their sweet scented flowers in June–July.

Methods of propagation 1. Cuttings in the low tunnel or in the cold frame and plastic in June. 2. Cuttings under mist in May. 3. Cuttings in the cold frame in September. 4. Cuttings in the open ground in December.

Method 1 Nodal cuttings of the current season's side shoots 3–5 in. (7.5–12.5 cm) long are inserted in June. Although up to 100% rooting can be expected without treatment with 0.8% IBA powder, this has been observed to give larger root systems. Those rooted under the tunnel are left *in situ* until the end of the season when they will be 12 in. (30 cm) or more high, with four or five shoots. Line out, prune back the young plants and grow on for a further season. If larger plants are required, grow on for two seasons.

Method 2 Basal cuttings 3–4 in. (7.5–10 cm) are inserted in May in a compost of two parts peat to one of sand after treatment with 0.4% IBA powder. Up to 100% rooting will occur in three weeks. The rooted cuttings, after hardening off, can be lined out in a cold frame for the rest of the season. By leaf fall they will be about 1 ft (30 cm) high, with four shoots. They can be sold as small plants or lined out for a further season's growth.

Method 3 Internodal cuttings 5–8 in. (12.5–20 cm) long, treated with 0.8% IBA powder are inserted in two parts moss peat to one of sand in September.

They will have rooted up to 100% when lifted the following April for lining out. At the end of the season, transplant, cut back and grow on for one or two seasons according to size of plant required.

Method 4 Strong growing cultivars can be rooted from hardwood cuttings inserted in the open ground. Treat the heel cuttings with 0.8% IBA powder. Transplant after one year and grow on for one or two seasons according to the size of plant required.

Philesia

Philesia magellanica (*P. buxifolia*) is a remarkable low growing narrow-leaved evergreen with rosy crimson tubular flowers 2 in. (5 cm) long. It is only successful in mild districts and should be grown in peaty soil. The plant sends up suckers, so propagation may be effected by detaching these when rooted. There is scope for experimenting with cuttings under mist.

Phlomis

Phlomis fruticosa is the Jerusalem Sage, a woolly, low shrub, 2–4 ft (0.6–1.2 m) high, noted for the whorls of hooded yellow flowers in late summer and autumn. It is a shrub for sunny well-drained situations. Propagate from nodal cuttings inserted in the cold frame in September, 3–4 in. (7.5–10 cm) long. Lift and pot in spring. Pot on during summer and sell as container grown plants in summer and autumn.

Phormium

Although *Phormium* is botanically a genus of herbs, it is generally included with trees and shrubs. As well as the New Zealand Flax (*P. tenax*) the smaller *P. colensoi* with laxer leaves and yellowish (not reddish) flowers is in cultivation.

Uses P. tenax, up to 9 ft (2.7 m) high will provide shelter even in the most windswept areas on boggy soil. In landscaping, more use could be made of the handsome purple leaved and variegated forms, particularly by the waterside. Not hardy in cold districts.

Method of propagation Both species can be raised from fresh seed, though their seedlings vary in habit. Sow out of doors or in a cold frame in spring. Division is a more usual method of propagation, carried out in spring. The old roots die and new ones emerge from the base of the stem.

Photinia

A genus of trees and shrubs belonging to the same family (*Rosaceae*) as *Crataegus* and *Cotoneaster*. *Photinia* has become popular through the introduction of the hybrids **Bermingham** and **Red Robin**. These, grown for the coppery-red young foliage are tolerant of lime soils where *Pieris* will fail.

Though basal cuttings of half ripened wood may be rooted as they become available in spring and summer, single node cuttings of the past season's growth taken in February give more material. Inserted in the warm bench and plastic upwards of 60% root in 15 weeks. Though slow to root, these cuttings will produce plants over 1 ft high (30–40 cm) by the end of the year if grown under glass. Prune hard back the following February to produce branched plants, utilising the prunings for a further crop of single node cuttings.

Cuttings may also be propagated in the white polythene tunnel in July (see p. 19).

Phyllostachys

See under **Bamboo**.

Picea

The spruces (*Picea*) have pendulous cones in contrast to the upright, barrel-shaped cones of the firs (*Abies*). As well as the common Christmas Tree (*P. abies* Norway or Common Spruce), the genus includes some outstanding ornamental conifers. Perhaps the best known are Koster's Blue Spruce (*P. pungens* **Kosteriana**) and the similar *P. p.* **Moerheimii**. These are likely to be surpassed for colour by the more recent *P. p.* **Hoopsii**. The Serbian Spruce *P. omorika* is notable for its narrow, spire-like habit. *P. breweriana*, Brewer's Weeping Spruce, is one of the most outstanding weeping trees, though this is the effect of the pendulous side branches only.

There are a large number of dwarf forms of *Picea* valued by enthusiasts, including the popular *P. albertiana* **Conica**.

Uses The tall species are valuable specimen trees for large gardens and parks. The dwarfs are very effective in rock gardens.

Methods of propagation 1. Grafting. 2. Cuttings in mist in July–August. 3. Seed.

Method 1 The rootstock used is *P. abies*. Plants with stems of pencil thickness are potted in spring and plunged in outdoor beds until grafting time. Though early August is commonly recommended for the grafting of the blue forms (**Kosteriana, Moerheimii** and **Hoopsii**) we have had better results from spring grafting (February–March). The scion must have three terminal buds to avoid lopsided growth in the developing plant. The rootstock is dried off and all the new growths are trimmed back leaving only the older shoots. The type of graft is a side graft on a foot (p. 32). As the bark is so easily detached in spruce at this time of the year, it is safer to cut one side only of the one-year-old scion-wood. The grafts are placed in a grafting case and it is vitally important that

166

they receive as much light as possible. Hence, permanent shading is not recommended, but rather the use of a cloth or coloured plastic material which can be removed during cloudy periods and replaced in strong sunshine. The grafts are plunged in peat in the grafting case with the union below the surface of the peat and a bottom temperature of 70–74°F (21–23°C) is maintained. When the union is callused (six weeks later) the grafts are planted in outdoor frames after the usual hardening off procedure. Lights are placed in position and left on during the winter and, again, no permanent shading material is used. In spring, when the shoots of the stock show 1 in. (2.5 cm) of growth, the rootstocks are cut back to just above the graft union and, when the scions start to grow, the plants are put out in well prepared outdoor beds.

Fig. 46. Side graft of *Picea*. Note top growth of stock left on until spring (left).

The failure rate with blue spruce can be high and, in such cases, the rootstock can be used for winter grafting (February) for the dwarfs. The grafted stocks are placed under a plastic tent in a glasshouse with a temperature of about 60–64°F (15.6–17.8°C), plunged into peat with the union covered. After about seven weeks, good callusing will be seen. The grafts can be planted into the outside frame during April. As with blue spruce, the shoots of the stock are cut back and, after the usual hardening off period, the plants lined out.

Method 2 Only the dwarf forms of spruce root readily from cuttings. Our best results (*P.a.* **Microsperma, Decumbens, Nidiformis, Dumosa, Repens** and **Tabuliformis**) are from cuttings taken in July and early August and placed under mist. After mid-August, rooting percentages rapidly fall away. Shoots of the current season's growth are taken, treated with 0.8% IBA powder and placed under mist in a medium of two parts peat to one of sand. Rooting percentages of 50–80% can be expected after three months. After rooting, the plants should be transferred to a cold frame for growing on. Three seasons later a saleable plant of 5–10 in. (12.5–25 cm) diameter should result. Many cultivars have similar growth habit and general characteristics and so the high rooting obtained with *P.a.* **Nidiformis** renders it a suitable nurseryman's cultivar.

Although rooting percentages of up to 60% have been obtained with the blue spruces from March cuttings in mist using a 4000 ppm IBA quick dip   167 hormone treatment, the slow development of the plant afterwards will discourage many from attempting this method of propagation.

Method 3 For horticultural purposes, seed raising is mainly of interest in connection with *P. omorika* and a few rare species. *P. breweriana* is very slow in the seedling stage. Purchased seed may be sown in frames in early spring or in open beds if much seed is to be sown. Small lots may be sown in pots, plunged out of doors and brought in on initiation of germination, for pricking off and growing on.

Pieris

A genus of evergreen shrubs with racemes or panicles of lily-of-the-valley like white flowers. *Pieris floribunda*, from USA, is hardy but slow growing. *P. taiwanensis* and *P. japonica* have copper coloured young foliage, but this feature reaches its greatest intensity in the best forms of *P. formosa var forrestii* and in the hybrid **Forest Flame**. The red coloured young leaves are susceptible to damage by late spring frosts, so plant with light overhead shade and shelter from the early morning sun. Most *Pieris* flower in March and April. *P. forrestii* flowers in May. All must be grown in lime free soil.

The species may be raised from seed. *P. taiwanensis*, for example, will seed itself in a peat bed, but the selected forms must be propagated vegetatively. Layering is an old method, but cuttings may be struck with up to 100% success. Basal cuttings of the current year's shoots are taken when extension growth has ceased (July). Treat with 0.8% IBA powder and insert under mist or in the warm bench with plastic, in moss peat. After about ten weeks the rooted cuttings may be potted up or hardened off and lined out in a cold frame. The young plants must be protected from spring frosts.

Cuttings may also be propagated in the white polythene tunnel in September–November (see p. 19).

Pinus

Apart from their value in forestry, many pines are very ornamental. As there are about 70 species, only a few can be mentioned here. Some, such as our own Scots Pine (*Pinus sylvestris*) and *P. pinea* the Stone Pine, assume picturesque shapes. Others have long graceful needles, such as the Bhutan Pine (*P. excelsa*) and the Mexican White Pine (*P. ayacahuite*). In mild districts the Mexican *P. montezumae*, remarkable for its long stiff leaves, is very striking. All these are large trees. The Mountain Pine (*P. mugo*) is sought after for the large rock garden, especially in selected forms like **Gnom**.

Methods of propagation 1. Seed. 2. Grafting.

Method 1 Pines may be sown out of doors by the method already outlined (p. 24) sowing broadcast or in drills 3–4 in. (7.5–10 cm) apart. Raised in this manner the seedlings will, in general, be about 3–4 in. (7.5–10 cm) by the end of the first season. The one year seedlings are lifted in early spring for lining out and the operation should be completed by early April. The seedlings are planted 2 in. (5 cm) apart in prepared beds in lines 6 in. (15 cm) apart.

Where small quantities of ornamental species are required, the seed may be sown in half pots or boxes under glass in February. With most species 60–70% germination may be expected after about 15 days. Prick off into 3 in. pots when the first leaves after the seed leaves are appearing (about 12 days later). For a few species like *P. pinea*, which produce large seedlings with long roots, pot into 4 in. 'Long Toms'. After returning the potted seedlings to the glasshouse for a few days to become re-established, they can be transferred to a capillary bed inside a plastic house.

The seedlings stop elongating for a period in July but then make a second flush of growth. By autumn they will be 5–12 in. (12.5–30 cm) high according to species. Among the vigorous kinds are *P. densiflora*, *P. thunbergii*, *P. patula* and *P. pinea*. Species noted as less vigorous under this treatment include *P. ponderosa*, *P. resinosa* and *P. ayacahuite*.

Purchased seed of most pines germinates well the same spring as sown but some, e.g. *P. cembra*, *P. pumila*, *P. coulteri* and, occasionally, others are apt to exhibit dormancy and may not come up the first year.

Method 2 The understock should be the same species or only closely allied to it. Pot selected pencil-thick stocks in spring in soil with some sand added, and plunge in outdoor beds. Lift in the following February and dry off the plants well. Use the side graft on a foot (p. 32) and select one-year-old scions. Cut only one side of the scion, removing the bark and a very thin sliver of wood only. Too deep a cut will produce poor callusing. The grafts are plunged in peat which is on the dry side and covered with 100 gauge polythene film. The bottom temperature should approximate to 60°F (15.6°C). These conditions are easily attained in a frame with bottom heating cables. A close watch should be kept on the grafts for any fungal symptoms and, after six or seven weeks, good callusing will take place. Harden off quickly and plunge the pots in a covered frame until the spring when shoots of the stock can be cut away. Line out in outdoor beds and grow on for a few years.

Piptanthus

Piptanthus laburnifolius (*P. nepalensis*) is known as the 'Evergreen Laburnum', a descriptive name, the shrub having evergreen trifoliate leaves and racemes of yellow laburnum-like flowers in May.

Uses As a specimen shrub up to 8 ft (2.4 m) or more high in the open or against a wall in cold districts, in any soil.

Method of propagation Seed is produced freely. The pods should be gathered when ripe in late summer or autumn and the seeds shelled out. Store under ordinary conditions and sow under glass in February. Germination to the extent of 60–70% takes place in seven to ten days. The seedlings will be ready to prick off into 3 in. pots after about 15 days. If kept in the glasshouse (minimum 60°F–15.6°C), development is rapid and three weeks later they will be 3–5 in. (7.5–12.5 cm) high. They can then be potted on into 6 in. pots or bags. Pinch when 18 in. (45 cm) high. If kept on a capillary bed in a plastic house they will be 6 ft (1.8 m) by autumn or, if hardened off and placed on a similar bed outside, they will be 18–24 in. (45–60 cm) high by the end of the season.

169

Pittosporum

A genus of evergreens from Australia and New Zealand, tender in most districts. *Pittosporum tenuifolium* is the most widely known. *P. tobira* is sometimes seen. The very tender *P. crassifolium* is used to form tall, narrow hedges in the Scilly Isles.

Uses *P. tenuifolium* is occasionally used for hedges in mild maritime districts. The foliage, especially of the finer leaved variants, is used in floristry. The variegated **Silver Queen** makes an especially handsome specimen.

Methods of propagation 1. Seed. 2. Cuttings in October in the cold frame with plastic. 3. Cuttings in October in the warm bench with plastic. 4. Grafting.

Method 1 *P. tenuifolium* produces seed freely. The sticky seeds can be gathered when the capsules split in October. In mild districts seedlings spring up spontaneously under the bushes and can be lifted and containerised. Growth is rapid — 1 ft (30 cm) a year. Seedlings vary in size of leaf and especially attractive small leaved forms can be selected. Otherwise sow under glass in February, prick off into 3 in. pots and grow on on a capillary bed under cover, pot on, harden off and transfer to an outdoor capillary bed when 1 ft (30 cm) high. Seed could also be sown in a cold frame in March, the seedlings thinned out and the remainder grown on until ready for containerisation.

Method 2 Apart from grafting onto seedling stocks in March or August, **Silver Queen** can be raised from cuttings inserted in October in the cold frame with plastic. Basal cuttings 3–4 in. (7.5–10 cm) long, wounded and treated with 0.8% IBA powder root 70–80% when lifted the following spring. The cuttings should be examined as early as March, for, if rooting is far advanced before they are lifted, there can be losses. As soon as rooting is evident, the cuttings should be hardened off, then potted into 3 in. pots. If kept under glass or in a plastic house, particularly if on a capillary bed, development is very rapid and the plants will require potting on once or twice. By the end of the year they will be bushy specimens 1 ft (30 cm) or more high. Sell as container grown plants.

Method 3 Cuttings treated as for Method 2 can also be rooted 70–80% in ten weeks by the warm bench and plastic method. They are lifted and potted in December and held in a frost free house until spring, when they can be hardened off, potted on and treated as above. Though this is a more expensive method of propagation, it may be convenient under some circumstances.

The uncommon *P. daphniphylloides* was rooted from basal cuttings of the current year's wood 3 in. (7.5 cm) long taken in July, treated with 0.8% IBA powder and inserted under mist. Potted up and kept under glass (minimum temperature 60°F, 15.6°C) they were branched plants 12 in. (30 cm) high by the following spring.

Method 4 Variegated and other coloured forms can be grafted in February–March onto seedlings of *P. tenuifolium* using the side graft (p. 31). The plants are placed in an unheated closed case. After two months if the union is secure the stock can be cut back and plants will reach saleable size (30 cm) in one season if grown under glass or polythene.

Platanus

The planes are distinct in producing round seed balls, hanging from the branches on long stalks. The London Plane (*Platanus x acerifolia*) is, however, a hybrid and so is propagated vegetatively by stooling or by basal cuttings of the past season's growth inserted in the open ground at leaf fall. It is also possible to propagate planes by softwood cuttings. We have no direct experience of this and understand that timing is important and that over-wintering may be a problem with this type of cutting.

Potentilla

In the large genus, *Potentilla*, there are only two shrubby species of horticultural importance, *P. fruticosa*, of which there are many cultivars, and *P. arbuscula*. The flowers may be yellow, orange or white. These potentillas are notable for their long flowering season.

Uses As specimens or ground cover in any reasonable aspect or soil.

Method of propagation 1. Cuttings in low tunnel in June. 2. Cuttings in the cold frame in September. 3. Cuttings in mist in July–September.

Method 1 Nodal or basal cuttings about 4–6 in. (10–15 cm) long are inserted under the low tunnel, after treatment with 0.8% IBA powder. Rooting should be 95–100%. The plants make good growth and by autumn should be up to 8 in. (20 cm) with four to seven shoots. They could be sold as small plants or lined out at 12 in. (30 cm) spacing for growing on for a further year. We have had better results by this method than from the cold frame with plastic. The use of IBA powder gives large root systems.

Method 2 Semi-hard basal cuttings of the current year's shoots are taken in mid-September 3–6 in. (7.5–15 cm) long. Remove any flower buds and treat with 0.8% IBA powder. When lifted in April 80–100% rooting can be expected. Line out in a nursery bed at 6–7 in. (15–17.5 cm) apart for growing on.

Method 3 Mist would be a relatively expensive way of producing potentillas but, on occasion, they can be a useful catch crop. Insert heeled cuttings 5–6 in. (12.5–15 cm) long, after treatment with 0.8% IBA powder. After three weeks all should be rooted. Harden off and plant out in a cold frame. By the end of the season these plants should be 7–10 in. (17.5–25 cm) high and suitable for lining out.

Prunus (Deciduous)

A large genus including not only the Japanese cherries, almonds and peaches but also the evergreen laurels (see under *Prunus*, evergreen).

171

Uses As flowering specimens for every type of garden, since they range from the dwarf *P. tenella* through the small *P. incisa* and through several medium sized trees such as *P. subhirtella*, *P.* **Accolade** and *P.* **Kursar** to the larger Japanese cherries like **Kanzan, Ukon** and **Tai Haku**.

Fig. 47. *Prunus incisa* develops faster from early cuttings.

Methods of propagation 1. Softwood cuttings in mist in April–May. 2. Semi-hardwood cuttings in mist in July. 3. Hardwood cuttings in November. 4. Stooling. 5. Budding and grafting.

Method 1 This method is suitable for a group of species and cultivars which includes *P.* **Accolade**, *P. subhirtella*, *P. incisa*, *P. tomentosa*, *P. triloba* **Flore Pleno**, *P.* **Hally Jolivette** and *P. tenella* **Fire Hill** (a much superior cultivar of *P. tenella* which does not sucker freely). *P.* **Kanzan** also responds to May cuttings, and such cuttings reach saleable size in 18 months as against 24 months for July cuttings. Suitable material is, however, scarce in May.

    P. triloba **Flore Pleno** will be ready for propagation early in May. Basal cuttings of the soft young shoots about 2½ in. (6.2 cm) long are taken when the flowers are just going over. Treat with 0.4% IBA powder and insert in two parts moss peat to one of sand in a mist unit. Though 80% rooting may be expected in four weeks, extra cuttings should be put in as the percentage can fall to 50% if conditions are not quite right, e.g. if the cuttings are slightly over-mature. Harden off and line out in a cold frame, replacing the lights and giving shade until the cuttings are established. A little growth is made before the following year but, after careful lifting and lining out in a sheltered situation, they will form a bush with three to five stems 2½ ft (75 cm) or more in height during their second year.

Extra cuttings of *P. tenella* **Fire Hill** also should be inserted, as only 30–40% rooting after eight weeks can be expected, though up to 80% is possible. Basal cuttings 1–2 in. (3–5 cm) long are taken in May. Treat with 0.8% IBA powder and insert in two parts moss peat to one of sand. After they have rooted, harden them off and transplant them carefully into a cold frame with shaded lights, until established. Though little growth is made during the rest of the year, by the end of the following season these rooted cuttings form a bush 1 ft (30 cm) high with up to three branches. If they are containerised early the next spring, they make attractive flowering specimens. *P. tenella* is especially prone to red spider.

The remaining species in this group root readily at this time of year. Softwood cuttings about 2 in. (5 cm) long are treated as for *P. tenella*. Four to five weeks later 60–100% rooting can be expected, *P. incisa* will even root in 18 days. After hardening off the rooted cuttings, they may be lined out as for *P. triloba*. *P. incisa* will grow to about 15 in. (38 cm) in its first year, reaching as much as 3 ft (0.9 m) the following year, freely branched and feathered *P. subhirtella* **Autumnalis**, *P.* **Accolade** and *P.* **Kursar** also grow strongly in their second year. *P. subhirtella* **Pendula** has been difficult to root from cuttings.

Method 2 The Japanese cherries can be propagated more successfully from semi-hardwood cuttings inserted in July. *P.* **Kanzan** is advertised in American trade Journals as 'callipering up quicker on its own roots'. We find that many other hybrids of this group come readily from cuttings. Of those tried *P.* **Kanzan**, *P. yedoensis*, *P.* **Tai Haku**, *P.* **Shimidsu Sakura** (*P. longipes*), *P.* **Hokusai** and *P.* **Taoyama Zakura** have rooted well and grown on into satisfactory trees. *P.* **Amanogawa** and *P.* **Mikuruma-gaeshi** have been difficult to grow on after rooting.

Basal cuttings of the current season's shoots when 4–8 in. (10–20 cm) long, according to cultivar, are taken in July, wounded, treated with 0.8% IBA powder and inserted in a medium of two parts moss peat to one of sand. After four to five weeks 80–100% rooting can be expected. The cuttings are hardened off and planted out in a cold frame, utilising shaded glass lights to get them quickly established. Though no shoot growth is made before leaf fall, the aim is to have well rooted and hardened off plants for lining out early the following spring, lifting them with the good ball that results from the peaty compost used in the frame. Strong growth is made during the summer, resulting in young trees 3–3½ ft (0.9–1 m) high. It is important that the soil should be fertile and in good heart. Top dress the trees with nitrogen e.g. 1½–2 oz per sq yd (50–66 g per sq m) calcium ammonium nitrate as they come into leaf. At the end of the year the stems are trimmed to form maidens. During the subsequent, i.e. the third growing season, side shoots are kept pinched at four or five leaves before final removal at the end of the year. Most cultivars can then be sold as half or full standards.

P. yedoensis is very satisfactory when used in this way, forming 8 ft (2.4 m) maidens two and a half years from the cutting, with four to five branches at 6 ft (1.8 m). At this stage it could be sold as a feathered maiden or grown on for a further year to form a standard tree, needing comparatively little training to make a good specimen. *P.* **Tai Haku** has been the next strongest, easily forming 6 ft (1.8 m) maiden stems. The familiar **Kanzan** runs to 4–5 ft 173

(1.2–1.5 m) under our conditions. In general, the other cultivars make 3–4 ft (0.9–1.2 m) of growth after two and a half years, sufficient for sale as half standards. **Kursar** is weaker and requires more time and care in the way of tying up and pinching to form a good specimen.

Where material is scarce single node cuttings of **Kanzan** (and no doubt other *P. serrulata* cultivars too) can be struck under mist in July. A few of the cuttings may make a little extension growth after rooting, but show no advantage over their fellows the following season, when whips up to 6 ft (2 m) can be trained up in a plastic house. Young lined out plants of *Prunus* are susceptible to simazine damage and should not be treated during their first season.

Method 3 Cultivars of *P. cerasifers* (e.g. **Pissardii**) can be rooted from stem cuttings 1 ft (30 cm) long, cut from strong smooth shoots of the past season's growth. These are taken in November, treated with 0.8% IBA powder and inserted half their length in an outdoor bed. They are lifted and lined out a year later for training as half or full standards.

Fig. 48. Five year old ornamental cherries raised from cuttings.

Method 4 *P. cerasifera* and its allies may also be propagated by stooling (p. 27).

Method 5 Budding is necessary for flowering peaches and almonds and is still the usual method for flowering cherries and plums. The technique is similar to that described for *Malus* (p. 158) and is a most successful method. Grafting is also carried out as described for *Malus* and, in addition, grafting by the whip and tongue method (p. 32) on to established stocks in the field in April is also practised. These are tied with raffia and waxed. Should a bush be required, then several developing buds can be encouraged and pinched at about 9 in. (22.5 cm) to encourage bushiness. Where half-standards or full standards are desired, the best developed bud is trained up and pinched at the necessary height. Autumn top working on trained up stocks is done by means of the whip and tongue method (p. 32) but is likely to lead to unsightly unions, except in the case of *P. subhirtella* **Autumnalis**, which is, indeed, better grafted owing to the abundance of flower buds on scion wood.

174

It is reported that the new rootstock **Colt** is superior to the older F 12/1 in imparting better girth and better flowering to the young trees.

Prunus (Evergreen)

Two evergreen species of *Prunus* are common in gardens, *P. lusitanicus*, the Portugal Laurel and *P. laurocerasus*, the Common Laurel. The latter has several cultivars, notably the low growing **Otto Luyken**.

Uses The Common Laurel has been much used for hedges and for 'Laurel lawns', i.e. trimmed to a uniform height to give a table-like effect, e.g. under trees bordering the entrance drives to large estates. Today the low growing and free flowering form **Otto Luyken** might be used to give a similar effect on a small scale and is a good ground cover plant. *P. lusitanicus* is also used as a hedging plant.

Methods of propagation 1. Cuttings in the cold frame in September. 2. Cuttings in the low tunnel in July–August. 3. Cuttings in mist in March.

Method 1 Basal cuttings about 4 in. (10 cm) long are treated with 0.8% IBA powder and inserted in the cold frame in September. No wounding is necessary. When lifted the following April, close on 100% rooting should have occurred. Line out in a prepared bed in the open, 8 in. (20 cm) apart. By autumn they should be about 7 in. (17.5 cm) high. Grow on for a further season to sell as plants about 8 in. (20 cm) high, 8 in. (20 cm) wide.

Method 2 Semi-hard cuttings about 3½ in. (8.7 cm) long will root 70–75% in the low tunnel, inserted in July–August and lifted the following autumn or spring. The use of 0.8% IBA powder gives a slight advantage in the number rooted. Lift and line out to grow on as above.

Method 3 Though mist is a relatively expensive system, it may be useful to propagate catch crops of *P. laurocerasus* cultivars during the February–March and August–September periods. Basal cuttings about 3½–4 in. (9–10 cm) long, wounded and treated with 0.8% IBA powder will root up to 100% in three weeks (spring) or six weeks (autumn). Harden off and line out in a prepared bed for growing on. By November (spring cuttings) or a year later (autumn cuttings) the plants will be 5 in. (12.5 cm) high. Grow on for a further year when they can be sold as plants about 8 in. (20 cm) high, 8 in. (20 cm) wide.

Pterocarya

Pterocaryas are large deciduous trees with handsome leaves like those of the Walnut. *P. x rehderana* is the finest and hardiest, with striking catkins 1 ft (30 cm) long, hanging on the tree all summer. The tree suckers freely at the base and these shoots may be taken as softwood cuttings with a heel in July when they are about 6 in. (15 cm) long. If treated with 0.2% IBA powder and put under mist, they root in about a month. Harden off and plant out in a cold frame. The following spring lift and line out in good soil in not too dry a place. Subsequent growth is vigorous.

175

Pyracantha

The firethorns (*Pyracantha*) comprise some half-dozen species of which *P. atalantioides*, *P. coccinea*, *P. rogersiana*, *P. crenatoserrata* (*P. yunnanensis*), their cultivars and hybrids are the most frequently seen.

Uses Mainly grown as wall shrubs as they are tolerant even of a north aspect and any soil but can be grown as bushes. Their main feature is their red, orange or yellow berries. Those of *P. atalantioides* ripen late and last into spring. For the maximum show of berries on wall trained specimens cut back all surplus shoots immediately after flowering.

Method of propagation Cuttings under mist in September. Though cuttings of *Pyracantha* can be rooted at any time from May to September, the latter

Fig. 49. Bigger plants of *Pyracantha* result from large late cuttings.

date is advantageous. In contrast to some other trees and shrubs, e.g. *Prunus incisa*, the growth of early struck cuttings does not catch up on that of larger cuttings taken later in the year. Moreover, plants grown from the latter flower in the spring following, so that berried specimens can be sold one year after inserting the cutting. Semi-hard, heeled, branched cuttings 1 ft (30 cm) long, wounded and treated with 0.8% IBA powder are inserted in two parts moss peat to one of sand under mist in September. Although the base of the cutting appears unpromisingly hard at this time, 70–80% of the cuttings should be rooted in three to four weeks. Pot up in 4½–5 in. pots, hold through the winter in a cold house or frame. In spring, place on a capillary bed out of doors and sell as berried plants in autumn.

Cuttings may also be propagated in the white polythene tunnel in September–November (see p. 19).

Quercus

From the horticultural point of view the important oaks are *Quercus coccinea* (the Scarlet Oak), *Q. rubra* (the Red Oak) from North America and *Quercus ilex* (Evergreen Oak) from the Mediterranean region.

Uses As specimen trees, the two deciduous species named above for autumn colour. *Q. ilex* grows well near the sea and is sometimes used for hedging. The American species prefer acid soils and should not be planted on shallow soils over chalk.

Method of propagation Seed. When collecting acorns there is much scope for selecting the mother trees. *Q. ilex*, in particular, varies much in vegetative and fruiting characters. Choose fruitful trees with large acorns. The ripening season is generally from early October to the end of November. The first acorns to fall are often poor and undeveloped. Watch that the crop is not lost, as acorns are eaten freely by pigeons, pheasants and squirrels.

Acorns should never be allowed to dry out. Small quantities may be sown immediately in boxes and kept slightly moist in a cool place until germination. Seeds of some American species send out a root in autumn, though the shoot does not appear until spring. Alternatively, they may be stored in polythene bags of slightly moist peat, hung in a cool place until spring. Beware of too much moisture or of any tendency of the seed to heat. Sow in prepared beds (p. 24) in lines about 3 in. (7.5 cm) apart and cover to a depth of 2 in. (5 cm). Simazine is a good means of weed control since the seeds are sown deeply.

Seedlings raised in boxes may be carefully lined out in frames when the second leaf has developed. Those sown in beds are lifted in early spring (before mid April) and lined out 2 in. (5 cm) in lines 10 in. (25 cm) apart. Oak seedlings should be transplanted regularly (every two years). *Q. ilex* should be only moved when growth is about to start (late May) or in September.

Rhododendron (large flowered hybrids)

The undoubted charm of these beautiful free-flowering plants make them amongst the most attractive of decorative subjects. They vary in vigour and period of flowering and their colours range from white (**Gomer Waterer**) through pink (**Pink Pearl**), red (**Cynthia**) to scarlet (**Britannia**).

Uses Specimen bushes may be planted, even in small gardens. In larger gardens they are unrivalled for mass planting. These plants maintain their attractiveness during the winter months with their glossy leaves and prominent flower buds.

Almost all rhododendrons need an acid loam or peaty soil.

Methods of propagation 1. Grafting through the winter months. 2. Cuttings in mist or warm bench and plastic in October.

Method 1 The rootstock used is *R. ponticum*, which is suitable for use when about pencil-thickness. The stocks are lifted from their growing place in November and brought into a glasshouse to be plunged in warm beds of temperatures around 60°F (15.6°C) so that new roots can develop. This happens after a few weeks and grafting can then commence. The cleft (p. 33) or the side graft method on a foot (p. 32) can be used and the scion material are those shoots which develop on the mother cultivars after the pinching of shoots in mid-June. The grafts are tied and returned to the grafting case which is covered with glass. The peat in the case should be fairly damp and the leaves of the grafts should come against the glass of the case. Since the plants make 177

Fig. 50. Removal of part of the leaves of *Rhododendron* has no effect on rooting.

such a good rootball in peaty soil, potting is not really necessary. During the first few days the temperature of the bed should be kept at around 60°F (15.6°C) and thereafter raised a few degrees with ventilation about twice per week. After about seven weeks the callus will be well formed and hardening off can start by means of more ventilation and by the reduction of the basal heat. The plants can then be placed on a bench with basal heat of about 55-60°F (13-16°C) and the growing points of any shoots pinched. In suitable weather in April–May, plant out for growing on in acid soil, in a well sheltered situation.

By starting the grafting of Rhododendrons in December, about four batches can be completed before the end of April.

Method 2 Thin semi-hardwood cuttings taken from the more shaded part of the plant are the most suitable as propagation material. The cuttings are nodal, about 4 in. (10 cm) long. The terminal growing point is removed and the number of leaves reduced to four or five. With some large-leaved cultivars it is necessary to reduce the leaf size and this is done by cleanly cutting away half of the leaf with a sharp knife. A sliver of bark is then removed from the basal inch (2.5 cm) of each side of the cutting, after which it is treated with 0.8% IBA powder. Insert the cuttings loosely in damp moss peat or two parts moss peat to one part non-calcareous sand and place under mist, or cover with a layer of thin polythene. Base temperatures should be kept at around 70°F (21°C). Ventilate each fortnight and remove any plant debris. After ten weeks heavy rooting (80%) will take place in such cultivars as **Pink Pearl, Hugo Koster, Gomer Waterer, Blue Peter, Purple Splendour, Cynthia** and **Professor Zaayer**.

A longer undisturbed period in the propagating bench (three to four months) will ensure rooting of up to 60% for the difficult-to-root cultivar **Britannia**.

After rooting, the plants are potted in 4 in. pots in a medium of peat only and left back on the propagation bench to establish. Liquid feeding with a

178

Fig. 51. *Rhododendron* **Pink Pearl** 15 months from a cutting.

Fig. 52. *R.* **Britannia**, less easy to root, needs more time in the propagating bench.

dilute (0.5%) solution of a compound feed should start after one week and thereafter each fortnight as a drench. In May the plants can be knocked from their pots and planted out in frames for growing on after first being pinched in order to produce basal breaks.

In autumn the plants are lifted from the frames and lined out in the nursery for growing on for one to two seasons more.

Rhododendron (Dwarf)

Since the beginning of the century large numbers of dwarf rhododendron species have been introduced from the mountains of western China and neighbouring regions. More recently hybrids from these species have been raised by plant breeders.

Uses The dwarf rhododendrons associate well with heathers and dwarf conifers. Like them, the rhododendrons should be planted in the mass or at least in groups, though single specimens have their place on the rock garden so long as it is not too dry.

179

Methods of propagation 1. Cuttings in the warm bench with plastic in
February. 2. Seed.

Method 1 These plants are normally rooted from cuttings of the current
season's growth, taken in June or July. Our investigations are based on the
system of production suggested for ericas (p. 126). Single shoot basal or nodal
hardwood cuttings are taken in February and the flower buds are removed.
In many cases this may not be practicable in view of their small size, so a
special watch is kept for botrytis in the propagation bench.

The cuttings are lightly wounded and treated with 0.8% IBA powder. They
are placed in moist peat in the warm bench with plastic and the base temperature is maintained at around 70°F (21°C). After eight to ten weeks, there
will be high rooting percentages (60–80%) in most types. The plants are
hardened off and planted into a frame with moss peat 5–6 in. (12.5–15 cm)
deep and liquid fed with 0.5% solution 9:7:7 feed, applied as a drench. The
frame lights are placed in position and shaded and the liquid feeding is
repeated each fortnight. When the plants are well established and growing
away, the lights should be removed gradually and the frames shaded with
laths. At the end of the first season, good liners will be produced (Figs. 53–4)
and, in fact, many species will have formed flower buds. These should be
removed and the plants lined out for one further season's growth when they
can be sold.

The following species and cultivars have responded well to this new tech-
ique: *R.* **Blue Tit**, *R. moupinense*, *R. hippophaeoides*, *R. leucaspis*, *R.*

Fig. 53. *R. leucaspis*.

180   Figs. 53 & 54. Dwarf rhododendrons can also be raised quickly from Jan./Feb. cuttings.

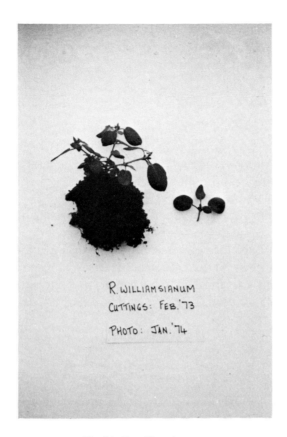

Fig. 54. *R. williamsianum*.

pemakoense, *R. desypetalum*, *R. williamsianum*, *R. impeditum*, *R. yakusimanum*, *R.* **Baden-Baden**, and *R.* **Bountiful**. No doubt many other species and cultivars will prove responsive to this new system.

Method 2 Rhododendron (species only) may be raised from seed sown under glass in February. As the seedlings are sensitive to over-fertilisation, a modified seed compost such as equal parts of moss peat and sand and sifted leaf mould is advisable. Indeed this sensitivity to too rich a compost applies to rhododendrons at all stages of their life. Prick off into a similar compost as soon as the seedlings are large enough to handle. When well established after pricking off, judicious liquid feeding can start, as advised for rooted cuttings. The young seedlings, after hardening off, are grown on in a cold frame, with well shaded lights and care in irrigation with lime-free water.

Rhodotypos

Rhodotypos scandens (*kerrioides*) is a deciduous white-flowered shrub allied to *Kerria*. It will reach 6 ft (1.8 m) and is useful for shrubberies in any ordinary soil.

Methods of propagation 1. Cuttings in the low tunnel or in the cold frame with plastic in June–July. 2. Cuttings in the cold frame in October.

Method 1 Use semi-hardwood basal or nodal cuttings about 4 in. (10 cm) long. No rooting powder is needed. Line out in autumn or spring for growing on. 181

Method 2 Heel cuttings of the current season's growth 6 in. (15 cm) long are inserted in two parts moss peat to one of sand. Treatment with rooting powder is not needed. Line out in spring for growing on.

Rhus

Now that the Venetian Sumach or Smoke Tree has been transferred to a separate genus (*Cotinus*), the remaining species in general cultivation is *Rhus typhina*, the Stag's Horn Sumach, a small tree or leggy shrub grown for the autumn colour of its pinnate leaves.

On a small scale propagation can be carried out by transplanting the suckers that often appear round the parent bush. Otherwise root cuttings can be taken in December, sectioned into pieces 1½ in. (3.7 cm) long and potted vertically in 3 in. pots under glass. Shoot emergence starts in February and by May they should be sufficiently established to harden off and line out in an outdoor bed for growing on. By autumn the plants will be 1–2 ft (30–60 cm) high and can be sold as small specimens.

Ribes

The most important flowering currant in the garden is *Ribes sanguineum* and its cultivars. *R. laurifolium* is an evergreen species that might be better known for its greenish-yellow flowers in winter. *R. odoratum* (*R. aureum*), though not very showy, has attractive yellow flowers in spring.

Uses For planting as specimens or in groups in gardens and parks.

Methods of propagation 1. Cuttings under the low tunnel or in the cold frame with plastic in June. 2. Cuttings in the open in October.

Method 1 Nodal cuttings of the current year's growth about three nodes long are treated with 0.8% IBA powder before insertion. About 95% of the cuttings root and when they are lifted at the end of the season they will be about 16 in. (40 cm) high, with four to six branches. Line out and grow on a further season; bushes will then be 4 ft (1.2 m) high with seven or eight shoots.

Method 2 Nodal hardwood cuttings are inserted in the open ground after treatment with 0.8% IBA powder. Line out in spring and grow on for two seasons, cutting back at the beginning of the second season to induce extra branching.

Robinia

Robinia pseudoacacia, the False Acacia, is a deciduous tree with spiny shoots. It is appreciated, especially on the Continent, for planting on well drained soils, and in industrial areas. The type may be raised from seed. To increase germination, scarification of the hard seed coat is recommended by many authorities. Machines have been devised for large scale operations.

Cultivars, if on their own roots, may be propagated by root cuttings; otherwise they are bench grafted onto seedlings of the type in January. Heel in the seedlings until required. After side grafting, heel the grafts in a bench of moist peat in a cold greenhouse. Improved results have been reported where the grafts, tied in bundles with damp moss around the roots and placed in open polythene bags, were given warm treatment (65–70°F or 18.3–21.1°C) for a few days to hasten callusing. The plants are then heeled in on the bench of peat. Line out in April.

Romneya

Romneya coulteri and *R. trichocalyx* are sub-shrubby, grey-leaved species of suckering habit and impressive, large, white, poppy-like flowers. They grow best in a warm sunny spot. Propagation is by root cuttings. Lift young mother plants in December, cut the roots into 1 in. (2.5 cm) lengths and pot in 3 in. pots, using sandy peat, laying the pieces horizontally. Stand the pots in a warm house, keeping them moist but avoiding overwatering. Shoots should appear in February but do not disturb the cuttings since roots may not form for a further period and, until then, the shoots may remain stunted or even wither. By May growth should be vigorous and the young plants may be potted on, hardened off and plunged outside for sale in autumn, as plants 1–2 ft (30–60 cm) high, many in flower.

Rosa

The enormous popularity of this genus of plants and the great diversity of its members does not require further elaboration in this book. Its versatility in a very great range of soils, its differing forms and multitudinous cultivars have established the rose as the almost inevitable choice for a great number of gardeners. Whether floribunda, hybrid tea, standard, climber, shrub or miniature, the rose will thrive in a sunny position in most soils and, where well maintained, will always be noted for the magnificence of its flower and its handsome foliage.

Uses The hybrid teas and floribundas are mainly used for formal bedding where the inclusion of standards will add to the interest by form or colour contrast. They may also be used with less effect as individual specimens, but for this role, the species roses and miniatures are more suitable. When supported against walls, or used on pergolas, the climbing roses display their attributes. More than any other, the climbers need constant attention to training and pruning so that their flowers will be produced as equally as possible along the length of their stems.

Methods of propagation 1. Seed (for species). 2. Budding. 3. Cuttings in the open ground in October. 4. Grafting (for miniatures).

Method 1 The production of rose species from seed is described first because, as is commonly known, there are a few species produced from seed for ornamental purposes, but the majority are for use as rootstocks on to which the modern rose hybrids are budded (see below). The species normally used for this purpose are *R. canina*, *R. dumetorum (laxa)* and *R. multiflora*. In each 183 case stratification of the seed is carried out. *R. canina* will germinate in the region of 30% in the first spring after harvesting at the beginning of October if one part of seed to two of moist sand are mixed and kept at a temperature of 70°F (21.1°C) for three months and thereafter kept at 32°F (0°C) for a further three months. *R. dumetorum (laxa)* harvested when ripe (orange/red stage) is similarly mixed and kept moist for two winters before germination will take place. The volume of seed and sand is turned once monthly and premature sprouting near the end of the second winter's stratification can be prevented by keeping the mass cool at 32°F (0°C) until sowing. *R. multiflora*, harvested at the beginning of October, should be mixed with fine sand and stratified in an outdoor pit for six weeks. If germination is proceeding while conditions are unsuitable for sowing outside, the process may be held back by keeping the seed cool at slightly above 32°F (0°C) until the soil conditions improve.

Seed is sown in beds 36 in. (90 cm) wide, five rows per bed. *R. multiflora* sowing rates are 30 lb per acre (33.6 kg per hectare), and *R. canina* and *R. dumetorum (laxa)* both at 50 lb per acre (56 kg per hectare). As straight, long root collars are required, a free draining sandy loam is best, high in humus and with a pH of 5.5 to 6.5. Both before and after germination attention to weed control is essential. During the growing season, a careful watch should be kept for mildew developing on the young stocks. Measures to control this include fortnightly sprays of preparations based on benomyl. Another disease which needs attention is rose blackspot for which the stocks should be treated with maneb.

The number of rootstocks produced at the recommended sowing rates will depend on the germination rate, which in turn will affect the ultimate size of each stock. Naturally, if germination is high, the mutual competition of the stocks will reduce the overall size of each. Thus, sowing rates need to be strictly adhered to and experience must be developed with seed stratification so that there is no great fluctuation in the overall stand of stocks produced by the end of the growing season.

Harvesting of rootstocks takes place in October/November and the lifting operation is made easier by a prior mechanical under-cutting of the plants. After lifting, the stocks should be graded into the four commercially acceptable sizes, i.e. 3–5 mm, 4–6 mm, 5–8 mm and 8–12 mm stem diameters. This is recommended because, apart altogether from the necessity to market in these grades, it is also convenient for the grower (should he be planting his own rootstocks) to have uniformity of growth in the plantation during budding.

Ornamental rose species may be raised from seed. The parent bushes should be isolated at least from others of similar characteristics to reduce the chances of hybridisation. The hips should be gathered as soon as they show colour and not left to get over ripe. This will reduce the chances of dormancy arising from the influence of chemical substances (e.g. abcissic acid) in the hip. The number of seeds per hip varies widely according to the species. *R. rugosa*, for example, can have as many as 60 seeds per hip but the small hips of *R. multibracteata* contain only one or two seeds. If possible, clean the hips from the flesh before sowing; otherwise crush up the hips with sand. Small quantities can be sown in pots or trays and left in a cold frame to be brought into heat at the initiation of germination. With many species, e.g. *R. moyesii, R. primula*, at least some germination occurs the first spring. Prick off these seedlings at the second rough leaf stage and return the trays to the cold frame to obtain a second flush a year later, if enough did not come up in the first spring. Other species need exposure to two winters before germination. The

Fig. 55. *Rosa primula* 2 ft 8 in. (80 cm) within one year from seed.

seedlings may be grown on under glass until May and then transferred to a plastic house. Some species respond markedly to this treatment, e.g. by late summer *R. setipoda* will be about 2 ft (60 cm) and *R. webbiana* about 2½ ft (75 cm). These can then be transferred to an outdoor bed to slow down and harden off before being sold in autumn. Slower species can be lined out in autumn to be grown on for a further season. This luxury treatment is of interest where it is desired to raise rose species in small quantities. For large scale operations, follow the procedure outlined above for the raising of rootstocks.

Method 2 To prepare for budding, the rootstocks are planted into good rich soil in February or March. If the soil is not fertile and little growth is expected, or in the case of a short growing season, the 5–8 mm rootstock is planted. Where the land is good and the growing season is long, the 3–5 mm and 4–6 mm stocks will make the necessary progress to enable the budding operation to take place with facility. The 8–12 mm stock is rarely used on a field scale, being kept for grafting under glass. Stocks are planted 6 in. (15 cm) apart and 3 ft (90 cm) between rows. It is usual to plant the stocks 'high' so that their root collars are clear of the ground. This will facilitate budding later in the season. Budding can start as soon as the sap is flowing in the rose stock, usually coinciding with the going-over of the first flush of flowers in the cultivars to be budded. The root collar is cleaned of any obstruction so that it is showing clearly above the ground. Budding is then carried out (p. 34) using budwood collected early in the day and kept damp whilst not being used. A T-cut is made in the centre of the root collar about 1 in. (2.5 cm) above the 185 roots. The bark is prised back with the back of the special budding knife used and the bud is now cut from the bud stick and swiftly placed in position. The overlapping top of the bud is trimmed and the entire area of the bud is covered by firmly stretching a rubber tie over it.

The bud will rapidly unite with the stock and the ties will fall off in due course. In the following February, the rootstocks are cut away about 1 in. (2.5 cm) above the bud. Frequently, the bud will have made some growth and this can also be trimmed back to about 1 in. (2.5 cm). Normal good cultural care will ensure a high proportion of first and second grade bushes in the following October. The bushes can be lifted and sold at any time from the beginning of November to the following early spring.

In the case of standard roses, the rootstock used is *R. rugosa*, produced as described in Method 3 below. Rather than one bud, it is usual to place two or three buds in the stem at the required height. Should a full standard rose be required, budding is carried out at 3½ ft (1.1 m), for a half-standard a foot lower, and for weeping standards 1½ ft higher. When buds shoot in the following spring it is recommended that they be cut back to produce a bushy head and also to ensure that physical rupture of the bud and stem by blowing out is obviated.

Method 3 The majority of hybrid tea and shrub species, can be rooted from cuttings. The method is also used for producing the stock used for standard roses — *R. rugosa*. Excepting the latter, it is extremely doubtful, however, that producing rose bushes from cuttings constitutes an economic proposition where any real numbers are contemplated. Although some shrub and miniature roses will root easily as softwood basal cuttings taken in June/July and placed under mist, the best method for rooting is from hardwood cuttings. Strong 9–12 in. (22.5–30 cm) cuttings uniformly of pencil thickness taken from the central portion of the stems are cut in October. They are heavily wounded and treated with 0.8% IBA powder. The cuttings are tied in bundles of 25 and firmly heeled in to two-thirds their length in a free draining sandy compost. Precautions against drying out must be taken. In mid March the cuttings are lifted and those that are callused are planted out directly into nursery lines and the remainder discarded. Root initials will have formed by this stage and growth will be uniform. These will remain *in situ* until the following autumn, when they are lifted and transferred to their final quarters.

In the case of *R. rugosa*, the cuttings are prepared as above and all buds, except the two uppermost, are removed. After callusing in March, they are lined out 6 in. apart (15 cm). The shoots are pruned back to ground level in the following spring and the most vigorous one emerging will be selected for training up an 8 ft (2.4 m) bamboo cane from ground level. During that growing season all side shoots are removed as tying-in proceeds. Under good conditions of growth, and with provision of irrigation, stems of up to 7 ft (2.1 m) can be produced after two years from when the cutting was taken.

Miniature roses can be produced from softwood cuttings in March/April forced from the previous season's stems and placed under mist in a medium of two parts moss peat to one of sand. A 0.8% IBA powder is a spur to rooting, which takes place in one month or less. Potting up follows and, when the plants have become established in warm conditions, they are transferred outside to grow on for that season, being potted on when necessary. Pinching shoots will promote bushiness and shape in the plants. They can be sold in the autumn of the first season or given a second season to produce a bush of some size.

Method 4 Grafting of miniatures is commonly practised. The mother plants are cut back hard in December and are potted and brought into a warm glasshouse — 68°F (20°C) — for forcing of the shoots to produce scionwood. Suitable stocks are heeled-in in a cold frame in November and as soon as the scionwood is ready (January), i.e. firm with a developed bud at the top of each shoot, grafting can start. The stock is cut back to about 1 in. (2.5 cm) from the roots and a vertical cut is made through the bark from its top towards the roots. A bud similar to a chip bud (p. 35) is taken from the scionwood and slid down the vertical cut of the stock inside the bark. The graft is tied and placed in a closed case with a bottom temperature of 75°F (23.9°C). In these humid conditions, precautions against fungus must be taken and it is advisable to syringe the plants with a fungicidal solution every second day. Uniting the scionwood and stock will be complete in ten days and gradual hardening off can begin by reducing the bottom temperature and increasing air to the case. The grafts can then be potted up and after establishment are grown on outdoors from May. Sell in November.

Rosmarinus

The well-known Rosemary (*Rosmarinus officinalis*) has a number of cultivars, some with especially deep blue flowers such as **Severn Sea**. The Prostrate Rosemary (*R. lavandulaceus*) is now regarded as a separate species.

Uses Appreciated for its aromatic foliage. Cultivation in any well drained sunny spot offers no difficulties, though the prostrate species is tender and has the best chance of survival if planted in the tops of banks and walls for good drainage.

Methods of propagation 1. Cuttings under the low tunnel or in the cold frame with plastic in July–August. 2. Cuttings in the cold frame in September–October.
   While cuttings strike at most times of the year, the above are two convenient methods.

Method 1 Softwood basal cuttings of the current season's growth about 3 in. (7.5 cm) long are inserted. Up to 100% will have rooted seven weeks later. Treatment with IBA powder has not been observed to be of advantage. The rooted cuttings can be lined out in prepared beds in a well-drained situation in autumn or spring for sale the following autumn. Of the two methods, the low tunnel has given better results in numbers rooted.

Method 2 Semi-hardwood basal cuttings of the current season's growth about 5 in. (12.5 cm) long are inserted in the cold frame. Lift and line out in spring for sale in autumn.

Ruscus

Ruscus aculeatus, the Butcher's Broom, is a low prickly sub-shrub, usually about 2½ ft (75 cm) high. It is useful for growing in shady places. Usually the male and female plants are separate. Every endeavour should be made to 187 obtain the hermaphrodite form so as to be sure of a good show of the scarlet berries in winter. This can be propagated by division in spring to ensure perpetuation of the true plant.

For *Ruscus racemosus* see under **Danae**.

Ruta

Ruta graveolens is a pungent leaved small shrub with glaucous foliage. A superior form is **Jackman's Blue** with glaucous-blue foliage for a sunny spot in the front of the shrub border.

Propagation is easily effected from cuttings in the cold frame in September–October, for lining out in spring.

Salix

The willows comprise a very large genus complicated for botanists by the freedom with which the species hybridise. Apart from the dwarf species for the rock garden those generally listed include *Salix alba* **Tristis**, *S. a.* **Vitellina**, *S. purpurea* **Pendula**, *S. pentandra*, *S. matsudana* **Tortuosa** and *S. daphnoides*.

Uses S. alba **Tristis** as a weeping tree where there is plenty of space on a lawn or near the water side. Weeping willows for smaller spaces are *S. purpurea* **Pendula** and *S. caprea* **Pendula**. For colour of the young shoots, plant *S. alba* **Vitellina** (yellow), *S. a.* **Britzensis** (scarlet) and *S. daphnoides* (purple). Those good for catkins include *S. aegyptiaca*, *S. daphnoides* **Agelia**, the native *S. caprea*, *S. gracilistyla* and for large gardens, *S. x smithiana*. *S. bockii* flowers in the late summer and autumn. *S. fargesii* is distinct in its large magnolia-like foliage..

Methods of propagation 1. Cuttings in the open ground in November–March. 2. Grafting.

Method 1 Willows are well known for the ease with which most of them strike from leafless cuttings even of material several years old. The tree sorts may be struck from lengths as much as 8 to 12 ft (2.4–3.6 m) long. Those grown for the beauty of the bark of the young shoots may be rooted from 1 ft (30 cm) long cuttings and the resultant bush may be cut hard every second spring to form a stool, often a convenient way of growing these willows within a limited space. *S. fargesii* however is best propagated from softwood cuttings, easily rooted during early June and can make 30 cm high by late autumn. Hardwood cuttings are slow to develop.

Method 2 Though grafting is frowned on by some authorities, *S. x smithiana* is used on the Continent for producing attractive small trees of the weeping *S. caprea* **Pendula** by top working. To keep such trees in good condition it is advisable to prune the branches hard back immediately after flowering. *S. aegyptiaca*, raised from soft or hardwood cuttings, has proved a satisfactory

understock under our conditions.

Salvia

In addition to the culinary Sage (*Salvia officinalis*), there are a number of tender shrubby species of which the red flowered *S. grahamii*, *S. neurepia* and *S. greggii* are occasionally seen in gardens in mild districts. They strike readily from cuttings. Perhaps the most convenient time and method is in October, when semi-hard basal cuttings of the current season can be inserted in the cold frame both to propagate and as an insurance against loss of the parent bushes during winter. Alternatively, semi-hard basal cuttings of the current year's growth, about 4 in. (10 cm) long may be inserted under mist in June. Treat with 0.8% IBA powder. These cuttings root quickly, upwards of 90% being ready to pot up in 3 in. pots in July. If they are grown on under glass or plastic, they will be 1 ft (30 cm) high by mid-August, with flowers. They could be sold at this stage as small plants for growing on or potted on into 4 in. pots to be overwintered and sold in spring.

Sambucus

The elders are not important as garden shrubs, though the variegated and fern-leaved forms of our native *Sambucus nigra* are interesting and quite attractive. They are readily propagated from hardwood cuttings of the past season's growth inserted in the open ground in January–February, taken with a heel to avoid exposing the pith. *S. racemosa* 'Plumosa Aurea' has ornamental ferny golden foliage.

Santolina

The Lavender Cottons are well known dwarf sub-shrubs grown mainly for their aromatic white foliage, though the yellow button-like flowers make quite a display in July. *Santolina chamaecyparissus* and *S. neapolitana* are allied species. There is a dwarf variety of the former. *S. virens* has green foliage.

Uses The white-leaved species make attractive mounds of white foliage in the front of the shrubbery in sunny aspects. They may be planted in groups for ground cover. Keep in good condition by trimming back after flowering. Occasionally a severe cutting back is needed if the bush becomes straggly.

Method of propagation Cuttings root readily at most times. A convenient method is to insert semi-hardwood cuttings in the cold frame in September and lift and line out in April.

Sarcococca

Sarcococcas are low growing evergreen shrubs with inconspicuous but very sweet scented white flowers in late winter. The flowers are followed by black berries in *S. hookerana* or red in *S. ruscifolia*.

Uses Valued as low-growing evergreens with glossy foliage which will thrive even in shade, and scent the air on the occasional warmer days of late winter or early spring.

Methods of propagation 1. Division. 2. Cuttings in April in mist. 3. Cuttings in cold frame in October.

Method 1 As the Sarcococcas spread freely by suckers, established clumps may be lifted and divided in early spring.

Method 2 Semi-hardwood basal cuttings 3–4 in. (7.5–10 cm) long, not wounded but treated with 0.8% IBA powder in a medium of moss peat or two parts moss peat to one of sand will root 100% in three weeks in the mist unit. Harden off and line out in a frame or well prepared shaded bed with peat incorporated and grow on for two to three years.

Method 3 Basal cuttings of the past season's growth about 3–4 in. (7.5–10 cm) long, treated as above, inserted in October will have rooted 75–80% when lifted the following May. Line out for two to three years in a well-prepared outdoor bed with peat incorporated.

Sasa

See under **Bamboo**.

Senecio

This genus, which includes our native Groundsel, has a number of shrubby species from New Zealand which are of value in the garden. These include *Senecio greyi*, *S. rotundifolius* and *S. compactus*.

Uses *S. greyi* is grown as a specimen shrub, the grey leaves being attractive at all seasons. In summer the bright yellow flowers are so profuse as to cover the bushes. *S. compactus* and *S. monroi* are similar but smaller and with wavy edged leaves. These are grown as specimens in full sun. *S. rotundifolius* has no beauty of flower but is outstanding for its resistance to seaside gales. The 4 ft (1.2 m) bush carries rounded leaves of thick leathery texture.

Methods of propagation The shrubby senecios are so easy to root that the method to use is largely a matter of convenience. The examples given below are some of the alternatives.
  1. Cuttings in the cold frame in September–October.
  2. Cuttings in the low tunnel in June–August.
  3. Cuttings in the cold frame and plastic in June–August.
  4. Cuttings in the mist or warm bench and plastic April–June.

Method 1 Basal or nodal cuttings, treated with 0.8% IBA powder, are inserted in a cold frame containing a compost of two parts moss peat to one of sand. By the following April 100% rooting can be expected and the rooted cuttings lined out for sale the following autumn.

Methods 2 and 3 Basal or nodal cuttings can be inserted in either the low tunnel or cold frame and plastic during the period June to August. Treatment with rooting powder is not necessary. By autumn 70–90% rooting can be expected. If the plants are lined out, then or during spring, good bushy plants will be ready for sale by the following autumn. *S. greyi* should be 1 ft wide by 1½ ft high (30 × 45 cm), *S. compactus* 9 in. wide by 6 in. high (22.5 × 15 cm).

Method 4 While these are relatively expensive ways of propagating such easy subjects, it may be useful to know that a catch crop can be put in at almost any time, using a compost of two parts moss peat to one of sand. Up to 95% rooting can be expected after seven weeks.

Sequoiadendron

S. giganteum is the 'Big-Tree' of California, formerly known as *Wellingtonia*. It is readily raised from seed and, though perfectly hardy, develops rapidly if kept under cover. For example, seedlings raised from seed sown in March and kept in a cold house were 9½ in. (24 cm) high by the end of the year and attained 26 in. (67 cm) after a further season in a plastic house.

Skimmia

The Skimmias are low-growing evergreen shrubs up to 4 ft (1.2 m) high, grown for the fragrance of their flowers and the long lasting scarlet berries. Various male and female clones of *S. japonica* have been given cultivar names (**Foremanni, Fragrans, Rogersii**, etc.). It is necessary to plant both sexes to ensure fruit. *S. reevesiana* is hermaphrodite but, unfortunately, does not thrive on alkaline soils.

Uses Valuable as dwarf shrubs for shady situations.

Methods of propagation 1. Cuttings in the cold frame with plastic in June. 2. Cuttings in mist in July. 3. Cuttings in the cold frame in September. 4. Seed.

Method 1 The apical portions of the shoots, cut at the first node, will root 60–70% in seven weeks if inserted in the cold frame and plastic in June. Treatment with IBA powder has not been advantageous. Line out and grow on for two to three seasons.

Method 2 Similar cuttings inserted under mist in July will root up to 100% in four weeks. Harden off and line out to grow on for two to three seasons.

Method 3 Basal cuttings of the past season's growth, not wounded but treated with 0.8% IBA powder will root up to 100% after insertion in the cold frame in September. Lift and line out in April for two or three seasons.

Method 4 Skimmias may be raised from seed, though cultivars will not come true, and the sex of the seedlings cannot be determined until they flower. Development is rather slow. Home saved seed sown under glass in February germinates about 70% after five to six weeks and, even if grown under cover, will be only about 3 in. (7.5 cm) at the end of their first year.

191

Solanum

In addition to the potato this genus includes a number of climbing shrubs, notably *Solanum crispum*, with its purple-blue flowers in late summer. It needs to be planted against a sunny wall and may ramble over a low building. The pale blue *S. jasminoides* will only thrive in the mildest areas.

Basal cuttings of current year's shoots, treated with 0.8% IBA powder, may be rooted under mist in July, but need to be removed promptly once rooted, as they are intolerant of wet conditions. Upwards of 60% rooting may be expected after seven weeks. Pot up the rooted cuttings, stake the young shoots and sell as small plants in autumn. Otherwise cut back the shoots in spring, containerise and sell in summer and autumn.

Sollya

The Australian Bluebell Creeper (*Sollya heterophylla*) is only hardy on walls in very mild localities, which is a pity, as it seldom reaches more than 3 ft (0.9 m) out of doors, is easily accommodated on a low wall and flowers over a long season. The blooms are bell-shaped, blue in colour. It is a twining plant that can clamber up a piece of wire netting. *S. parviflora* is similar with smaller leaves and flowers.

Method of propagation As *Sollya* is tender, it is a wise precaution to strike a few cuttings for overwintering under glass. Softwood nodal cuttings about 4 in. (10 cm) long can be struck under mist in October. After seven weeks 60% strike may be expected. Pot up in 3 in. pots. If a warm house is available, the plants will be 18 in. (45 cm) high by March. They can be hardened off and planted out as soon as danger of hard frost is over. Seed may also be sown under glass in February. Germination occurs in 14–20 days. Prick off into 3 in. pots in April and pot on into 4 in. pots in early June. If at this stage they are placed on a capillary bed in a plastic house, they will be 2 ft (60 cm) high by autumn. Stake as the plants develop and sell as container grown plants in autumn or spring.

Sophora

Sophora tetraptera is a large shrub or small tree with elegant pinnate leaves and showy yellow, pea-shaped flowers in clusters in May.

Uses As a specimen shrub or small tree in the milder parts of the country. Plant in a sunny position.

Method of propagation Sophora is best from seed. The curious winged and jointed pods are usually freely produced from which the seeds may be shelled out in autumn and stored in ordinary room conditions until sown in spring. If they are sown under glass in February, germination will be 50–60% after 15–20 days. It is stated that imported seed should be soaked in hot water for two hours before sowing. Prick off at the second rough leaf stage, about 15 days later, into 3 in. pots. By June the plants will be large enough to pot on into

6 in. plastic bags. They may be grown on in a plastic house on a capillary bed and sold in autumn as freely branched plants 12–15 in. (30–37.5 cm) high.

Dwarf forms are available and can be raised from seed.

Sorbus

The genus Sorbus can be divided into two main groups (a) the mountain ashes with pinnate leaves, e.g. our native *S. aucuparia* and (b) the whitebeams with simple or lobed leaves (*S. aria*, *S. intermedia*, etc.).

These are some of the most valuable of our smaller trees for decorative purposes. Many attractive Asiatic species and hybrids are available and are becoming more appreciated.

Uses As specimen trees in gardens, parks and on roadsides for the white foliage in spring of the whitebeams and the red, pink, yellow or white berries and autumn foliage of the mountain ashes.

Methods of propagation 1. Budding. 2. Grafting. 3. Seed.

Method 1 Central buds from well developed bud sticks are taken in July. These are budded as near the ground as possible onto stocks of *S. aria* for whitebeams or *S. aucuparia* for mountain ashes, field lined from the previous autumn. The system employed can be either T-bud or chip bud (p. 34). Sell after one season as a whip or grow on at greater spacing until a good standard develops, usually three and a half years from budding. It should be noted that *S. intermedia* is incompatible with the *aria* type cultivars **Wilfred Fox** and **Mitchellii**. This was confirmed in a trial where all 25 buds of these failed, though the two aucuparia types tried at the same time, **Sheerwater Seedling** and *S. arnoldiana* **Shoutan**, succeeded.

Method 2 Bench grafting (p. 30) using the whip method is carried out in February, using stocks and scions of pencil thickness. Bind, wax and heel in a covered cold frame or in a shed in moss peat. As growth starts, line out and, should standards or half standards be the aim, select the best shoot and cut away the remainder of the few buds which will develop from the scion. Sell as whips or grow on as above.

Method 3 Raising from seed is complicated by the problem of dormancy (p. 22) and as this problem may vary in intensity with the source of the seed and particularly with its treatment, this is an added inducement for the nurseryman to have his own mother trees, perhaps in groups of three or four, as isolated as he can manage. He then can gather the berries as soon as they show colour and sow them immediately. This, in itself, is a means of avoiding some types of dormancy and of being able to repeat tried procedures each year.

Our experience with the cultivars of the Aria group, e.g. *S. aria* **Majestica**, and *S. latifolia* is that they give uniform seedlings. Since some Sorbus are known to be apomicts (i.e. producing seed by a process of budding within the ovary, without cross or self fertilisation) this means that they will come true from seed despite the fact that the parent tree may be a hybrid or cultivar. This gives a special interest to the raising of *Sorbus* from seed.   193

By using home saved seed and sowing it immediately, we have obtained around 25% germination the first spring with *S. esserteauiana, S. scalaris, S. insignis* and *S. hupehensis.* Higher germination (30–55%) was obtained with *S. rehderiana, S. latifolia, S.* **Joseph Rock** and *S. vilmorinii. S. aria* **Majestica** gave 68% germination. Other species gave low percentages or even no seedlings the first year.

It must be borne in mind that these figures are only examples. The degree of germination obtained the first spring may vary considerably between different lots of seed of the same species, especially from different localities. Purchased seed will have been subjected to unknown conditions. These are arguments in favour of home saved seed, where operations are under the control of the grower. The percentages quoted are, however, a guide to what may be expected using home saved seed.

If only small numbers are needed, the seed can be sown in pots or boxes which are left outside in a frame under a north wall, where they should be kept under observation. When germination is seen to begin they may be brought under glass. Prick off at the second rough leaf stage, which is generally from about twelve days to a month later, according to the vigour of the species.

Fig. 56. *Sorbus rehderiana* ten months from sowing the seed, grown under glass and plastic (left) and outdoors (right).

The pots or boxes may then be returned to the shaded frame and left until the following spring to obtain a second flush of seedlings.

From the pricking off stage there is a remarkable difference in response between the aucuparia and aria types. Three to five weeks later the former will be ready to pot on into 6 in. polythene bags. If they are transferred then to a capillary bed inside a plastic house, growth will be so strong that by autumn they will be whips 2½–6 ft (0.75–1.8 m) high according to the species.

In contrast, seedlings from seed sown out of doors will usually only be 2–3 in. (5–7.5 cm) high at this stage. This system could be of interest to a nurseryman wishing to raise a limited number of uncommon species annually. Since mountain ashes grown under cover can develop mildew in hot weather a protective spray of dinocap should be given. The aria types do not show a worthwhile response to this system of rapid growing.

Where larger numbers of plants are required, the seed may be sown in a well prepared seed bed. Under our conditions we find it convenient to sow in a frame. Even though the lights are not used, there is a degree of protection from pests as well as from extremes of weather and conditions are under better control generally. It is usually advised to crush the berries and mix them with sand before drilling them in the frame in rows 2 in. (5 cm) apart. We have sown whole berries of *S. aucuparia* and *S. aria* **Majestica** with successful results. Perhaps other species could be treated similarly. At the end of the first season lift and line out in a nursery bed all seedlings that have appeared. The seed bed may be left for a further year to obtain the second flush of seedlings. After one year in the nursery bed the seedlings may be lined out in the field. Weaker growing species may need two years in the seed bed. *S. koehneana* and *S. vilmoriniana* are apt to produce side shoots from the base in the seedling stage and unless these are trimmed off bushy specimens will result instead of single stemmed trees.

Spartium

Spartium junceum, the Spanish Broom, is a shrub with rush-like stems that grows to 12 ft (3.6 m). It is valued for its large yellow pea-shaped flowers carried for a long season during summer and autumn. Plant in a sunny position. Trim back in March to avoid a leggy habit. Good for seaside gardens.

Propagation is by seed which may be gathered in autumn and stored under ordinary condtitions. If sown in February under glass, around 80% of the seeds will germinate in seven or eight days. After four to five weeks, the seedlings will be about 6 in. (15 cm) when they can be pinched and transferred to a capillary bed either inside a plastic house or out of doors. By early June those under plastic will be about 1 ft (30 cm) high with several branches. At this stage it is advisable to transfer the plants to an outdoor capillary bed or frame. If kept too long in the warm, humid conditions of the plastic house, they become drawn and leggy. They can be sold in autumn as container grown plants or held over into the following year.

Spiraea

A large genus of deciduous shrubs ranging from dwarfs to large bushes.

Uses Spiraea bullata, 18 in. (45 cm) for the rock garden or small beds. It has crimson flowers. *S. albiflora* (white) and *S. x bumalda* **Anthony Waterer** (crimson) for the front of the shrub border. *S. thunbergii* (white), *S. trichocarpa* (white) and *S. x vanhouttei* (white) for the middle border. Taller (6 ft–1.8 m or more) are *S. x arguta* (white) and *S. veitchii. S. salicifolia* is a suckering species with terminal inflorescences of pink flowers, too invasive for the choice border.

195

Methods of propagation 1. Division. 2. Cuttings in the cold frame with plastic in July. 3. Cuttings in the low tunnel in June. 4. Cuttings in the warm bench with plastic in July. 5. Cuttings in open ground in October–November.

Method 1 *S. salicifolia* in particular, and other species on occasion, can be propagated by lifting and dividing in early spring the clumps formed by the growth of suckers.

Method 2 Nodal cuttings 2–3 in. (5–7.5 cm) long of the current year's shoots are inserted in the cold frame with plastic in July. The use of root promoting substances or wounding is not necessary. After five weeks up to 100% rooting can be expected. Harden off and line out in autumn or spring for growing on.

Method 3 Similar cuttings can be inserted in the low tunnel in June. Though up to 100% rooting can be expected without the use of root promoting substances, bigger root systems at lifting time in autumn have been noted from cuttings treated with 0.8% IBA powder. Line out in the open ground and grow on.

Method 4 Nodal cuttings of the current year's shoots may also be rooted by the warm bench and plastic method, inserting the cuttings in two parts moss peat to one of sand in July. Up to 100% rooting can be expected after six weeks. Treatment with root promoting substances is not needed. Harden off and line out in cold frames for a further season, after which the young plants can be lined out in the open or sold, according to species and vigour.

Method 5 Many species can be rooted from hardwood cuttings about 6 in. (15 cm) long inserted in the open ground. Lift a year later and line out for a further season.

Stransvaesia

Large evergreen shrubs or small trees with heads of white flowers resembling cotoneasters of the *C. frigida* type and, like them, grown for their berries. The most commonly seen species is *Stransvaesia salicifolia*. This may be raised from seed or gathered before the berries are fully ripe and either sown directly or stratified over winter before sowing in spring. Germination is good the first spring. The yellow berried form (**Fructuluteo**) may be struck from basal cuttings in late autumn under mist or in the warm bench and plastic. Wound the cuttings and treat with 0.8% IBA powder. They may be left in the containers and potted up in early spring.

Sycopis

A genus of evergreen shrubs related to *Hamamelis*. *S. sinensis* blooms in March, with clusters of flowers without petals, but with reddish brown bracts surrounding the yellow anthers. Basal cuttings taken in September and treated with 0.8% IBA root well under mist in ten to eleven weeks.

196

Symphoricarpos albus is the Common Snowberry, familiar for its white fruits in winter. It is a useful shrub for rough places. *S. orbiculatus* **Variegatus** is an attractive delicately growing shrub with golden variegated leaves. More recently, hybrid snowberries with pink berries have been introduced.

Method of propagation is simple, on a small scale by division, or by hardwood cuttings 6 in. (15 cm) long in the open ground in December. Lift and line out a year later. *S. orbiculatus* **Variegatus** may be propagated from basal cuttings of the past season's growth treated with 0.8% IBA powder, inserted in September–October in the cold frame or under mist.

Syringa

The familiar garden lilacs are derived from *Syringa vulgaris*. A number of species, e.g. *S. reflexa, S. sweginzowii*, are valued also, including the Canadian hybrids (*reflexa x villosa*).

Uses The lilacs, universally popular on account of their scent and colour, are widely planted both in gardens and parks. Full sun and good feeding help to give the best results. The species may be grown in shrubberies if they can be given ample room to display their laxer panicles of flowers.

Methods of propagation 1. Grafting. 2. Layering. 3. Cuttings in the mist in April–May. 4. White polythene tunnel (see p. 19).

Method 1 Grafting is carried out either in August or February. For August grafting, pot pencil thick specimens of *S. vulgaris* or *S. reflexa*, in spring. Plunge the pots outside until grafting time, when the pots are lifted and all but 2 in. (5 cm) of the stem of the rootstock is cut away. Graft by the cleft method (p. 33) with perfectly healthy scions, i.e. free of leaf infecting fungi. If fungus is present, the leaves will fall off in the frame or case and this will stimulate the buds into growth which will die back during the winter. After tying, place the grafts in a cold frame under double glass or in a closed case in the glasshouse. Callusing will take place quickly and, when the callus turns brown, harden off the plants immediately. Plunge the pots in frames until spring, when the plants are put out in nursery beds 12–18 in. (30–45 cm) apart. Plant deeply to encourage scion rooting.

For grafting in February lift and bench graft the rootstocks, using the whip method (p. 32). After tying and waxing the grafts, heel them into a shaded cold frame or shed. In early spring plant them out deeply in nursery beds 12–18 in. (30–45 cm) apart.

Plants grafted onto *S. reflexa* (*S. tomentilla* is also used) have the advantage that suckers are easy to distinguish. Both these species can be raised from softwood cuttings.

Method 2 Shoots from well established stool beds are pegged down firmly when the buds are swelling in spring (p. 27). Cut a tongue 2 in. (5 cm) long in the section to be covered in the soil. The following spring sever the rooted layers from the mother plant and line out 12–18 in. (30–45 cm) apart.

197

Method 3 Cuttings are an uncertain method owing to liability of infection with bacterial disease due to *Pseudomonas syringae*. The softwood basal cuttings are taken when about 2 in. (5 cm) long, around flowering time, treated with 0.2% IBA powder and inserted under mist. Rooting will occur after five to six weeks. Harden off and line out in a cold frame. By the end of the year the stronger growing cultivars will be 6 in. (15 cm) high. Lift and line out to grow on for a further two seasons.

Preliminary results with rooting softwood cuttings in the white polythene tunnel (p. 19) are promising and the indications are that *Pseudomonas* is not a major hazard. The raising of lilacs from cuttings is attractive as it does away with the problem of suckers.

Taiwania

Taiwania cryptomerioides is a rare conifer from Formosa (Taiwan), very elegant with its gracefully curving branches and drooping branchlets. *Taiwania* thrives best in the mild south western counties. The thick awl-shaped leaves give it the general aspect of *Cryptomeria*. While we have no great experience of its propagation, we can record that 4 in. (10 cm) basal cuttings treated with 0.8% IBA powder inserted under mist in July had rooted 82% by October. Potted up and placed in a plastic house the following spring they were 8 in. (20 cm) high at one year old.

Tamarix

The tamarisks most commonly seen in gardens are *Tamarix tetrandra* and *T. gallica* usually seen as shrubs up to 10 ft (3 m) high. Both have feathery foliage and bear pink flowers in May–June and July–September respectively.

Uses Especially useful on sandy soils near the sea. Wind resistant.

Method of propagation Sections of the current year's shoots 8–10 in. (20–25 cm) long may be inserted in the open ground in November–December adding extra sand to heavy soils. Lift and line out the following autumn.

Taxodium

Taxodium distichum is the Swamp Cypress, one of the comparatively few deciduous conifers. Though thriving in wet ground it will grow well in ordinary soil. Capable of reaching 100 ft (30 m).

Uses As specimen trees in parks and large gardens.

Methods of propagation 1. Seed. 2. Cuttings in the cold frame in October.

Method 1 Sow small lots thinly under glass in February or larger quantities in an outdoor bed in March, with provision for irrigation. Those sown under glass may be hardened off in a cold frame and lined out the following spring. Outdoor sowings can be lined out one or two years later.

Method 2 Hardwood cuttings 4–5 in. (10–12.5 cm) long are treated with 0.8% IBA powder and inserted in a well shaded and dampened cold frame. In April lift and line out in further cold frames at 6 × 6 in. (15 × 15 cm) spacing. In autumn line out in nursery beds for a further two seasons.

Taxus

The familiar Golden and Irish yews are forms of our native *Taxus baccata*. In North America and other regions with cold winters, the Japanese Yew (*T. cuspidata*) is grown on account of its greater hardiness.

Methods of propagation 1. Seed. 2. Grafting. 3. Cuttings in the cold frame in September–October.

Method 1 The type species can be raised from seed though germination is a slower process than might be thought from the self sown seedlings that appear in the vicinity of female yew trees. (The male and female flowers are borne on separate trees.) Perhaps naturally sown seed benefits from having passed through the digestive system of birds. Be that as it may, yew seeds do not come up the first spring if sown direct. It is necessary to stratify the seed for two winters in moist peat and sand. Sow in March in outdoor beds or frames. Even then, some of the seed may not come up until the year following.

Method 2 The understock used is *T. baccata*. Pot up two-year-old seedlings in April and plunge in outdoor beds until August. Lift and bring indoors, removing small side branches to show a clean stem of about 5 in. (12.5 cm). Use a side graft with lip (p. 31) and strong upright growing scions of the current season's wood. Place the graft in dampened peat in a grafting case in the glasshouse or under double glass in a cold frame and maintain a minimum temperature of 72°F (22.3°C). Callusing will take place in five or six weeks. Harden off and transfer, still in pots, to an outside frame to overwinter. In spring knock from the pots and cut away the stem of the understock above the graft union. Plant out for growing on.

Method 3 The majority of the cultivars of *T. baccata* can be propagated from cuttings, as can *T. x media* **Hicksii**, *T. x m.* **Hadfieldii**. 6 in. (15 cm) long stem cuttings of the current season's wood are inserted in a cold frame in September/October in a medium of two parts peat to one of sand. Wounding is not necessary and the cuttings, in accordance with Dutch recommendations, should receive a steep in a solution of 50 mg/litre NAA. Rooting will be well advanced in the following June and the plants are transferred to a well prepared outdoor bed for growing on.

Thuja (Arbor vitae)

The thujas are evergreen conifers superficially resembling *Chamaecyparis* but distinguishable by the overlapping scales of the cones. As with *Chamaecyparis*, there are numerous cultivars, including dwarfs and coloured forms.

Uses T. occidentalis and *T. plicata* can be used for hedges and screens. *T. p.* **Zebrina** makes a large tree with variegated foliage. Some of the medium 199 sized forms of *T. occidentalis* make neat screens for the smaller garden, e.g. **Fastigiata** and **Spiralis**. The dwarf forms include the well known **Rheingold**. Dwarf forms of *T. orientalis* with juvenile foliage include **Juniperoides** and **Meldensis**. The latter turns a plum purple colour in winter.

Methods of propagation 1. Cuttings in mist or warm bench with plastic in April. 2. Cuttings in the cold frame in September–October. 3. Seed.

Method 1 The propagation of thujas can conveniently follow *Chamaecyparis*, being less dependent on early insertion. Stem cuttings 3–4 in. (7.5–10 cm) long or 2 in. (5 cm) long for the dwarfs, are treated with 0.8% IBA powder before insertion into a medium of two parts moss peat to one of sand. Rooting takes seven to eight weeks when 70–85% success may be expected, with up to 100% possible. Harden off, line out in cold frames placing shaded lights over them until established. Plant out at the end of the year for growing on for two, three or more years according to the vigour of the cultivar and the size desired.

Method 2 Cuttings of a similar sort to those in Method 1 are inserted in September. Here also the use of 0.8% IBA powder is advantageous. Under our conditions the addition of extra sand to the base of the cutting (as has been advocated) did not prove advantageous. Lift the following May and line out as above.

Method 3 The type species may be raised from seed sown as early in spring as practicable. Little growth is made the first year so it is convenient to sow thinly and not line out until the second spring. Our particular experience is with *T. orientalis* which, sown in March, germinated quickly. Although early season growth was slow, the seedlings were potted into 3 in. pots and placed on a glasshouse bench until well established. Then after containerising in 6 in. bags the plants were transferred to a capillary bed in a plastic house and by autumn were 9 in. (22.5 cm) high.

Thujopsis

Thujopsis dolabrata is a conifer resembling *Thuja* but with broader leaves conspicuously marked with white beneath. There is a variegated form and also a dwarf (**Nana**). Stem cuttings, treated as for *Thuja* will root 60–70% in eight to ten weeks. The type may be raised from seed.

Tilia

There are many species of lime trees. Those most planted today include *Tilia cordata* (slow-growing), *T. euchlora*, *T. petiolaris*, *T. platyphyllos* and *T. tomentosa*.

Uses Much used as avenue trees in the past and today often used as street trees. *T. euchlora* has the advantage of keeping free of aphids.

200

Methods of Propagation 1. Seed. 2. Layering. 3. Grafting. 4. Cuttings in mist in June–July.

Method 1 is not very satisfactory as the seeds come up over a period of years.

Method 2 All of the limes can be successfully propagated by layering. This can be done by using the French layering system (p. 28) or the simple system (p. 27). The majority will be fully rooted in two years but *T. americana* and *T. europaea* will root in the same year, after being layered in April.

Method 3 The rootstock used are imported seedlings of *T. platyphyllos* and bench grafting is carried out in February by the whip technique (p. 32), using rootstock and scions of equal diameter. These are heeled in in a cold frame with lights or in a shed and planted out in the field in April, under favourable conditions, as soon as they begin to grow. A whip can be produced in the first season and to ensure straightness of stems, the plants should be staked. Crown formation is encouraged the following season and the plants grown on to produce sizeable specimens.

Method 4 Dutch investigations have proved successful with cuttings of *T. cordata* and *T. europaea*. Shoots are cut at the end of June or beginning of July and treated with 2% IBA powder. The growing point is left intact and the cuttings placed under mist. The types mentioned rooted 82% and 67% respectively and, after being hardened off and planted in a frame, had an 86–90% survival rate after two years.

Ulex

Double Gorse (*Ulex europaeus* **Plenus**) is one of the most brilliant shrubs in the garden in April and May. The Irish Gorse (**Strictus**) though of picturesque fastigiate habit is disappointing in that it flowers very sparsely. The Double Gorse should be cut back hard every few years immediately after flowering to prevent the bush becoming open and straggly.

Methods of propagation 1. Cuttings in the cold frame in September. 2. Cuttings in June and July in the cold frame with plastic.

Method 1 Basal cuttings of the current year's growth 4–6 in. (10–15 cm) long are treated with 0.8% IBA powder and inserted in two parts moss peat to one of sand in a cold frame. When lifted and containerised the following April 90–95% should have rooted. Containerise in 6 in. plastic bags and grow on on an outdoor capillary bed for sale as plants 12 in. (30 cm) high by late summer and autumn.

Method 2 Softwood basal cuttings about 3–4 in. (7.5–10 cm) taken in June–July are inserted in two parts moss peat to one of sand in the cold frame with plastic. 95–100% rooting can be expected after 11 weeks. When rooted, the plants are lifted and containerised into 5 in. bags. If kept in an outdoor capillary bed they will make saleable plants about 6 in. (15 cm) across by autumn.

201

Ulmus

The most important elms from the horticultural point of view have been the fastigiate and weeping kinds. Among the former may be noted the Wheatley Elm (*Ulmus stricta* **Wheatleyi**). *U. glabra* (*montana*) **Pendula** is a striking weeping form.

However, the future of these elms in many districts is precarious in view of the ravages of the Dutch Elm disease, to which they are susceptible. Indeed, elms are being replaced by plantings of other genera, but are now in a position to make a come-back as cultivars resistant to this disease have been identified. Though at present these are unfamiliar they should be obtained and propagated by enterprising nurserymen. Some of these disease resistant elms are listed below.

U. x hollandica **Christine Buisman**.	Eventually forms a large rounded tree.
U. x hollandica **Bea Schwarz**.	Forms a tree of no distinctive shape.
U. x hollandica **Dampieri**.	A tree of narrow conical habit.
U. pumila **Hansen**.	Hardy and vigorous, with large leaves.
U. glabra **Camperdownii**.	A small weeping tree suitable as a specimen tree, e.g. on a lawn.

Methods of propagation 1. Cuttings, including root cuttings. 2. Grafting. 3. Layering.

Method 1 The disease problem has stimulated interest in the propagation of elm clones from cuttings. Our own experience is that 6–8 in. (15–20 cm) cuttings root 60–70% in six weeks under mist in August. They may be heeled cuttings or in the case of long shoots, the apical or middle portion, wounded and treated with 0.8% IBA powder. After hardening off, the rooted cuttings may be lined out in a cold frame or in a well prepared outdoor bed. Growth the following year is strong. The young trees may be trained to a single stem from their second year.

Other methods recommended by various authorities include softwood cuttings under mist, inserting the cuttings singly in Japanese paper pots (as the new roots are brittle). After three weeks about 70% rooting can be expected. A Dutch method involves the taking of root cuttings from three- to four-year-old mother plants. The roots are placed vertically in a seed tray of peat-sand mix, with the top ½ in. (1.2 cm) protruding. Place the trays on the bench with bottom heat 68°F (20°C) and cover them with polythene suspended 9 in. (22.5 cm) above the cuttings. The tops of the roots will first form green callus and then send out shoots. When these are six to eight leaves long and becoming woody (about nine weeks after insertion), cut them off at the base, treat with a root promoting substance (0.8% IBA powder would probably suit) and root under mist or in the warm bench and plastic. Further shoots will arise from the root cuttings.

Conventional root cuttings, about pencil thickness and 2½ in. (6.2 cm) long may be taken from young plants in December–January. After dusting them with a fungicide they are placed singly in pots, the right way up and placed in a frame or cold glasshouse. When well established the young plants are lined out. The use of pots is advised on account of the brittle nature of the young roots. *U. hollandica* **Christine Buisman** is mentioned as responding well to this method.

Method 2 As the Dutch Elm disease is carried by elm bark beetles feeding on the young shoots it is considered safe to retain grafting and budding as means of propagation of resistant cultivars. The species used as the understock (*U. vegeta*) does not sucker, therefore there should not be any shoots of the understock present to attract the beetles.

The seed of *U. vegeta* should be collected in June as soon as the seed wings are brown and before the seeds are scattered by the wind. Sow at once, as the seed loses viability very quickly — even in a few days. It is stated that seed may be stored for several years in sealed containers at a temperature of 0–4.4°C (30–40°F).

The understocks are bench grafted (p. 30) in February or March, using one- or two-year-old scion wood. Heel in the grafts after tying or waxing in a shed or shaded cold frame. As the buds begin to move in spring, plant out in nursery beds for growing on.

Chip budding in July, August and early September is also recommended. Some species have very small buds and, for these, twig budding has been recommended. This resembles ordinary T-budding but is carried out in a glasshouse in March–May, using one-year-old dormant twigs instead of buds.

Method 3 Simple layering (p. 27) is carried out in August. Good roots will have developed after two years, when the plants can be cut away from the stock plant.

Vaccinium

This genus includes the native bilberry (*Vaccinium myrtillus*), not of decorative importance. Other deciduous species include *V. corymbosum* from which the American Highbush Blueberry has been derived by selection and hybridisation with other species. As well as yielding fruit, these are worth planting for the autumn colour of the foliage. The native *V. vitis-idaea* is a creeping evergreen. *V. glauco-album*, not hardy in cold districts, grows up to 4 ft (1.2 m) and is attractive in its 2 in. (5 cm) long leathery leaves, blue-white beneath. All species of Vaccinium need lime free soil.

Method of propagation V. corymbosum, including the named fruiting blueberries, is best propagated from side shoots of the current year when about 1½ in. (3.7 cm) long in April–May. Treatment with rooting powder is not needed. Root in peat by the warm bench and plastic method or under mist; harden off and grow on in frames of fertilised peat. Unless rooted early and grown on well, the young plants may not overwinter satisfactorily. *V. vitis-idaea* can be multiplied by simple division in spring; other evergreens by cuttings in the cold frame in September.

Viburnum (Carlesii group)

This group includes *V. carlesii*, *V. x juddii*, and *V. x carlcephalum*.

Uses Deciduous spring flowering shrubs notable for sweet scented blooms. Plant as specimens or in small groups. *V. x juddii* grows 3 ft (0.9 m) high and is suitable for the foreground. *V. carlesii* reaches 4 ft (1.2 m) and *V. x carlcephalum* 5 ft (1.5 m). They flower successively in that order. All are hardy. 203

Methods of propagation The viburnums of this group are commonly grafted onto *V. lantana* and this has been the spoiling of many a fine specimen, however advantageous grafting may be in the short term. Often we have been called on to admire a specimen of *V. carlesii*, for instance, only to find that it had become three quarters *V. lantana*. The suckers from the stock are very vigorous, reaching as much as 3 ft (0.9 m) in one season and are still a nuisance on specimens we planted ten years ago. By shooting up in the middle of the bush they evade detection until they are woody enough to make removal difficult. Perhaps such suckering is due to the use of rootstocks raised from seed rather than from cuttings prepared by the removal of the lowest buds.

Be that as it may, these viburnums can be raised from cuttings given a little care and patience. These are two possible methods.

1. Softwood basal cuttings in April in the mist or warm bench and plastic.
2. Semi-hardwood basal cuttings in July–August in mist or warm bench and plastic.

Method 1 Earliness of cuttings is highly important if the plants are to develop sufficiently to avoid overwintering losses. Viburnums do not force well but development of the young shoots is helped by the removal of flower buds in February. The shoots of these viburnums usually terminate in three buds, of which the centre one may be a flower cluster. When the central bud is vegetative, the shoot arising from it is especially suitable. 5–20% more rooted cuttings have been consistently obtained from such shoots than from those to each side of it. Good growing on conditions in the frames is another essential to success, e.g. loamless compost and irrigation. Flower buds frequently form on the young plants and should be removed. At the end of the first season the young plants are only 4–6 in. (10–15 cm) in height. These young plants need two growing seasons in the frame before they are saleable. While in the frames, large spreading root systems form, which can lead to transplanting check.

Method 2 Late summer cuttings root quickly (four weeks) and form good root systems. However, if they are then planted out overwintering losses can be heavy. It is safer to leave the rooted cuttings in the boxes in a cold frame until spring, keeping them on the dry side.

Treat cuttings with 0.8% IBA. Wound summer cuttings but not those taken in spring. The rooting medium is two parts moss peat to one of sand. Under mist 50–100% rooting can be expected in 4–6 weeks. Propagation by the warm bench and plastic method gives 5–20% less rooted cuttings.

Though not notably bad transplanters these viburnums should be handled gently and planted while fully dormant, otherwise severe transplanting check may occur. Alternatively the young plants may be container-grown thus removing the transplanting hazards of open-grown plants.

Viburnum (Deciduous winter flowering)

These include *V. farreri*, more familiarly known as *V. fragrans*, and *V. x bodnantense*.

Uses As specimens, flowering in winter with fragrant blooms. Eventually they reach 8 ft (2.4 m) or more in height.

Methods of propagation 1. Softwood cuttings under warm bench and plastic in early May. 2. Hardwood cuttings in a cold frame in October. 3. Layering. 4. White polythene tunnel (see p. 19).

Method 1 Softwood cuttings are treated with 0.8% IBA powder and are not wounded. The rooting medium used is two parts of moss peat to one of sand. Up to 100% rooting can be expected in three to four weeks.

Good subsequent growth is important in relation to good overwintering, hence the cuttings should be taken as soon as possible (2½–3 in., 6.2–7.5 cm long) and treated well. The cuttings come out in better condition from under plastic than from under mist. This can influence their subsequent performance, e.g. mist propagated cuttings of *V. farreri* measured only 5–6 in. (12.5–15 cm) by the following October compared with 1–1½ ft (28–45 cm) in the case of similar cuttings from under plastic.

Though treatment with IBA powder does not increase the number of rooted cuttings, better root systems have been observed in those so treated. Line out and grow on.

Method 2 Untreated flowering specimens do not produce sufficient suitable material owing to their twiggy habit of growth. A hedge of mother plants should be established. These plants are cut back hard to a stool each winter. In this way long, vegetative shoots are produced, some 3–4 ft (0.9–1.2 m) long. At leaf fall these are sectioned into nodal cuttings some 5 in. (12.5 cm) long. The basal part of the shoot is the most suitable. Treat with 0.8% IBA powder and insert into a compost of two parts moss peat to one of sand in a cold frame in October so deep that only the top ½ in. (1.2 cm) shows. Space at 2½ × 4 in. (6.2 × 10 cm), water in and place the glass in position. In spring harden off gradually as the cuttings leaf out; irrigate and feed (e.g. a 0.5% solution containing 9% N, 9% P and 7% K, fortnightly). Line out in the field in autumn.

Method 3 Small quantities can be produced by French layering (p. 28).

Viburnum (evergreen)

Evergreen species include *V. tinus*, *V. davidii*, *V. x burkwoodii*, *V. rhytidophyllum*, etc.

Uses The order in which they are named above corresponds to their commercial importance.

V. tinus is a well known dense growing shrub with white flowers in winter and early spring. It is so tolerant of rough conditions that it is often seen so shaded and starved as not to develop its best qualities. It is sometimes used for hedges. Height 6–10 ft (1.8–3 m).

V. davidii is increasing in importance owing to its suitability as a ground cover shrub. It can ultimately reach 3 ft (0.9 m) in height but is usually low and spreading. The clusters of white flowers are produced even on small plants and are followed by blue berries, though their production is erratic and some clones appear to berry more freely than others.

V. x burkwoodii and *V.* **Park Farm Hybrid** are similar in general appearance, having a loosely spreading habit and heads of fragrant white flowers early in the year, mainly in April and May. They are planted as specimens for their fragrance, growing up to 5 ft (1.5 m) in height.

V. rhytidophyllum is not very important commercially. It is only planted as a specimen shrub where there is plenty of space as it can reach 10 ft (3 m) or more. Though striking in appearance with its large rough surfaced leaves (up to 7½ in.–18.8 cm long) it has a lugubrious aspect in cold winter weather when the foliage droops. The large heads of flowers are seldom followed by berries unless more than one clone is planted for cross-pollination.

Methods of propagation 1. Cuttings in mist or warm bench and plastic from February to April (*V. davidii, V. x burkwoodii, V.* **Park Farm Hybrid**). 2. Cuttings in the cold frame and plastic in June (*V. davidii, V. tinus*). 3. Cuttings in the low plastic tunnel in June. 4. Cuttings in the cold frame in September (*V. davidii, V. tinus*).

Method 1 Take hardwood cuttings of the previous season's growth, 3–4 in. (7.5–10 cm) long, remove, any flower buds, wound and treat with 0.8% IBA powder. Internodal cuttings are satisfactory. Root in two parts moss peat to one of sand. Up to 100% rooting results in three weeks. Harden off and plant out in frames in April–May. Line out the following April–May.

V. x burkwoodii will make 4 in. (10 cm) extension growth the first year and can be sold at the end of the second year as a freely branched plant 1½–2 ft (45–60 cm) high.

Method 2 Young but firm cuttings 2½–3 in. (6.2–7.5 cm) long of the current season's growth are wounded and treated with 0.8% IBA powder. Internodal cuttings root more profusely than nodal and give 90% or more rooted after two weeks. Harden off by removal of the plastic in easy stages. Lift in October and line out in the open ground 9 in. (22.5 cm) each way and leave for two seasons.

Method 3 *V. tinus* has given over 70% rooting in the low plastic tunnel in June. Insert nodal cuttings, do not wound but treat with 0.8% IBA powder. Lift and line out in autumn or spring for growing on.

Method 4 Semi-hard basal cuttings about 5 in. (12.5 cm) long, treated with 0.8% IBA powder, are inserted in the cold frame in September in a medium of two parts moss peat to one of sand. Remove any flower buds before insertion. Rooting of 85–95% will take place by the following April. Harden off and line out 9 in. (22.5 cm) each way and grow on for two seasons.

Viburnum (Lacecap group)

It is convenient to call this the lacecap group by analogy with the lacecap hydrangeas. As in the latter, the outer ring of the flower head is composed of larger, sterile florets surrounding the inner fertile florets.

Well known are the species *V. opulus* (Guelder Rose) and *V. tomentosum*. Both have several important cultivars.

The native Guelder Rose has attractive red berries. The yellow fruited form **Xanthocarpum** deserves to be better known but commercially the most important cultivar is **Sterile**, the popular 'Snowball Tree', with round heads of blossom in June.

V. tomentosum **Plicatum** is also commercially important. This, the 'Japanese Snowball Tree', has larger heads of bloom. *V. tomentosum* **Mariesii** is one of the best of the flowering shrubs with horizontally disposed branches in tiers, crowded with rows of flower heads. **Lanarth** is similar, less horizontal in habit and more vigorous, suitable only for larger gardens.

The foliage of all colours well in autumn.

Uses As specimens in gardens and parks.

Methods of propagation 1. Hardwood cuttings in October in the cold frame. 2. Softwood cuttings in mist in May. 3. Layering.

Method 1 *V. tomentosum* and its cultivars may be propagated from hardwood cuttings. The mother plants should be pruned hard during winter to produce vigorous non-flowering shoots. From these shoots nodal cuttings of 4–5 in. (10–12.5 cm) long are inserted in cold frames in October, placing them deeply so that only one pair of buds shows at the surface. Line out one year later.

Method 2 Soft cuttings of *V. tomentosum* are taken in May, rooted under mist, hardened off after rooting and planted out into cold frames. It is important to induce good shoot growth to ensure successful overwintering. Line out in early spring. Transplant with care for, despite good root systems, this species can often move badly. *V. opulus* also roots easily from soft cuttings inserted under mist in May. Line out rooted cuttings in frames for the remainder of the season. Grow in open ground the second year.

Method 3 When smaller numbers of large plants are needed *V. tomentosum* can be propagated by simple layering (p. 27). The straight shoots arising from the crown of the mother plant, when layered, root readily and at lifting time in autumn have formed well-branched specimens about 2 ft (60 cm) high. These are lined out for one year to become fully established. At least 20 plants can be expected from a six-year-old mother plant.

Vinca

The periwinkles are well known cover plants, often growing in the roughest places. An attractive way to grow the Lesser Periwinkle (*Vinca minor*) is to cut back the stems hard each January, so that the plants form tufts covered with flowers almost like blue primroses.

Methods of propagation 1. Soft cuttings under mist or by warm bench and plastic in July. 2. Cuttings of firm shoots in October in the cold frame. 3. Division.

Method 1 Soft cuttings 8–12 nodes long, treated with 0.4% IBA powder, root 80–90% after five weeks in a medium of two parts moss peat to one of 207 sand. Harden off and plant out in well prepared beds at 6 in. (15 cm) spacing. Leave for two seasons to form good clumps.

Method 2 Insert cuttings 3–4 in. (7.5–10 cm) long. Lift in spring and line out as above.

Method 3 Clumps may be lifted in spring, split into small pieces and lined out.

Vitis

See **Parthenocissus** (p. 163).

Weigela (formerly Diervilla)

The familiar *Weigelas* or *Diervillas* are hybrids from several Asiatic species.

Uses Deciduous shrubs valued for their flowers in May and June. They may be planted as specimens in the private garden or as groups in parks and other public places. There are many white, rose, pink and red cultivars. **Eva Rathke** and **Newport Red** are good red-flowered forms. **Mont Blanc** is a good white. *D. florida* **Variegata** is very attractive with variegated leaves and pink flowers. *D. florida* **Folius Purpureus** forms a smaller, more compact bush with purple flushed leaves and pink flowers.

Methods of propagation 1. Cuttings in the open ground in October–November. 2. Cuttings in the cold frame with plastic in June. 3. Cuttings in the low tunnel in June.

Method 1 Select substantial shoot sections 9 in. (22.5 cm) long and bundle them in 25's after leaf fall. Wound and treat with 0.8% IBA powder. Heel in the bundles outside in a sheltered spot, burying the cuttings two-thirds of their length. In March lift the bundles and select out all cuttings which have callused. Line these out in nursery beds. Plants after one season will have five to seven shoots about 12–14 in. (30–35 cm) high. The plants can then be lifted and sold as good liners. As an alternative, cut them back and grow for a further season to obtain more substantial bushes.

Method 2 Basal 5 in. (12.5 cm) long cuttings are taken in June and inserted in a cold frame of two parts of peat to one of sand after treatment with 0.8% IBA powder. Cover with 100 gauge polythene and place well-shaded lights in position. Up to 100% rooting can be expected in six to eight weeks. Leave until September, lift and plant out in nursery beds to grow on. After one season sell as liners or after a further season as bushes.

Method 3 Basal softwood cuttings about 4–5 in. (10–12.5 cm) long are inserted in the low tunnel in June. Treatment with 0.8% IBA gives improved results; up to 100% rooting may be expected. Lift in autumn and line out for one or two seasons as in Method 2.

Wisteria

The wisterias are well known deciduous climbers. The two species are important, *W. sinensis* and *W. floribunda*. A sunny situation is essential.

Uses Wisterias are usually seen on walls and pergolas. *W. sinensis* is recommended for the former, *W. floribunda* for the latter. Prune back hard in late winter to keep in bounds and shorten back the leafy shoots in August. Wisterias may be grown as bushes and standards by pruning in this way. There are named cultivars of both species, notably *W. floribunda* **Macrobotrys** with very long racemes. It is sometimes called *W. multijuga*.

Methods of propagation 1. Root grafting. 2. Layering. 3. Cuttings in mist in June.

Method 1 Propagate the named forms by grafting onto roots of *W. sinensis*. Two-year-old seedlings may be used or roots may be lifted from older plants and held over winter in sand in a cold frame. In late March, when growth is about to start, cut the roots up into 3 in. (7.5 cm) pieces. The tops of seedlings are cut off at the neck. Select scions of two or three eyes of the cultivars required and graft using the cleft technique (p. 33). Place the grafted plants in a warm case in the glasshouse with the graft below the compost level in 'Long Tom' pots. Maintain the bottom temperature at 68°F (20°C). Place the glass 6 in. (15 cm) above the tops of the grafts. As soon as the eye begins to grow, pinch. Harden off and transfer to an outside frame with shaded lights in place. Harden off further and about two weeks later plant out in the nursery or in containers. If the latter, and the plants are grown under polythene on a capillary bed, they will be ready for sale as three or four stemmed 2 m high plants at the end of the first season. Outdoor culture will provide plants for sale two seasons after grafting.

Method 2 Select the long shoots in the spring and lay on the ground in the manner described on p. 29 (serpentine layering). The part below the ground will form roots and that above shoots. The small plants are cut out in the autumn. Pot up and grow on for two or three seasons or plant out in nursery beds. The plants must be staked. Wisterias are sold as container grown plants.

Method 3 Basal cuttings of short jointed side shoots are inserted under mist in late June-early July. (Cuttings taken too early will defoliate and fail to root.) The rooting medium is two parts peat to one of sand. The use of root promoting substances has not been helpful. After six to seven weeks 80–90% rooting may be expected. Pot into 4 in. pots and replace in the glasshouse or plastic house to re-establish. No shoot growth will occur until the following spring when the plants should be potted on into 5 in. pots and staked. Sell during the season as container grown plants.

Yucca

Yuccas are well known as they are conspicuous for their sub-tropical aspect, forming clumps of narrow leaves, topped in late summer by spire-like racemes of white flowers. The hardier species include *Y. filamentosa*, *Y. flaccida*, 209

Y. glauca, *Y. gloriosa*, *Y. recurvifolia* and their hybrids.

Uses Striking plants as specimens or in groups in well drained soil in full sun. *Y. recurvifolia* is recommended for town gardens and parks.

Method of propagation The smaller species, e.g. *Y. flaccida* can be increased by division in spring. Most species can be easily propagated by root cuttings. Lift the mother plants in April when examination of the root system will show the presence of swollen buds ('toes'). If these are cut off and potted with the apex just below the surface in 3 in. pots and placed in a glasshouse at 65°F (18.3°C), shoots will appear as quickly as a fortnight later. By autumn the young plants will be 4–6 in. (10–15 cm) high with 10–12 leaves.

PART THREE
Nursery Management

9

Economics and the Nurseryman

Few nurserymen today can operate a nursery as a hobby, for the pleasure of propagating rare plants, rather than as a method of earning a living. For all but the most wealthy, a nursery must be profitable.

In the past few years, however, it has become more and more difficult to run a nursery profitably. Costs have increased rapidly, with oil prices and labour prices going up particularly fast, and nurserymen can only maintain their profitability by being more efficient. They must be more efficient in production, producing more plants with the same resources, and they must be more efficient in marketing, selling a larger quantity at a better price.

In the next few chapters we are going to show how the nurseryman can use economics to improve his marketing and his production and to increase profits.

Farmers have been using economic management techniques on a large scale since 1945 and farm management economists have now reached the stage where farm planning is largely routine and is accepted by all but the most conservative farmers in Britain.

Nurserymen have realised the need for economic planning and for a management system like that used by farmers but in the past there has been no satisfactory system. A nursery is one of the most complicated businesses in the country: several hundred different products are produced and dozens of different production systems are used — rhododendrons may be rooted in mist, or in warm bench and plastic, or they may be grafted; they may be propagated at different times of the year; and they may be grown on for one year for sale as liners, or for up to six years for sale as specimens. With three propagation methods, three times of the year and six different ages at sale, there are $3 \times 3 \times 6$ or 54 production systems for rhododendrons alone. The only industries that are as complicated as this are the giant firms like Unilever or Philips, firms which produce hundreds of different products in different ways.

The economic planning systems used by these industrial giants are far too complex for the nurseryman. He would need a staff of hundreds of accountants to operate the system. At the other extreme, he would find the system used by the farmer hopelessly inadequate as it is developed for the simple farm with a dozen or so enterprises.

In the next few chapters we will explain an economic management system which will make it possible for a nurseryman to produce an economic plan fairly rapidly. The system is not perfect: a perfect system would need dozens of accountants to keep it operating. Nevertheless, it works; it can show which are the least profitable production plans, and it can give a choice of production plans which may suit the individual nurseryman.

213

Planning is quite as important to the small nursery as to the large nursery business. The saving, in money terms, is less, but a saving of £5,000 a year, which does not mean much to a large business, means the difference between surviving and failing to the small businessman.

The small nursery gets a greater proportional saving from planning, because the manager is fully occupied with the day-to-day running of the nursery and spends much of his time trouble-shooting. This means that he may not see the wood for the trees; he may be so involved with solving problems that he does not have time to plan the nursery to avoid them. Only if he makes a conscious effort to plan the nursery can he see what are the bottlenecks that are slowing production. Only if he makes a marketing plan can he be sure that he is growing the plants that will sell in three years' time rather than the plants that he has got used to growing over the past ten years.

When the nurseryman looks for credit he will find that a bank manager is more likely to lend money to a businessman who can produce a detailed plan to show why he wants the money, when he will repay it and how much profit it will produce.

Planning is particularly important for long-term crops; farmers producing short-term crops frequently have no farm plan and they get away with it because they are growing only a few crops and they can see fairly easily what is likely to go wrong with their crop in the next three to eight months. The nurseryman has to be much more careful. It is all too easy for him to strike cuttings, plant them in a frame and then to find that the labour is not available to transplant them so they must be abandoned. He may even find that after nurturing a crop carefully for three years, he has not the labour to lift and sell it, or that when it matures no one wants to buy it. There can be few nurserymen who have not had experiences of this sort. These breakdowns in planning are far more expensive to the nurseryman who has spent years on a crop than they would be to a lettuce grower who has spent only weeks.

The higher the risk the more important it is to plan. People growing long-term, low risk, crops like raspberries tend to have at least sketchy plans though they, too, may manage without; but people with long-term, high-risk crops should always plan. The risk can be reduced by careful planning, by choosing safer crops, or by choosing a combination of crops so that some crops benefit from the very wet weather that damages others, or by reducing the risks in other ways, perhaps by installing sprinklers to beat frost and drought. Alternative cropping systems can be prepared in case of crop failure or the failure of a batch of cuttings. Marketing risk can be substantially reduced by proper market research. Even though no plan will work exactly as hoped, because of disease, weather etc., the risk can be reduced.

The methods of planning production and marketing that are developed in this book are sound in theory and they can be justified by common sense. They can be used without the help of a mathematician, computer expert or an economist and they can be managed by the average nurseryman. The methods are considerably less time-consuming than some of those currently being used and it is hoped that most nurseries will be able to spare the time to use them. No attempt has been made to show the theoretical justification for the methods or to describe methods which are of no practical interest to the nurseryman, either because his business is too small to justify the time spent or because he would have to employ a mathematician to do the work.

In this chapter we will explain some of the basic economic techniques that we will be using in planning production and marketing. Then in Chapter 10 we will show how the nurseryman can use market research to forecast what plants will be most in demand in the future and what prices he will be able to charge for them. In Chapter 11 we show how the nurseryman can use this information to find the production plan which will give the most profit. Finally, in Chapters 15 and 16 we will give a more detailed explanation of some of the techniques that can be used and show when they should or should not be used.

Gross margins

The planning system presented in this book is a common-sense system, making use of two economic techniques which are readily understood, discounted cash flow analysis and gross margin analysis. Gross margin analysis will be familiar to many farmers, and discounted cash flow analysis (DCF) will be familiar to most people who have been in forestry. Since nursery stock production is a combination of farming and forestry, we have developed a combination of farming and forestry management techniques to deal with the nursery business.

Gross margin planning was developed as a simple planning tool for farmers and retailers. It is a simpler and more accurate system than the earlier, full-accounting system where the cost of each item of expenditure is split between the different crops and each crop is expected to show a return greater than the cost of production.

The full-cost system broke down because it is *impossible* to calculate the cost of any one crop, theoretically or practically. There is no meaningful way of deciding how much of the glasshouse cost should be charged to ericas and how much to azaleas. There is no meaningful way of splitting the cost of management, of tractors, or of packing sheds between the different crops. One could split the costs according to the value of the crop or the time spent on it or the glasshouse space it occupies but there is no logical reason why any one way should be any better than another.

Instead, economists divide all costs into fixed and variable costs. *Fixed costs* are those which the nursery incurs whatever crops it grows or, in the short run, whether or not it grows any at all. These costs include the manager's salary, interest on borrowed capital, machinery costs, and general maintenance. Most of these costs, in fact, are incurred even if nothing at all is grown.

There is another set of costs, the *variable costs*, which can be charged to the individual crops. These include the costs of fertilisers, herbicides, fungicides and packaging materials. Where nothing is grown there are no variable costs. As production increases, so the variable costs increase. The variable costs *vary* with the level of production, hence the name. Fixed costs, on the other hand, remain the same whatever the level of production.

There are many costs which are, strictly speaking, variable costs but which cannot be split between the different enterprises at all accurately, even with a great deal of work. Fuel is an example; obviously the fuel used varies directly with the amount of heat applied to a crop and the length of time the crop is in the glasshouse, but, in practice, it is virtually impossible to divide the fuel cost between the different crops unless there is only one glasshouse on the nursery and there are only one or two crops in the glasshouse. For this reason we treat them as overhead costs to the nursery as a whole and lump them together with fixed costs as *common costs*, common to all crops.

Planning is made more simple when the common costs are the same for a wide range of production plans, and we can concentrate on the changes in the variable costs from one plant to the next. There are, however, some costs which vary a lot from one plant to another. Labour is the prime example; two plans may be virtually identical in all their other costs, but one will have no labour peaks so all the work can be done by permanent labour, while another will have peaks. Casual labour, or more permanent labour will be required at the peaks; these costs are, in a sense, variable but they vary according to the labour plan of the nursery as a whole, rather than to the size of any one crop, so we will call them *semi-variable costs*.

As far as the nursery as a whole is concerned, *net revenue*, or profit, is total revenue from all sales, minus total fixed costs, minus variable costs. Total revenue minus total variable costs is *total gross margin*. In the nursery situation where it is not feasible to divide costs into fixed and variable, and we are talking of common costs, semi-variable costs and variable costs, the gross margin is the total revenue minus the common costs, minus the semi-variable costs.

We have already said that we cannot meaningfully divide fixed costs between the different crops, but we can fairly accurately divide both revenue and variable costs. For each crop we can work out the gross margin, which is the revenue from that crop less the variable costs that can be charged to it. The sum of the gross margins from each crop is the total gross margin referred to in the last paragraph.

Taking the nursery as a whole, the higher the total gross margin, the higher the total profit, for profit is the total gross margin minus the common costs and semi-variable costs. It follows that we can work out the profit for a nursery more quickly and easily by adding the gross margin from each crop and subtracting the fixed cost and semi-variable cost for the nursery as a whole than we could by arbitrarily dividing the fixed cost between the different crops, working out the profit per crop and then adding up the profit per crop. The total profit is the same under both systems.

Calculation of the variable costs for each crop takes a lot of time and accountancy, more than the small nursery or most large nurseries can spare, so in this book we are going to take the system one step further. In a nursery most of the costs are common costs or semi-variable costs and those costs which can be satisfactorily allocated to a crop, the true variable costs, account for only a small part of the total costs. What is more, there is not a great deal of difference between the variable costs for the different crops. We are going to lump the variable costs together with the common costs, and make no effort to charge the costs to the individual crops. This saves a lot of work at the sacrifice of a little accuracy. A large nursery which can handle the extra work can modify our system very slightly to charge variable costs to individual crops.

We are going to make use of labour timings and figures for the glasshouse space requirements of the different crops to develop nursery plans which are *possible*. We will then calculate the total cost of these plans, first charging the common costs, then the semi-variable costs, then any new costs that may arise from changing the plan — the construction of new frames, for example. We then work out the revenue from the nursery plan. The revenue minus the common costs minus the semi-variable costs is the profit.

We will take one set of capital resources, say 846 sq ft of glasshouse bench space, 15,000 sq ft of frame space and three acres of land, then work out a feasible plan for this. We will then work out the common costs and semi-variable costs for this plan, and subtract them from the total revenue to give the net revenue. We will then work out another feasible plan, using the same set of resources. The common costs will be assumed to be the same, so we only have to work out the semi-variable costs (labour) and the revenue. We will do the same for several feasible plans and we can expect to produce some that are more profitable and some that are less profitable than the first one.

We will then take another set of resources, taking perhaps another 846 sq ft of glasshouse bench space, and do the same thing, working out common costs for this basic production plan and using them for several feasible plans. If one of the feasible plans obviously has very different common costs, perhaps because only half the frames are used, then naturally new common costs have to be worked out.

As the plans are worked out it will become clear that the same bottlenecks are hampering each plan and the nurseryman may turn his attention to removing these. It will also become clear that some crops are making demands on labour in, say, September, which are quite out of proportion to their revenue and these crops will be dropped from the plan. Several of the feasible plans are likely to prove more profitable than the existing one and the nurseryman can adopt one which suits his temperament.

Why labour costs are not charged to individual crops

Labour costs are charged as semi-variable costs and are never charged to individual crops. Under our system the time taken to do each job is important and labour records are kept, so there is a great temptation for the nurseryman who has collected details of the time spent on taking cuttings, bench preparation, potting, weeding etc., to put a cost on this labour and to work out the cost per plant of producing each crop. This is impossible, both in theory and in practice, and anyone trying to do so will miss valuable business opportunities.

In a typical nursery the staff may consist of the owner/manager, two or three skilled workers, one of whom may be a skilled grafter, two or three less skilled workers and some casual workers from time to time. The skilled workers are very valuable indeed and it would be difficult to replace them if they left; the same is true, to a large extent, of the less skilled workers. It is often necessary to train replacements over a period of years as skilled men cannot easily be recruited. The hard fact is that a nurseryman cannot take on or get rid of labour whenever he wants. Still less can he lay off skilled labour for a month or two in the slack season. If we charge labour as a variable cost we are assuming just that; we are assuming that when labour is not charged to any one crop, that it is not being charged at all and the workers are not being paid.

Take, for example, a time of the year when the nursery is relatively slack and one worker has nothing to do. Since he cannot be dismissed he must still be paid. His wages cannot be charged to any one crop. He may, in fact, carry on working with the other workers, all working slowly to spread out the work. Let us suppose that the owner now comes up with a new proposal, a crop which has variable costs of £30 and which will be sold for £300 at the end of three months, giving a gross margin of £270. The crop can be grown quite easily, using existing resources, and it uses the labour of one man for three months, the surplus man.

217

If we take it that the man is going to be employed anyway, whether or not the extra crop is grown, that, in other words, his cost is fixed, then, clearly,

TABLE 1 COSTS AND REVENUE FROM THE TWO PLANS:

	Growing the crop	Not growing crop
	£	£
Wages	300	300
Variable costs	30	0
	330	300
Revenue	300	0
Net Income	− 30	− 300

the business is £270 better off by growing the crop. If, on the other hand, we cost that man's labour at, say, £100 per month, the crop will cost £30 variable costs plus £300 labour costs, a total of £330. Since the return is only £300, there is a loss of £30 so, if we use the full-cost system, we do not grow the crop. This decision loses the nursery £270 as shown in Table 2.

Since the labour is paid whether or not the crop is grown, it must either be put in equally for both plans, as in Table 1 or, much better, be left out as in Table 2.

TABLE 2 COSTS AND MARGINS FROM THE TWO
PLANS: GROSS MARGIN METHOD

	Growing the crop	Not growing the crop
	£	£
Variable costs	30	0
Revenue	300	0
Increase in total gross margin	+ 270	0

Using our system rather than the gross margin system we would say

Common costs stay the same.
Semi-variable costs stay the same.
Revenue increased by £300.
Therefore we are £300 better off.

This conclusion is not quite right, because we have not allowed for variable costs, but the right decision has been made, to grow the new crop, so we are £270 better off than we would have been had we been charging labour to the crop. We have said that in a nursery the variable costs that can be meaningfully and accurately charged to any one crop are small in relation to the total costs, so the error is small, much smaller than the error due to disease or weather damage. There is another reason why the error due to putting variable costs with common costs may not be as high as the example suggests. Where the average variable cost is £20 an acre over four acres, the extra variable costs of bringing another quarter acre into cultivation may not be £5 as assumed in the gross margin system but nearer £1. In this case our system would be more accurate than the gross margin system when deciding whether or not to bring the extra quarter acre into cultivation. In a farm, where variable costs may be much higher in relation to total costs, the error from our system could be substantial, but in a nursery it is acceptable.

The lesson to be learnt from this is that *if a man has nothing to do, his time is free*. This is vitally important to the nurseryman. Efficient use of labour and other resources, such as glasshouse space, can only be attained if the fixed costs are ignored. What counts is that the profit to the firm as a whole — the total revenue minus common costs minus semi-variable costs — should be as large as possible.

If there is any spare labour, any new crop that produces a revenue higher than the *increase* in total costs, but does not require more fixed resources (like glasshouses) than are available, will increase total profit. It is not necessary that the crop should cover its share of fixed costs, only that it increases total revenue more than total costs.

There are other reasons why it does not make sense to cost labour. The owner and the skilled workers are paid more than the unskilled workers yet they may all be working on the same job, say handweeding. It would be foolish to charge one rate when a labourer is handweeding the azaleas and another when the manager is handweeding the rhododendrons. This would make it seem that the rhododendrons were less profitable than the azaleas, when in fact it was only a matter of chance that the manager was not working on the azaleas. For the same reason one cannot distinguish between permanent and casual labour. This does not mean that we ignore labour in our planning. Labour is clearly one of the two or three critical factors in most nurseries and it must be fully accounted for throughout the planning process. In our system, though, we work on the hours taken to do each job, rather than on the cost.

Disadvantages of Gross Margin Analysis

Gross margin analysis is widely used in farm management but it cannot be used, in its pure form, for nursery management. This is because farmers tend to plan from year to year while nurserymen must plan for at least three years in advance, as the plants propagated this year may not be sold for three or even six years.

Fixed costs and variable costs lose their meaning when we do long-term planning. If a new nursery is to be built, all costs are variable, so the system has to be used with the greatest care. For example, when one considers building a glasshouse solely so that rhododendrons can be grown, the cost of the glasshouse is a variable cost, chargeable to rhododendrons. Once the glasshouse is built, it becomes a fixed cost as interest and maintenance charges are incurred whether or not the glasshouse is used. It is a cost to the nursery as a whole and it is available for any crop that can use it profitably. It follows that all costs are variable at the construction stage.

The other main disadvantage of gross margin analysis is that it does not allow for the fact that returns are different each year. It is one thing to say the gross margin for wheat is £50 a year and it will be about the same next year and the year after. It is quite another thing to deal with a crop like Japanese azaleas where the returns are zero in the first year, £4,443 at the end of the second year, £10,252 at the end of the third year, and £11,255 at the end of the fourth year, and to compare it with a crop like rhododendrons with zero return until the end of the third year, when £29,577 is earned. The gross margin system, by itself, cannot say which of these two systems is profitable or whether, indeed, either is. To handle questions like this, we have to combine the gross margin system with the discounted cash flow system. This is shown in later chapters.

The Nursery Plan

We have said that our planning system is based on Discounted Cash Flow analysis and on Gross Margin analysis. The most important lesson we have taken from Gross Margin analysis is that it is useless to try to cost individual crops: we are concerned only with the total profit of the nursery as a whole. We have shown with an example that we will not find the most profitable plan if we charge the fixed costs, such as labour, to a crop. The most profitable plan for the nursery as a whole is not found by ranking crops in order of profitability then taking the three or five most profitable as the nursery plan. Not only is it unlikely that this will be the most profitable plan but it is virtually certain that it will not be possible to grow a reasonable amount of this crop combination with the labour and glasshouses available. This approach also ignores the marketing side, the difficulty of selling plants if one third of the nursery's output is of one variety.

We start our analysis by seeing what crops the nursery can grow with the resources available and then seeing what costs and revenues, to the nursery as a whole, come from each combination of crops. After this we can compare the profitability of the schemes, but, since some schemes produce rapid profits while others take longer but make larger profits, we use discounted cash flow to compare the schemes. This is shown in Chapter 12.

In Chapter 11 we give an example of how to plan a nursery using these techniques, but first in Chapter 10 we examine marketing, for without proper market research we do not know what will sell and what price it will get — basic information for any production planning.

10

Marketing

At one time horticulturists felt that their job was to grow plants and that they could ignore marketing but now they realise that marketing is all-important. Their whole production plan is based on the need to produce something they can sell and something they can sell profitably. It is for this reason that we discuss marketing before we give a detailed example of a production plan.

Two major problems face the nurseryman — first what crops should he grow and secondly what price should he charge for them? In this chapter we discuss pricing policy; what price should the nurseryman charge? should he always try to cover his costs? Then we discuss the question of what the nursery should produce and show how the nurseryman can do his own market research to answer the question.

Pricing

Often we are asked 'How can I set a price which will cover my costs and give me a fair profit?'

The answer is that costs of production have nothing to do with prices in agriculture. Supply and demand determine prices. Beef producers and vegetable producers know that they cannot set a price which will cover their costs of production and leave them a fair return for their trouble. They must take the price offered in the market and hope that, on average, the price gives them a fair return. If they were to set a price which gave them a fair return, they would have no difficulty in getting this price when the market was under-supplied but they would sell nothing at all when the market was over-supplied. Their *average* return would then be very much below the cost of production. Nurserymen are in the same position; they can seldom fix their price, they can only take the market price.

The aim must be to get as high a total return as possible from a given supply. The nurseryman has to dispose of the plants he has on his hands and he must not let himself be influenced by the cost of production — all expenditure in the past is ancient history.

We are sometimes asked 'I have access to a cheap source of cuttings so I can produce magnolias 20% cheaper than my rivals. What price should I charge?' We may even be asked 'Most of my eucalyptus were killed by the frost so the cost of production per plant is twice the market price. What price should I charge?' When the two questions are put together in this way, the answer is obvious: the nurseryman cannot get away with charging twice the market price for his eucalyptus so why should he sell his magnolias cheaply? The profits on one will help to compensate for the losses on another.

221

Naturally, nurserymen feel pangs of conscience about putting up their prices by 10% every time changing exchange rates put up Dutch prices by 10%. If they were going to make a fair profit at the first price, they will make an enormous profit at the new price, they think. It is only when the next bills come that they realise that all imported raw materials, fertilisers, herbicides, fungicides and mother plants have risen by 10% and that wages are about to go up again and it is not until five years later that they realise that the glasshouse that cost £100,000 in 1979 is going to cost £400,000 to replace in 1989, and that they have not put enough away in depreciation to cover this. If they are reticent about charging the full market price, they are not allowing for inflation and they could easily find that their working capital has vanished.

There is another reason why nurserymen should concentrate on the market price rather than on their cost of production. Market prices show what the customer wants. If the market price of conifers doubles while other prices stay the same, this is a good indication that the customers want more and more conifers and that the demand for some other crops may be falling. It might equally indicate that there was a shortage of supply.

Sometimes a nurseryman will say 'All my production was sold as soon as I issued my catalogue' or 'All my production for the next year was sold in advance'. This is a sure sign that prices have been too low. The ideal is to have exactly enough orders to sell all that is available. If there are too few orders, the price is too high or the quality too poor, or the market has collapsed, while, if there are too many orders, the price is too low. The only way the nurseryman can be sure his price is not too low is to have a slight surplus at the end of the selling season, perhaps 5% of the total. This surplus is not always wasted; with some crops it can be sold next season.

It may not pay to charge the maximum possible price. There is a danger that the goodwill that exists will vanish if the customer feels that he is always being pressed for the last penny. On the other hand, there is no evidence that retailers or wholesalers in other businesses are unduly worried about the effect on goodwill of charging the full market price.

This brings us to the question 'How do I decide whether to sell a plant this year or to keep it until next year and sell it for a higher price?' The answer to this question is in the Discounted Cash Flow technique discussed in Chapter 12. £1.25 next year is the same as £1.00 this year at 25% discount rate. If a plant is worth £1.00 this year and £1.35 next year and the variable cost of maintaining it for another year is 5p, then the rate of increase in value is more than 25% and the plant should be kept for another year. In fact, it has been shown in the last chapter that most of the costs of maintaining the plants for another year are fixed costs, like labour, rent and interest, and these should be ignored in this calculation. If the nurseryman applies this principle rigidly, he will keep all plants as long as their value increases by 25% per annum and he may end up keeping all his plants until they are mature specimens for landscape architects and selling little or nothing for the first ten years.

There are two main reasons why he will not do this: first, few nurserymen have enough land to plant out ten years' production to grow to maturity: second, cash is needed to live on, to pay expenses and to repay loans, so something must be sold each year. The nurseryman must keep those plants whose price will rise most, and sell those plants whose price will rise least. In a nursery that is short of cash, only those plants that double their value in a year will be kept, while in an established nursery with plenty of spare cash and not many other investment opportunities, 15% may be the breakeven line.

There are times when it may pay to charge more than the market price and to leave some plants unsold, or to sell them at a low price to another nurseryman in a different part of the country. This might happen where the nursery has some locational advantage. Most nurserymen find that, because of competition from neighbouring nurseries, they can sell everything they have at any price up to the market price but that sales fall rapidly if they increase their price over the market price. Some find, however, that they have locational advantages that make their demand steadier. They may be on a main road on the edge of a city, for instance, or they may have no competitors within easy driving distance. They find that they can sell all they can produce at any price below the market price but that they lose relatively few customers if they charge more than this. It is so inconvenient to go to rival nurseries that only the customers nearest the other nurseries change. In this case, a 1% rise in price leads to a less than 1% fall in sales. Here the nurseryman can increase his total revenue by restricting supply.

TABLE 3   TOTAL REVENUE AT DIFFERENT PRICES

Local Price	Number sold locally	Number sold wholesale elsewhere	Total Revenue
£1	5,000	0	£5,000
£2	4,200	800	£9,200
£3	3,200	1,800	£11,400
£4	1,800	3,200	£10,400

Table 3 shows the total revenue a nurseryman gets selling his plants locally, when he sells his surplus to other nurserymen at £1 each. By restricting the supply in the local market and selling the surplus elsewhere he can push up the price in the local market. His maximum revenue is not where the home price is as high as possible but at an intermediate stage where the price is £3 or a little higher. The calculation of the price at which the maximum revenue is obtained is simple. The one difficulty is to estimate what sales will be at any level of price. This can only be done by experience, seeing what sales are each year at different prices and making a guess at the effect of inflation. Still, the example shows that it is well worth your while to see if total revenue can be increased in this way.

Published market research

The published statistics on the nursery stock industry are of little value to the individual nurseryman. One knows that Britain and Ireland import a large quantity of plants and that most of these come from the Netherlands.

The trade press often has articles or new items which point out a trend in production or demand. For instance, it has been suggested that more and more amateurs are renting land and producing short-term, low-value plants on it. This may mean that there will be a surplus of these plants in the near future. It has also been suggested that the land on either side of the motorways is going to be heavily wooded with indigeneous species.

The trade press also keeps nurserymen informed of coming promotions, but there is seldom enough advance notice for the nurserymen to grow plants especially for this. It is worth looking ahead to see if you can identify occasions when a campaign will be launched, or when local authorities can be expected to make special plantings for the celebrations. News items like these are difficult to interpret. Often a very minor decision, referring to a small area, is given widespread publicity while major policy decisions are ignored. Even when there is an obvious and clearly defined trend, it is difficult to know how to react to it. Too often one news item catches the imagination of all growers and all of them switch crops at the same time, producing a glut.

We feel that a nurseryman cannot get a lot from published market research and that he should concentrate on doing his own market research to solve his own problems.

Market research for the retail nurseryman

The market research needed by the retail nurseryman is quite different from that needed by the wholesale nurseryman, because he is dealing direct with the final purchaser, while the wholesaler is indirectly influenced by the final demand and is strongly influenced by the supply at a national and regional level. In this section we will discuss the market research needed by the retail nurseryman.

The retail nurseryman wants to know, first of all, what his customers want. What plants do they want? Will they want the same plants next year or the year after? Do they know what they want or do they need advice? Do they want fertilisers, herbicides or equipment as well as plants?

Next he wants to know if he is getting all the customers in the neighbourhood. Is someone else taking his business? If so, is it because he does not have the right plants? Is it because he does the wrong advertising? Is it because the customers have never heard of him? Finally, he wants to know how he can increase his sales.

The first step is to find out who the customers are and what they buy. Every nurseryman will be on very good terms with some of his customers and will know what they want and what they buy, but there are many customers he knows very little about.

The only way to get a good idea of the market is to ask customers some questions. We describe below two surveys the nurseryman could carry out himself. Some nurserymen would prefer not to ask these questions, both because they are embarrassed about asking a stranger a lot of questions and because they arc afraid their customers will be offended. In this case, there should be no difficulty in getting students of agriculture, horticulture, statistics or business economics from the local agricultural college, polytechnic or university to do the survey. Often they have to do research papers as part of their course and they would be delighted to do the survey for you, provided you cover their expenses and give them something for themselves.

Customers may feel happier about taking part in an official university survey than in your private survey so the response may be better. We have drawn up a questionnaire (p. 225) with the most important questions. The questions may have to be changed if the nursery is unusual in any way but the questionnaire should not be any longer. In some parts of the country customers may not want to answer the questions on their age and income but we feel that if a customer is asked to fill in the questionnaire and is then sat at a table where he can do this comfortably and privately and is given a box like a ballot box to put the answer in, he will answer all the questions. We have not asked the customer for his name so he can be sure his answers will be confidential and there will be no follow-up marketing.

About 100 or at most 200 questionnaires should be filled in. Even the nationwide opinion surveys in Britain have only 1,400 or so questionnaires so 100 will give a good cross section of a nursery's customers. The survey should be spread over at least a month and preferably over one winter to give a broad picture of the type of customers. If you have 10,000 customers in a season, you should ask one in every 100 or one in every 50 customers to fill in questionnaires. Customers must be chosen at random, using a special technique. It is very tempting to pick out the better dressed, the more polite customers or the regular customers but this would ruin the survey. The aim is to have a chance selection where the man carrying out the survey cannot alter the selection according to his personal tastes.

The way to do this is to wait until 90 customers have gone (assuming a 1 in 100 sample), then say 'The tenth customer from now is my man.' When he comes, ask him to fill in a questionnaire. If he refuses, do not take the next man, but the tenth man after him — otherwise one can subconsciously choose someone who looks more helpful. If you ask politely and explain that you are trying to improve your service to customers, you should not have any trouble getting the forms filled up. If you do, it might be an idea to give a present of a plant to anyone who co-operates — choosing a cheap line that must be cleared fast.

EXAMPLE OF MARKET RESEARCH QUESTIONNAIRE

CONFIDENTIAL

We are trying to find out more about our customers and what they want so that we can give them a better service. We should be grateful if you would answer these questions. The answers are confidential and we do not ask for your name.

Where do you live?   ....

            ....

When did you last come to this nursery?

	Less than 10 days ago	☐
	Less than 6 weeks ago	☐
(Please tick)	Less than 3 months ago	☐
	Less than 18 months ago	☐
	Never been here before	☐

How old is your house?

	Less than 1 year old	☐
(Please tick)	Less than 3 years old	☐
	Less than 5 years old	☐
	More than 5 years old	☐

225

Is it your own house? Council house? Rented?

When you came here today did you buy anything?   Yes ☐   No ☐

If you did, what did you buy?

Were you coming past here anyway as part of a shopping or pleasure trip or did you make a special journey to come here?

Pleasure trip	☐
Shopping trip	☐
Special journey	☐

How did you find out about the nursery?

Advertisement in the paper	☐
Notice at roadside	☐
Recommended by a friend	☐

In the last year which of these did you buy for your garden?

Fertiliser	☐
Weedkiller	☐
Peat	☐
Lawn seed	☐
Flower seed	☐
Vegetable seed	☐
Hedging	☐
Roses	☐
Flowering shrubs	☐
Trees — conifers	☐
others	☐
Climbing plants	☐

Is there anything that you would like to buy for your garden that we do not sell?

Which age group are you in?

	Under 25	☐
	25 and under 30	☐
(Please tick)	30 and under 40	☐
	40 and under 60	☐
	Over 60	☐

What is the combined income of everyone living in your house?

	Under £3,000 (£58 per week)	☐
	£3,000 and under £4,000 (£58–£77 per week)	☐
(Please tick)	£4,000 and under £6,000 (£77–£115 per week)	☐
	£6,000 and under £10,000	☐
	£10,000 and under £15,000	☐
	£15,000 and under £20,000	☐
	Over £20,000	☐

The results of the survey will tell you a lot about the weaknesses of your marketing. If a pin is put in the map at the place given on each questionnaire, it is easy to see where the customers come from. It is at once obvious if all the customers come from the immediate neighbourhood, suggesting that no one anywhere else knows of the nursery. Possibly all the addresses are where the customers pass the nursery on the way to work or on the way to the shopping centre, suggesting again that very few people know where the nursery is. There may be no customers from some suburbs and a lot from others. By cross checking with the income group of the customers and by using your own appraisal of these areas, you can get some idea why this is. We have noticed, for instance, that in many new estates the new residents do not know where the nearest nursery is and they may travel to the nursery nearest their old house.

The questionnaire asks how old the customer's house is. This is important because people moving into a new house are likely to spend money on establishing a garden, planting a lawn and hedges the first year then, as their financial situation improves, planting trees, then shrubs. When they have established a mature garden, they will develop it by exchanging cuttings and plants with friends. This pattern of establishing a garden when the house is new may or may not apply in your area. This can easily be checked from the questionnaire — what type of plants are the people with the new houses buying? Are they any different from the plants bought by people with the older houses? Do people who buy older houses remodel the garden or leave it much as it was?

Do different income groups buy different plants? There are keen gardeners in all income groups but some of the gardens in council estates rely on beautifully kept hedges and lawns, while gardens in wealthier areas are larger and rely more on expensive shrubs and trees. The nurseryman is, of course, more interested in people who buy expensive plants, even if they are poor gardeners and have to replace the plants every few years. A look at the questionnaires will show who the customers are and what they buy. If nearly all customers are wealthy, although the nursery is in an area with a mixed population, this is a sign that some of the market is not being served. You must ask yourself:

Do I supply the plants this income group wants?

Do I provide the requisites they need?

Do I make people welcome however much or little they buy?

Have they ever heard of me?

If most of the customers are wealthy, one must see what they are buying. Are they buying a few cheap plants, once a year or so, or are they buying expensive plants? The plants available should suit the customer's pocket and his taste. If most of the customers are wealthy and have large gardens, there should be expensive, large plants that can be displayed to best advantage in a large garden. If nearly all customers are in the lower income group, there is no point in displaying large numbers of six-year-old trees.

Age can be a useful indicator. If the only people buying roses are in the over-60 age group, the nurseryman can draw the conclusion that the market will decline rapidly in the next few years — even though many people take to gardening late in life. Young people will tend to be poorer and to live in newer houses than middle aged people but their choice of plants may indicate the trends for the future.

The questions on when the customer last bought in the nursery make it possible to divide the customers into casual customers, occasional shoppers and regular customers. The higher the proportion of customers who return to buy again, the better, so something is very wrong if nearly all customers are casual. If there are no casual customers, on the other hand, this means that there is no chance of gaining new regular customers — in this case something is wrong with the advertising or the nursery is too difficult to find.

A survey of this sort is sure to provide valuable information, to show up weaknesses in the present marketing system and to show new marketing opportunities.

It is surprisingly quick to sort the questionnaires into piles, those earning under £4,000, those earning under £6,000 etc. You can then divide each pile into 'old houses' or 'new houses' or into 'requisites' 'roses' or 'trees'. While you do this you will find yourselves noticing a lot of relationships you had not thought of looking at. Perhaps the young people do not like roses for instance.

The following table is an example of what can be done. This shows clearly

TABLE 4 PERCENTAGE OF PEOPLE WITH DIFFERENT INCOME GROUPS
LIVING IN DIFFERENT TYPES OF HOUSES

| Income group | Age of house | | | | |
	0–1 year	1–3 years	3–5 years	5 years +	Total
£4,000 and under	15	10	20	25	20
£4,001 to £6,000	30	30	35	35	32
£6,001 to £8,000	25	30	30	25	25
£8,001 to £10,000	20	15	10	10	10
£10,001 and over	10	15	5	5	13
	100	100	100	100	100

that the lower the income group, the more likely it is that people live in an older house.

In analysing these tables, small differences in percentages can be ignored as these could occur by accident. Where the difference is important there is usually a marked difference in the figures, becoming more marked as the customer gets richer, older, etc.

A marketing strategy

An example of the use of the survey in drawing up a strategy can be given here.

The survey showed that the nurseryman had almost no customers at all in any of the new housing estates nearby, in spite of the fact that there had been a lot of new building in the area in the last few years. Most of the customers lived in houses over ten years old and none lived in houses less than one year old. Few of the customers were less than 30 and those that were lived in council houses or flats and were in the lower income groups.

The analysis suggested firstly that something should be done to tell new residents that the nursery existed. It had a large notice facing the road but the road was a side road which few of the customers would travel on. It seemed that a lot might be achieved by handing out leaflets in the new estates, with a map showing were the nursery was. A simple statement that the nursery was good or was the best in town might be made but it was unlikely to carry conviction. Something more than this was needed to attract the residents and to

get them to come again.

The answer seemed to be to offer a bargain, one that would attract customers but which would not, at the same time, cost the nursery too much. The bargain should, therefore, appeal only to new customers. Lawn seed and hedging seemed to be possibilities. If leaflets were put in new houses offering either or both at a much reduced price, possibly at cost, there would be a big incentive for people moving into the neighbourhood to search out the nursery and buy. Existing customers would not get the advantage of the offer as they have lawns and hedges already so no money would be wasted trying to attract existing customers.

The customers were not in a position to spend a great deal in the first year as they had all the costs of moving into a new house but they would know where the nursery was and know that it was cheap so they would visit it when their finances improved.

The estates that had grown up in the last four years proved more of a problem. Cheap lawn seed and hedging would not interest these customers as they already have their lawns and hedges. Leaflets would help but it was difficult to say how much.

The solution that appeared was to approach the local residents' association and to offer a discount for bulk purchases. The residents' association was offered 25% discount on all public trees, plants at the side of the road, etc., and the same discount was offered for orders of over 100 plants by the estate. If 25 residents each ordered four rose bushes, they got 25% off, if 100 residents each ordered a prunus, they got 25% off. If over 25 plants were ordered 10% discount was given. All orders were given in advance at the nursery and discount was given on the total orders for the estate. The nursery could then order the plants from the wholesale nursery and deliver them to the estate. The discount of 25% was not too much considering the standard mark-up was 100% and handling and carrying costs were reduced. The full discount can only be obtained on the most popular species, 10% or nothing being obtained on others. The scheme was only publicised in the new estates but if existing customers had heard about it and had complained of discrimination, the scheme could have been extended to their estates too. Because the gardens there were mature, they would not have qualified for the 100 rate on more than one or two items.

This strategy would attract new customers who had never before shopped at the nursery. The chief cost would be printing the leaflets. The discount would be compensated for by an immediate and large profit.

Here the logic of Gross Margin Analysis applies again. The nursery does not have to cover all costs on increased sales. As long as the price covers the variable cost and makes some contribution to fixed costs, profits increase. For this reason, cut prices and special offers can increase profits providing

(a) prices more than cover variable costs

(b) most of the cut prices and special offers are taken up by new customers rather than existing customers.

In most cases a survey of this sort would provide all the information needed but it must be remembered that the people interviewed are already customers. The people who do not buy nursery stock and the people who buy elsewhere have not been interviewed. If there are areas where you would expect to get customers but where you do not in fact get them, it may pay to call on some houses in the evening and ask a few questions. Call at every tenth or every twentieth house, knock at the door, say 'Good evening, I am carrying out a market survey, could I ask you a few questions? I am not selling anything and I have nothing to do with encyclopaedias.' Then ask the person at the door the questions. This kind of work is best done by a woman as people are less suspicious — a man is more likely to be a mugger or an encyclopaedia salesman. The interviewer should carry some identification showing the name and address of the firm. Again, it might help to present them with a sample plant.

When interviewing, concentrate on getting facts: do not argue, do not make exclamations like 'Is that all?'. Above all, do not try to sell. Do not mention the name of your nursery unless asked, do not criticise your competitors. Remember that door-to-door salesmen practise the hard sell, getting people to buy something they don't want at an inflated price. They do not look for repeat orders and, in fact, it is not the salesmen but a special debt-collecting squad that collects the money. You on the other hand, want them to visit your nursery, look around, choose something they want, recommend you to their friends and come again. Any foot-in-the-door salesmanship would lose you customers.

Market research and the wholesale nurseryman

Wholesale nurserymen will obtain most of their market information from discussion with their customers and the larger wholesalers may do a market survey of their customers. Beyond this, there is little they can do except keep an eye on trends reported in the trade press.

11
Simple Planning

In this chapter we present a super-simple planning technique. It has been designed so that the average nurseryman can handle it without getting bogged down in paperwork and masses of figures.

In order to make it simple, we have had to cut corners and to ignore a lot of costs. This means that the system is not accurate and it does not always show up the most profitable plan for the nurseryman. However it will show up plans which are among the most profitable, and it will reject many plans as being certainly unprofitable.

We believe that any planning is better than none at all, and we strongly advise the nurseryman to try this system. Once he has mastered it and has seen how it helps him, he can develop it into a more accurate system. The way to do this is shown in later chapters where new costs and new problems are taken into account, step by step, until a much more accurate, but more time-consuming planning system is achieved. The smaller nurserymen may be happy with the very simple system presented in this chapter, because they do not have much time to spare, and any planning is time-consuming. Obviously the large nurseries will stand to make more money from planning in detail, and will be more willing to devote the necessary time to it. However, even the most complicated planning system presented in this book may not be enough for the giant nursery businesses, which need, and can afford to pay for, very complicated computer models (which will however be based on the same principles).

Most practical nurserymen hate the tedious messing around with figures that planning involves: they would rather be in the glasshouse taking cuttings, or in the field helping with weeding. However, the payoff from planning is very much higher. If, as a result of spending a month planning his nursery, a nurseryman puts up future earnings by £15,000 (which is not that difficult), he is earning money at the rate of £180,000 a year, for that month at least.

Information needed

The following information on each crop is needed before the planning can begin:
  When it enters the glasshouse
  When it enters the frame
  When it is planted out
  When it is lifted and sold
  Number of cuttings per square foot
  Number of plants per square foot glass (if being established under glass)
  Number of plants per square foot frame

231

Number of plants per square foot land
%cuttings rooting
%plants leaving frame
%plants sold
Price of plants this year.

This information can be laid out as in Table 5. It is convenient to put plants with similar production systems close together in the table, but, in the range of plants produced by any one nurseryman, there are not likely to be more than two or three plants which are exactly the same in all respects from spacing to prices. Naturally, each nurseryman has his own climatic and soil factors to take into account, and different techniques will produce different success rates, so each nurseryman will want to make different estimates for Table 5, based on his own experience. To reduce the calculations at a later stage, and to make it easier to compare profitability of different crops, the cost of packaging materials, labels and burlap is subtracted from the price at this stage, so the quoted price is the selling price less cost of packaging materials and other unusual costs (but not labour).

Naturally we do not expect that each crop will be grown according to plan, with no disease or insect damage. However, proper planning means that you plan the best possible cash flow for your nursery, after taking into account the amount of risk in the crops you select. We must explain here that we have chosen ten crops for this example, purely for illustration. When we say ericas, we mean all plants propagated in the same way; when we say santolinas, we mean all similar cheap plants propagated in frames in the autumn. The propagation systems costed are not necessarily the best systems, but have been chosen as convenient examples. Indeed, we show later that there is no 'best' or 'cheapest' propagation system — the one to choose is the one that fits best into the plan for the nursery as a whole.

Bottlenecks

There is no point in costing out a plan if it is not practicable. The first step in planning must be to identify the bottlenecks and to devise some production programmes that can be carried out. Only after this should they be costed.

Any nursery has bottlenecks. There may not be enough glasshouse bench space for the programme; there may be more work than the grafter can do; there may not be enough skilled labour available in September; there may not be enough frames. There may be several bottlenecks, and which one is critical will depend on which production plan is being considered — with one plan glasshouse space may be critical, with another, labour may be the problem.

In the simple system covered in this chapter we concentrate on two constraints — amount of glasshouse bench space and amount of frame space. The amount of ground for planting out is less often a problem, but it can easily be taken into account in the same way. Obviously labour is often a critical factor and it *should* be taken into account. It is not difficult to do so. However, it is quite time consuming to calculate the labour requirements for all the crops. In addition, very large tables are needed to show labour inputs, crop by crop, week by week, over three years, and we want to avoid large tables in the simple system. For this reason labour planning has been put into a separate chapter. It is worth looking at the introduction to this chapter when first reading through the book, but the tables and calculations can be left until the nurseryman has mastered the simple system and is ready to move on a stage.

TABLE 5 SPACE REQUIREMENTS OF DIFFERENT CROPS

	How propagated	When propagated	Into frame	Into ground	Sold	Cuttings/ sq ft	Plants/ sq ft glass	Plants/ sq ft frame	Plants/ sq ft ground	% cuttings rooting	% plants leaving frame	sold	Price per 1000 £
Ericas	Cold frame + P	Sept./Oct.	April/May	—	Oct. Y1/Y2	100	—	12	—	72	90	100	150
Ericas	Warm bench + P	Jan./March	April/May	Nov. Y0	Oct. Y0/Y1	100	—	12	9	72	90	100	150
Prunus	Cold frame	Sept./Oct.	—	April/May	Oct. Y3	40	—	—	12/3	90	—	80/90	400
Viburnum	Cold frame	Sept./Oct.	—	April/May	Oct. Y3	25	—	—	12/3	95	—	80/90	400
Cotoneasters	Cold frame	Sept./Oct.	April/May	October	Oct. Y2	75	—	20	12/5	85	—	80/90	300
Santolina	Cold frame	Sept./Oct.	—	April/May	Oct. Y1	35	—	—	3/1½	91	—	90	200
Dwarf Rhododendrons	Warm bench + P	February	April/May	Oct. Y0	Oct. Y3	40/50	—	20	10	60/70	95	90/95	850
Rhododendrons	Warm bench + P	October	May/June	Oct. Y2	Oct. Y3	23	13.5	6	6.2	60	81	90	2,000
Deciduous Azaleas	Warm bench + P	April/May	July/Aug.	Oct. Y1	Oct. Y2	42	—	10.5	6	70	86	100	1,300
Japanese Azaleas	Warm bench + P	June/July	Aug./Sept.	Oct. Y1	Oct. Y2	42	—	9	9	72	67	100	453
Viburnum	Warm bench + P	August	—	Sept./Oct. Y0	Oct. Y3	25	—	—	8/4	70/90	—	80	850

Note (1) As each nurseryman will decide on spacing for himself we did not think it necessary to give metric equivalents in this section.

(2) Y0 is the year in which the crop is planted, Y1 is the next calendar year and Y2 the year after.

(3) P = Plastic.

TABLE 6 NUMBER OF CUTTINGS AND AMOUNT OF GLASS, FRAME SPACE AND GROUND NEEDED TO PRODUCE 6 1000 PLANTS FOR SALE

	No. of cuttings	Cuttings per sq ft	Sq ft glass needed	Glass for growing on	Frames for cuttings	Plants put in frames	Plants per sq ft	Sq ft frames needed	Plants into ground	Sq ft ground needed	Replanting ground needed	No. plants sold
Ericas (a)	1543	100			16	1111	12	92	0	0		1000
Ericas (b)	1543	100	16			1111	12	92	1000	111		1000
Prunus	1307	40			31	1176			1176	98	392	1000
Viburnum (a)	1237	25			50	1176			1176	98	392	1000
Cotoneaster	1384	75			19	1176	20	58	1176	98	236	1000
Santolina	1221	35			35	1111			1000	333	750	1000
Dwarf Rhododendron	1760	45	40			1144	20	57	1000	100		1000
Rhododendrons	2286	23	100	102		1371	6	228	1111	179		1000
Deciduous Azalea	1667	42	40			1167	11	111	1000	167		1000
Japanese Azalea	2075	42	50			1494	9	166	1000	111		1000
Viburnum (b)	1562	25	62			0			1249	156	312	1000

Note: This table is just a reworking of Table 5

TABLE 7 GLASSHOUSE BENCH SPACE NEEDED AND NUMBER OF PLANTS PRODUCED FROM THE PROPOSED PLAN

	Sq ft per 1000 plants sold	No of plants	January	February	March	April	May	June	July	August	September	October	November	December
Rhododendrons	100	8400	840	840	840							840	840	840
Ericas	16	0	0	0	0	0								
Dwarf Rhodos	40	0		0	0	0	0							
Decid. Azaleas	40	21000				840	840	840						
Jap. Azaleas	50	16800							840	840				
Viburnum	62	13580								842	842	842		
Total Bench space required			840	840	840	840	840	840	840	842	842	842	840	840

Bench space

Here, a plan will be developed for a nursery specialising in ericas, azaleas and rhododendrons. The nursery has only 840 sq ft of bench space. At first sight, bench space seems to be the bottleneck, as all the most valuable plants must be propagated in the glasshouse. The first step, then, is to develop a programme which makes full use of the bench space.

Figure 57 shows the months when the ericaceous crops are in the glasshouse. Rhododendrons, for instance, can go in at the beginning of October and leave in mid-March, or they can go in as late as mid-December and leave at mid-April. The right-hand edge of the block shows the latest propagation time under the system, and the left-hand edge of the block shows the earliest time. These are not the only possible propagation systems and it is worth putting down any others — June propagation of ericas is one obvious example, but it is also immediately obvious that this will clash with Japanese azaleas or

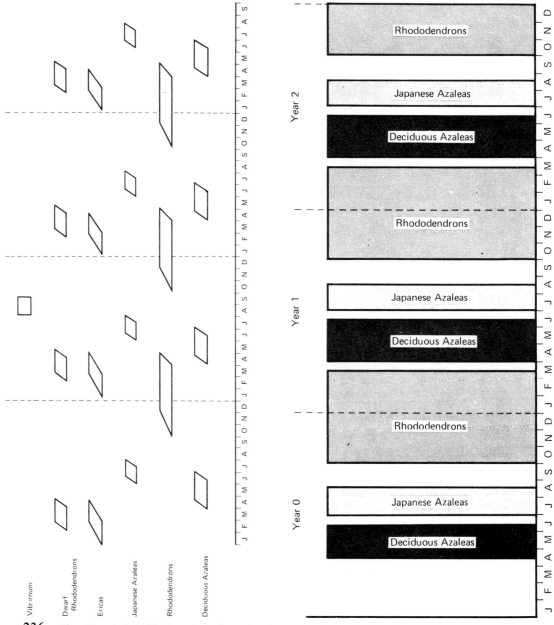

236   Figs. 57 and 58. Utilisation of glasshouse bench space.

deciduous azaleas. We have two ready alternative ways of producing ericas, January/February propagation under warm bench and plastic or September/ October propagation under cold frame and plastic.

The dwarf rhododendrons, the large-flowered hybrid rhododendrons, the Japanese azaleas and the deciduous azaleas are the most valuable crops, so the first step is to see how they fit into the glasshouse. There is a clash between dwarf rhododendrons and large-flowered rhododendrons, so any system must grow one or the other, or else reduced quantities of both. At first we assume that only one crop will be grown at a time. We can try modified systems after examining this fully.

Figure 58 shows how deciduous azaleas, Japanese azaleas and rhododendrons fit into the bench space. In the first year there is nothing in the glasshouse until mid-April. This space can be filled by putting in ericas at the beginning of January and following them with dwarf rhododendrons in

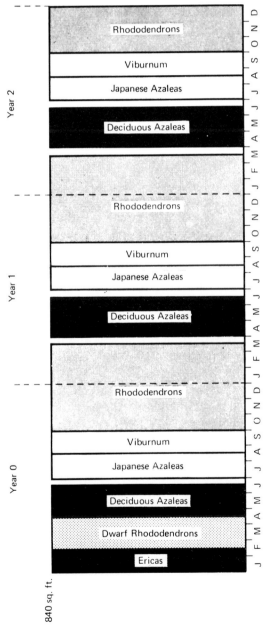

Fig. 59. Utilisation of glasshouse bench space.

237

mid-February. In each year there is an empty space between mid-August and the end of September. The nurseryman looks for a high-value ericaceous plant to fill this gap, but if it is not available, he must fill the gap with something else, perhaps Viburnums. The glass is then fully used, as shown in Figure 59.

However, there are still times when the bench space is not being fully used. These can be filled as shown in Figure 60, putting in viburnums in August and September and putting in crops of ericas and dwarf rhododendrons in the first year — in later years they cannot be grown, because the space is occupied by rhododendrons.

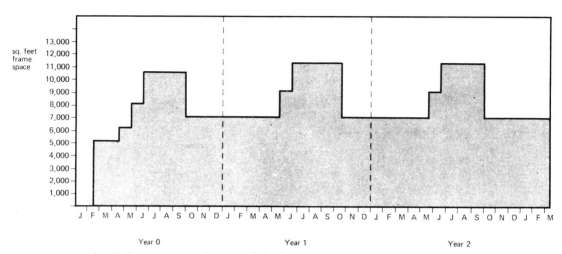

Fig. 60. Frame space requirements of six glasshouse-propagated crops.

Having decided what crops are to be grown in the glasshouse, the next thing is to work out how many cuttings will be needed and how many saleable plants will be produced.

Table 6 shows the number of cuttings and the glass, frame space and ground needed to produce 1000 saleable plants. The figures have been worked out from Table 5. First the number of plants and cuttings was worked out. In the last column was entered the number of saleable plants, 1000, then the number of cuttings needed was worked out from this and the survival rates quoted in Table 5. With rhododendrons, for instance, 1000 was divided by 0.9, to get the number of plants leaving the frame, 1111, because only 90% (which is the same as 0.9) of the plants survive the field. This figure, 1111, is divided by 0.81, as only 81% of the plants survive the frame, to get 1371 plants going into the frame. This figure is divided by 0.6 (the proportion of cuttings rooting) to get 2286 cuttings needed to produce 1000 finished plants.

Once one knows the number of cuttings and plants at each stage, it is easy to get the square feet needed. Just divide the number of cuttings by the figure for cuttings per square foot shown in Table 5. Similarly, for frame space, divide that number of plants by the number of plants per square foot, to get square feet frame space.

Now we know the number of square feet needed per plant sold, it is a simple matter to work out the number of plants that will be produced by the plan in Figure 59. Just divide the number of square feet per thousand plants into the 840 square feet available. This gives 8400 rhododendrons, 21,000 deciduous azaleas and 16,800 Japanese azaleas. This is shown in Table 7, which shows the space needed fortnight by fortnight.

238

Frame space

Frame space is the next limiting factor. The nursery has only 15,000 square feet available. The frame space required per thousand plants sold has already been worked out. The first step is to work out how many square feet will be needed to grow on the plants that were propagated in the glasshouse. This is done in Table 8, which is worked out using the level of production obtained in Table 7, and which uses the same logic.

To make the figures clearer, the frame space required for the crops planted in Year 0 and Year 2 go on one line, and those for the crops planted in Year 1 and Year 3 on the next line. This avoids the need for adding up when two crops overlap.

At the foot of the table is written the total number of square feet of frame space needed for all the crops together. These figures show whether there is enough frame space available, and, at the same time, whether all the frame space is efficiently used. The totals can be plotted on a graph, Figure 60, which shows very clearly the variations in the use of frame space. Between October and mid-May the amount of frame space is 62% of the amount used between mid-June and October. From this it can be seen that any crops that use the frames between October and mid-May get what is, in effect, free frame space.

The possibility of growing dwarf rhododendrons every year instead of growing the large-flowered hybrids can be considered later. From Table 8 though, it can be seen that these use frames at the time of the year when the frames are most in demand and not at all the rest of the year, so, from this point of view, the crop is undesirable.

There are several plants that can be propagated in September or October in a cold frame and removed from the frame in April or May. In the data sheet, Table 5, several of these, prunus, santolina and viburnum, have been given as examples. There are also examples of plants which are propagated in this way but which are transplanted into frames for summer, ericas and cotoneasters for instance.

Since the nursery has 15,000 square feet of frame space available, there is excess capacity, with nearly 3000 square feet excess even in August, September and October, and 8000 square feet available in the winter months. How can this space best be used? In Table 9, a programme for plants to be propagated in the frames is added on to the programme already prepared for the crops propagated in the glasshouse. The programme set out here is not worked out by any complicated method: it is just a first guess at a feasible programme, more or less in line with the present production system. The programme is the glasshouse crops mentioned above, plus 15,000 plants a year of ericas, prunus and cotoneasters and 40,000 santolinas. This first estimate turns out to be practical. There is a shortage of frame space in October, but it should be possible to get round this by lifting plants at the beginning of the month and putting in cuttings towards the end. However, it is clear that careful planning will be needed during this period.

The number of plants mentioned here is very large indeed. While a specialist nurseryman may well produce 21,000 dwarf rhododendrons, many nurserymen will not see 40,000 santolinas in their entire career. It must be remembered that we are using santolinas to represent all cheap plants propagated in frames in this way. Before putting this plan into effect, the nurseryman will select the ten or twenty plants produced in this way which he can sell for the best price, and which give him the best catalogue. He will produce perhaps 4000 of each of these, instead of 40,000 santolinas.

TABLE 8 MONTHLY REQUIREMENTS OF FRAME SPACE FOR A PRODUCTION PROGRAMME

Sq. ft per 1000 plants applies to the **Cuttings** and **Plant out** columns.

	Plants sold	Cuttings	Plant out	J	F	M	A	M	J	J	A	S	O	N	D
Year Zero															
Rhododendrons	8400	0	228					1915	1915	1915	1915	1915	1915	1915	1915
	8400	0	228												
Ericas	0	0	92												
	54890	0	92		5050	5050	5050	5050	5050	5050	5050	5050			
Dwarf Rhodos.	21700	0	57				1237	1237	1237	1237	1237	1237			
	0	0	57												
Decid. Azalea	21000	0	111							2331	2331	2331	2331	2331	2331
	21000	0	111												
Jap. Azaleas	16800	0	166										2789	2789	2789
	16800	0	166												
Viburnum	13580	0	0												
Ericas	0	16	92									0	0	0	0
Prunus	0	31	0									0	0	0	0
Viburnum	0	50	0									0	0	0	0
Cotoneaster	0	19	58									0	0	0	0
Santolina	0	35	0									0	0	0	0
Total frame Space reqd.				0	5050	5050	6287	8202	8202	10533	10533	10533	7035	7035	7035
Year One															
Rhododendrons	8400	0	228	1915	1915	1915	1915	1915	1915	1915	1915	1915			
	8400	0	228					1915	1915	1915	1915	1915	1915	1915	1915
Ericas	0	0	92					0	0	0	0	0	0	0	0
	54890	0	92												
Dwarf Rhodos.	21700	0	57												
	0	0	57												
Decid. Azalea	21000	0	111	2331	2331	2331	2331	2331	2331	2331	2331	2331			
	21000	0	111							2331	2331	2331	2331	2331	2331
Jap. Azaleas	16800	0	166	2789	2789	2789	2789	2789	2789	2789	2789	2789	2789		
	16800	0	166											2789	2789
Viburnum	13580	0	0												
Ericas	0	16	92	0	0	0	0	0	0	0	0	0	0	0	0
Prunus	0	31	0	0	0	0	0								
Viburnum	0	50	0	0	0	0	0								
Cotoneaster	0	19	58	0	0	0	0	0	0	0	0	0	0		
Santolina	0	35	0	0	0	0	0	0							
Total frame Space reqd.				7035	7035	7035	7035	8950	8950	11281	11281	11281	7035	7035	7035
Year Two															
Rhododendrons	8400	0	228					1915	1915	1915	1915	1915	1915	1915	1915
	8400	0	228	1915	1915	1915	1915	1915	1915	1915	1915	1915			
Ericas	0	0	92	0	0	0	0	0	0	0	0	0	0		
	54890	0	92												
Dwarf Rhodos.	21700	0	57												
	0	0	57												
Decid. Azalea	21000	0	111						2331	2331	2331	2331	2331	2331	2331
	21000	0	111	2331	2331	2331	2331	2331	2331	2331	2331	2331			
Jap. Azaleas	16800	0	166											2789	2789
	16800	0	166	2789	2789	2789	2789	2789	2789	2789	2789	2789	2789		
Viburnum	13580	0	0												
Ericas	0	16	92	0	0	0	0	0	0	0	0	0	0		
Prunus	0	31	0												
Viburnum	0	50	0												
Cotoneaster	0	19	58												
Santolina	0	35	0												
Total frame Space reqd.				7035	7035	7035	7035	8950	11281	11281	11281	11281	7035	7035	7035

TABLE 9 MONTHLY REQUIREMENTS OF FRAME SPACE FOR A FEASIBLE PRODUCTION PROGRAMME

Year Zero

	Plants sold	Sq. ft per 1000 plants — Cuttings	Plant out	J	F	M	A	M	J	J	A	S	O	N	D
Rhododendrons	8400	0	228					1915	1915	1915	1915	1915	1915	1915	1915
	8400	0	228												
Ericas	0	0	92												
	54890	0	92		5050	5050	5050	5050	5050	5050	5050	5050	5050		
Dwarf Rhodos.	21700	0	57												
	0	0	57				1237	1237	1237	1237	1237	1237	1237		
Decid. Azalea	21000	0	111												
	21000	0	111							2331	2331	2331	2331	2331	2331
Jap. Azaleas	16800	0	166												
	16800	0	166										2789	2789	2789
Viburnum	13580	0	0												
Ericas	15000	16	92									240	240	240	240
	15000	16	92												
	15000	16	92												
Prunus	15000	31	0									465	465	465	465
Viburnum	15000	50	0									750	750	750	750
Cotoneaster	15000	19	58									285	285	285	285
	15000	19	58												
Santolina	40000	35	0									1400	1400	1400	1400
Total frame Space reqd.				0	5050	5050	6287	8202	8202	10533	10533	13673	16462	10175	10175

Year One

	Plants sold	Cuttings	Plant out	J	F	M	A	M	J	J	A	S	O	N	D
Rhododendrons	8400	0	228	1915	1915	1915	1915	1915	1915	1915	1915	1915			
	8400	0	228					1915	1915	1915	1915	1915	1915	1915	1915
Ericas	0	0	92												
	54890	0	92				0	0	0	0	0	0	0	0	0
Dwarf Rhodos.	21700	0	57												
	0	0	57												
Decid. Azalea	21000	0	111	2331	2331	2331	2331	2331	2331	2331	2331	2331	2331		
	21000	0	111							2331	2331	2331	2331	2331	2331
Jap. Azaleas	16800	0	166	2789	2789	2789	2789	2789	2789	2789	2789	2789	2789		
	16800	0	166											2789	2789
Viburnum	13580	0	0												
Ericas	15000	16	92	240	240	240	240	1380	1380	1380	1380	1380	1380	690	690
	15000	16	92									240	240	240	240
	15000	16	92												
Prunus	15000	31	0	465	465	465	465					465	465	465	465
Viburnum	15000	50	0	750	750	750	750					750	750	750	750
Cotoneaster	15000	19	58	285	285	285	285	870	870	870	870	870	870		
	15000	19	58									285	285	285	285
Santolina	40000	35	0	1400	1400	1400	1400	1400	1400				1400	1400	1400
Total frame Space reqd.				10175	10175	10175	10175	12600	12600	13531	13531	15271	14756	10865	10865

Year Two

	Plants sold	Cuttings	Plant out	J	F	M	A	M	J	J	A	S	O	N	D
Rhododendrons	8400	0	228					1915	1915	1915	1915	1915	1915	1915	1915
	8400	0	228	1915	1915	1915	1915	1915	1915	1915	1915	1915			
Ericas	0	0	92	0	0	0	0	0	0	0	0	0	0		
	54890	0	92												
Dwarf Rhodos.	21700	0	57												
	0	0	57												
Decid. Azalea	21000	0	111						2331	2331	2331	2331	2331	2331	2331
	21000	0	111	2331	2331	2331	2331	2331	2331	2331	2331	2331	2331		
Jap. Azaleas	16800	0	166											2789	2789
	16800	0	166	2789	2789	2789	2789	2789	2789	2789	2789	2789	2789		
Viburnum	13580	0	0												
Ericas	15000	16	92	690	690	690	690	690	690	690	690	690	690		
	15000	16	92	240	240	240	240	1380	1380	1380	1380	1380	1380	690	690
	15000	16	92										240	240	240
Prunus	15000	31	0	465	465	465	465						465	465	465
Viburnum	15000	50	0	750	750	750	750					750	750	750	750
Cotoneaster	15000	19	58									285	285	285	285
	15000	19	58	285	285	285	285	870	870	870	870	870	870		
Santolina	40000	35	0	1400	1400	1400	1400	1400					1400	1400	1400
Total frame Space reqd.				10865	10865	10865	10865	13290	14221	14221	14221	15256	15446	10865	10865

Note: the apparent overlap in October may be overcome by careful planning. One crop may leave the ground at the beginning of the month while the next is planted at the end.

Ground for planting out

If the nursery is short of ground for planting out, exactly the same exercise can be carried out using square feet ground instead of square feet frame space. While this is not a particularly important constraint for most nurseries, it is worth working it out at least once — especially if a nursery switches from producing liners to producing specimen trees.

Revenue

Once a feasible plan has been worked out, the next step is to work out the revenue. This is straightforward: write down the number sold in each year from Table 9 and multiply by the price (Table 5). This gives the layout in Table 10.

In this table the revenue from each crop is put in the year of harvest, under the assumption that payment is made immediately. With ericas the bigger plants are sold the first year and the others are left to grow on for a year so 7500 are sold in Year 0, but in later years 15,000 are sold, 7500 from the previous year and 7500 from the current year.

For the simple system we ignore inflation. We work out all sales at the current prices unless we have reason to believe that some crops are going to go up in price much more than others. Even so, this is a complication that is probably best left to later chapters and a more complicated planning system.

It is assumed that the nursery is sold off in Year 10. This is done so that the nurseryman can take into account his capital appreciation. Again, current prices are used, though allowance should be made for any increase in real value — the spread of the suburbs may make it suitable for building or for conversion into a garden centre. Remember, though, that it is usually the developer who makes the big profits, not the owner of the land.

The nurseryman who is now planning buying the nursery should put in purchase, investment and establishment costs in the year they are incurred. This will mean that the bottom line shows exactly what the cash flow is. It will also make it possible, using the technique set out in the next chapter, to see if the venture is profitable at all, if he would not be better putting the money into the savings bank.

The nurseryman who has already bought the nursery and has invested money in it should allow for this, so that the costing can show whether he would not be better off selling up and putting his money in the savings bank. To do this the net current value of the nursery, the selling price minus the amount owed, should be put in as a cost in Year 0. Future financial charges, interest and repayments are put in the column for the year the payments are made. The bottom line then represents the cash flow on the assumption that the first figure is the amount paid into the business by the owner — which is what it is.

For the simple system we make no attempt to work out costs. It is enough to put in roughly the present level of costs. One reason for this is that it is assumed that switching from one production plan will not greatly affect costs. Even in the full system we assume that most costs stay the same unless there is a major change in the system. The other reason is that calculation of costs is time consuming, and, especially for the simple system, it is not worth the effort. When the half dozen most profitable plans have been selected, it may then be worth going into a little more detail in costs, as shown in later chapters.

TABLE 10   TOTAL REVENUE FROM THE PROPOSED PLAN

	No. of Plants	Price in pounds	Year 0	Year 1	Year 2	Year 3	Year 4	Year 5	Year 6	Year 7	Year 8	Year 9	Year 10
Rhododendrons	8,400	2.00				16,800	16,800	16,800	16,800	16,800	16,800	16,800	33,600
Ericas (glass)	54,890	0.15	4,117	4,117									54,600
Dwarf Rhodos.	21,700	0.85				18,445							15,221
Decid. Azalea	21,000	1.30			27,300	27,300	27,300	27,300	27,300	27,300	27,300	27,300	23,086
Jap. Azaleas	16,800	0.45			7,610	7,610	7,610	7,610	7,610	7,610	7,610	7,610	
Viburnum	13,580	0.85				11,543	11,543	11,543	11,543	11,543	11,543	11,543	
Ericas	15,000	0.15		1,125	2,250	2,250	2,250	2,250	2,250	2,250	2,250	2,250	4,500
Prunus	15,000	0.40				6,000	6,000	6,000	6,000	6,000	6,000	6,000	12,000
Viburnum	15,000	0.40				6,000	6,000	6,000	6,000	6,000	6,000	6,000	12,000
Cotoneaster	15,000	0.30			4,500	4,500	4,500	4,500	4,500	4,500	4,500	4,500	9,000
Santolina	40,000	0.20		8,000	8,000	8,000	8,000	8,000	8,000	8,000	8,000	8,000	16,000
Sale of nursery													250,000
TOTAL REVENUE			4,117	13,242	49,660	108,448	90,003	90,003	90,003	90,003	90,003	90,003	430,007
less NET CURRENT VALUE less TOTAL COSTS			200,000 70,000	70,000	70,000	70,000	70,000	70,000	70,000	70,000	70,000	70,000	70,000
equals NET REVENUE			(265,883)	(56,758)	(20,340)	38,448	20,003	20,003	20,003	20,003	20,003	20,003	360,007

Discount rate 5%
NET PRESENT VALUE £
3,376

Once the cash flow has been worked out, the Net Present Value should be calculated. It is suggested that a 5% discount rate should be used. Because we are using current prices, inflation can be ignored. The bank borrowing rate is affected by inflation, so that, too, can be ignored. The 5% discount rate makes some allowance for risk and for the fact that the nurseryman might be able to make a fair income from some other investment.

Other plans

One feasible plan has now been worked out, and its profitability has been calculated. The next step is to move back to the beginning and work out another feasible plan. Trial and error is the best way of finding out what can be done and what the profit is. Naturally, the nurseryman must take into account his own preferences, the need to produce a balanced catalogue, the resources available and estimates of the market size.

Choosing a plan

When several plans have been worked out, the most profitable must be selected. This is not as easy as it sounds. Some plans will be more profitable in early years, others in later years. To make a useful comparison it is necessary to have some way of comparing two cash flows to decide which is the most profitable. The next chapter shows how two of these methods, Discounted Cash Flow and Breakeven Period, work.

12
Choosing a Plan

This chapter shows, first, how to see whether a plan which produces a flow of revenue over a 10-year (or longer) period is profitable at all. It answers the nurseryman's question 'Wouldn't I be better off selling up the nursery, investing the money and living off the interest plus my salary?' Second, it shows how to decide which of two plans with very different cash flows is the most profitable. Thirdly, it shows that profitability is not the only important factor: cash flow can be critical. The cash flow is the amount of money going into, or out of, a business enterprise over a period. Table 11 shows how a cash flow is drawn up. The business or the investment, perhaps the purchase of new glasshouses, starts at the beginning of the first year, at a time we will call year 0, with an expenditure on mother stock, glasshouses, frames, etc. of £40,000. During the first year, wages, fertilisers, machinery costs, etc., amount to £5,000. There is a small income, £500, from surplus mother stock and from plants bought for growing-on, so the net cash flow is only − £4,500. (The minus sign means that the firm is paying this out.) In the second year, expenditure remains the same, but income rises as more of the plants bought for growing-on reach saleable size, so the net cash flow is (− £5,000 + 1,500) or − £3,500. Over the year, income rises until, when all production systems are producing, it levels off at £10,000 a year. As expenditure is only £5,000, the business has a net income of £5,000 or a net cash flow of + £5,000. At the end of year 9 the business is sold up, so the nurseryman recovers the value of the growing plants, plus the value of his land and the value of the 10-year-old glasshouse. His net cash flow in this year is + £65,000.

This cash flow, like the other cash flows in this chapter, is rather simplified, so that the method of doing Discounted Cash Flow Analysis can be shown simply and clearly.

Discounting the cash flow

The nurseryman has to look at cash flows from different systems of production and to decide whether they are profitable at all and which of them is the most profitable. To do this he *discounts* the cash flow, using the compound interest method. The idea is this: if, instead of investing in a nursery, the nurseryman puts his money in a savings bank, he will receive perhaps 10% interest. For every £100 he deposits he will receive £10 at the end of the year. If, however, he leaves the £10 interest in the bank, then at the end of the second year he will receive 10% of his original £100 plus the 10% on his £10 interest, so he will receive £11. If he leaves all this £121 in the bank a third year he gets another £12.10, bringing his bank balance up to £133.10.   245

TABLE 11   CASH FLOW FOR A NURSERY ENTERPRISE

Year		Flow out £	Flow in £	Net cash flow £
0	Purchase of land, erection of glasshouse, frames, etc.	40,000		− 40,000
1	Wages, fertilisers etc.,	5,000		
	Sale of first plants		500	− 4,500
2	Wages, materials.	5,000		
	Sale of plants		1,500	− 3,500
3	Wages, materials.	5,000		
	Sale of plants		5,000	0
4	Wages, materials.	5,000		
	Sale of plants		7,000	+ 2,000
5	Wages, materials.	5,000		
	Sale of plants		10,000	+ 5,000
6	Wages, materials.	5,000		
	Sale of plants		10,000	+ 5,000
7	Wages, materials.	5,000		
	Sale of plants		10,000	+ 5,000
8	Wages, materials.	5,000		
	Sale of plants		10,000	+ 5,000
9	Wages, materials.	5,000		
	Sale of plants		10,000	
	Value of growing plants		40,000	
	Value of land etc.		20,000	+ 65,000

This case, where he is getting interest on interest, is called *compound interest* and the amount can be calculated very quickly with a calculating machine. The amount put in the bank is multiplied by $(1+r)$, where r is the rate of interest, every year it remains in the bank. For example:

	£
Amount put in the bank in Year 0	= 100
End of 1st year £100 × (1+0.10)	= 110
End of 2nd year £110 × (1.10)	= 121
End of 3rd year £121 × (1.10)	= 133.10
End of 4th year £133.10 × (1.10)	= 146.41

Here the amount in the bank at the end of each year is multiplied by $(1+r)$ to give the amount in the bank at the end of the next year. This same calculation can be written slightly differently as follows:

	£
Amount in bank in year 0	= 100
End of 1st year £100 × 1.10	= 110
End of 2nd year £100 × 1.10 × 1.10	= 121
End of 3rd year £100 × 1.10 × 1.10 × 1.10	= 133.10
End of 4th year £100 × 1.10 × 1.10 × 1.10 × 1.10	= 146.41

This calculation is quite straightforward as long as it is remembered that 0.10 is 10% so that $(1+r) = (1 + 0.10) = (1.10)$. Where r is 5%, $(1 + r) = (1.05)$. *Most mistakes in discounted cash flow analysis come from forgetting this point.*

The businessman wants to know firstly whether he should put his money into a savings bank at 10% interest or whether he should invest in a certain project. If the project involves investing £100 in Year 0 and collecting £146.41 at the end of Year 4, he is equally well off as we have just shown (inflation aside). If he gets not one payment at the end of four years, but a flow of payments over 10 years, a *cash flow* like that in Table 4, in fact, the problem is equally simple, but a little more time consuming.

When we have a cash flow like that in Table 11 we want to know what it is worth in terms of today's money. To do this we find for each year's payment, how much money put in the savings bank now would produce this sum of money. For instance, if £100 is put in the bank at 10% now, it will be worth £146.41 in four years' time, so the present value of £146.41 in four years' time is £100 at 10%. If we work out the present value of each year's cash payment and add them up we will have the present value of several years' cash flow. If this money is put in the savings bank now, we can draw out the higher payments in future years. We are saying, then, that a given sum of money at the present value, is worth exactly the same to the nurseryman as a larger future amount of money. If the present value is negative, the losses are bigger than the profits.

The calculation of the present value of the cash flow in Table 11 is shown in Table 12, which took less than four minutes to work out with an ordinary calculating machine. It would take an even shorter time with a business calculating machine which is already programmed to do this calculating, or

TABLE 12   PRESENT VALUE OF A FLOW OF INCOME AT 10%

Year end	Net cash flow £	Discounting factor (1.10)	Present value Cash flow — factor £
0	− 40,000	1.00	− 40,000
1	− 4,500	1.10	− 4,091
2	− 3,500	1.21	− 2,892
3	0	1.331	0
4	+ 2,000	1.464	+ 1,366
5	+ 5,000	1.610	+ 3,106
6	+ 5,000	1.772	+ 2,822
7	+ 5,000	1.948	+ 2,567
8	+ 5,000	2.144	+ 2,332
9	+65,000	2.358	+27,567
			− 7,223

with a computer. In the first column are the years. At the end of Year 0, the beginning of Year 1, the investment is made. The second column, the net cash flow, comes straight from Table 11. The third column, the discounting factor, is worked out from $(1 + r)$. The present value of £40,000 in the hand is £40,000 in Year 0, because this is the money you have not yet spent, so the discounting factor is 1.00. At the end of the first year you would get your original deposit × (1.10) from your savings bank at 10% so the discounting factor is 1.10. At the end of the second year you would get your original deposit × (1.10) × (1.10) from the savings bank so your discounting factor is (1.10) × (1.10) or 1.21. At the end of the third year you would get your original deposit × (1.10) × (1.10) × (1.10) so your discounting factor is (1.10) × (1.10) × (1.10) or 1.331. Each figure in this column is just the previous figure times 1.10.

The fourth column is the present value and it is calculated by dividing the cash flow (Column two) by the discounting factor. If you are borrowing at 10%, an overdraft of £4,091 now is the same as an overdraft of £4,500 in one year's time so the present value of − £4,500 in one year's time is − £4,091 now. If you put £27,567 in the savings bank at 10% now you will get £65,000 at the end of 9 years — 2.348 times as much as your original investment. The *present value* of £65,000 after 9 years at 10% is £27,567. The total of the fourth column — add all the plusses, then take away all the minuses — gives the present value of the cash flow. This can be done automatically in the calculator's memory. In this cash flow the present value is minus £7,223. In other words, the businessman who puts his money in this business instead of putting it into the bank is throwing away £7,223.

One reason why the project is unprofitable is that the present value of the £65,000 at the end of year 9 is only £27,567, or 42% of its cash value. If the interest rate was lower, the present value would be higher. Table 13 shows the position if the interest rate was as low as 7½%. Here the future income is worth relatively more and the nursery is slightly more profitable than the savings bank as an investment.

TABLE 13   PRESENT VALUE OF A FLOW OF INCOME AT 7½%

Year end	Net Cash Flow	Discounting factor $(1.075)^n$ £	Present value Cash flow ÷ factor £
0	− 40,000	1.00	− 40,000
1	− 4,500	1.075	− 4,186
2	− 3,500	1.156	− 3,028
3	0	1.243	0
4	+ 2,000	1.336	+ 1,497
5	+ 5,000	1.436	+ 3,482
6	+ 5,000	1.544	+ 3,238
7	+ 5,000	1.660	+ 3,012
8	+ 5,000	1.785	+ 2,801
9	+ 65,000	1.919	+ 33,872
			+ 688

This point is very important. When interest rates are high, distant returns have a low present value, so investments with a fast return are more profitable. When interest rates are low, distant returns become more profitable. This is why countries build hydro-electro power stations, with high capital costs and low running costs, when interest rates are low and thermal power stations, with relatively low capital costs and high running costs, when interest rates are high.

The choice facing the nurseryman is shown in Table 14. There are two possible projects. In Project A, half the investment is recovered in the first year and returns tail off until the nursery is sold in year 15. This nursery might start by buying plants from Holland, growing them on for two or three years and then selling them. For the remainder of the 15 years the investor runs the nursery as a Production Nursery growing cheap plants.

Project B is more like the cash flow from a normal nursery. The capital expenditure takes place at the beginning of the first year; at the end of the first year some returns are obtained from sale of mother plants and plants bought for growing-on and, from the second year onwards, increasing returns come from plants with a three, four or five year production period. Finally, in year 15, the nursery is sold. (In Chapter 10 it will be shown how the returns from short-term and long-term plants are combined to make a cash flow for a nursery business.)

TABLE 14   THE PRESENT VALUE OF TWO INVESTMENT PROJECTS AT
10% DISCOUNT RATE

Year	Cash flow		Discount factor $(1.10)^n$	Present value	
	A	B		A	B
0	− 20,000	− 20,000	1.0	− 20,000	− 20,000
1	10,000	+ 1,000	1.1	9,091	+ 909
2	8,000	500	1.21	6,612	413
3	6,000	1,000	1.33	4,511	752
4	4,000	1,000	1.46	2,740	685
5	3,000	1,000	1.61	1,863	621
6	2,000	2,000	1.77	1,130	1,130
7	1,000	3,000	1.95	513	1,538
8	1,000	4,000	2.15	465	1,860
9	1,000	5,000	2.39	418	2,092
10	1,000	6,000	2.61	383	2,299
11	1,000	6,000	2.87	348	2,091
12	1,000	6,000	3.16	316	1,899
13	1,000	9,000	3.48	287	2,586
14	1,000	15,000	3.83	261	3,916
15	10,000	50,000	4.21	2,375	11,876
				£11,313	£14,667

Table 14 shows that at an interest rate of 10% Project B, the normal nursery, has a present value of £14,665, while the quick-return investment, Project A, has a present value of £11,312. This means that the investor will be £11,312 better off if he invests in Project A than if he invests in the savings bank, so

TABLE 15   THE PRESENT VALUE OF TWO INVESTMENT PROJECTS AT
15% DISCOUNT RATE

Year	Cash flow		Discount factor $(1.10)^n$	Present value	
	A	B		A	B
0	− 20,000	− 20,000	1.0	− 20,000	− 20,000
1	10,000	1,000	1.15	8,696	870
2	8,000	500	1.32	6,060	379
3	6,000	1,000	1.52	3,947	658
4	4,000	1,000	1.75	2,286	571
5	3,000	1,000	2.01	1,493	498
6	2,000	2,000	2.31	866	866
7	1,000	3,000	2.66	376	1,128
8	1,000	4,000	3.06	326	1,307
9	1,000	5,000	3.52	284	1,420
10	1,000	6,000	4.05	247	1,481
11	1,000	6,000	4.66	215	1,288
12	1,000	6,000	5.36	187	1,119
13	1,000	9,000	6.16	162	1,461
14	1,000	15,000	7.08	141	2,119
15	10,000	50,000	8.14	1,229	6,143
				£6,514	£1,308

clearly he is not interested in the savings bank. Project B has an even higher present value than Project A so he will be £3,354 better off if he adopts Project B than if he adopts Project A. If, however, the interest rate is 15%, rather than 10%, the position is reversed. Table 15 shows that in this case the present value of Project A is £5,206 more than that of Project B. As the interest rate has risen, the project with the quick returns has become more profitable.   249

At any given rate of interest, then, the investor will be better off if he chooses the project with the highest net present value, but different projects will be more profitable at different rates of interest. The nurseryman can use any of several rates of interest to calculate the present value, for instance the interest he gets from investments in a building society, the overdraft rate he pays to the bank or the rate of inflation. These are discussed in Chapter 16. Most nurserymen will not want to read this discussion until they are actually planning the nursery.

Internal Rate of Return

There is another measure of profitability, the Internal Rate of Return. It is based on the same logic as the Net Present Value, and should rank plans in the same order. It offers no advantages over the other system, and could easily lead to confusion, so we suggest that it is avoided. The nurseryman should stick to the Net Present Value, but for those that are interested, a brief description of the Internal Rate of Return follows: The internal rate of return is the discount rate which yields a present value of zero. This is found by choosing different discount rates and calculating the present value until one gets a present value near to zero. For example, the cash flow in Table 13 had a present value of −£7,223 at a discount rate of 10%. Obviously, since the big payments were in the distant future, a lower interest rate would give a higher present value. The next step is to calculate the present value at a lower rate, 5%; this produces a figure of +£10,669.

Since 5% is too low a discount rate and 10% is too high, a mid point, 7.5% can be tried. This is shown in Table 6 where the present value works out at £709, which is near enough to zero, so 7.5% is the internal rate of return. Another ten minutes calculation would show that the true figure is 7.7%.

Some people prefer using the internal-rate-of-return to using the present value so they can say 'My investment is yielding 17.2%,' instead of saying 'The present value of my investment is £132,000'. In fact, the two systems give the same result providing the financial charges, etc. are handled in the way suggested in this chapter. We have used the present value method rather than the internal rate of return method because the internal rate of return can easily be confused with 'rate of return on capital invested' — a rather pointless measure often used in business. We are not concerned with the rate of return on all capital invested, including borrowed capital, but rather on how the nurseryman can get the maximum return from *his own* capital so instead of saying the firm is making 10% on capital employed (£100,000 including borrowed money) we say it is making 50 per cent on the owner's investment of £20,000 after paying all interest, financial charges etc.

The most profitable project is the one with the highest present value or the one with the highest internal rate of return. The two systems, internal rate of return and present value, will rank projects in the same order if:

Reinvestment opportunities are examined and fully utilised. That is to say all profits, over and above the directors' salaries, are reinvested in the most profitable way and only drawn at the end of the 10 or 15 year investment period.

The same capital outlay is considered for each investment. It is usually a lot easier to select a really profitable investment requiring £2,000 than to select an equally profitable investment requiring £200,000.

The same investment period is used for each project. Otherwise if cash flows are appraised using the Present Value method it is assumed in effect, that all profits can be reinvested at the discount rate, 10%. If, instead, the internal rate of return is calculated, it is assumed, in effect, that all profits can be reinvested at the internal rate of return, 25%, for Project A and 16% for Project B.

In order to meet these conditions when evaluating nursery projects we will assume that:

(a)   The investor has a sum of money available, all of which will be taken into account in his cash flow. If he invests only half of it and puts the rest in a Building Society, both the nursery and the building society will be included in the cash flow. This means that the same capital outlay is considered for each investment.

(b)   The directors will be paid a fee which may rise over the years. All profits over this will be reinvested. (Alternatively the investors may withdraw all profits as they are made, but difficulties do arise with this.)

(c)   At the end of the project, after 10 or 15 years, all assets will be valued.

The present value system and the internal rate of return system then rank projects in the same order.

Breakeven Period

When several plans have been prepared, which one should be chosen? Other things being equal, the one with the highest Net Present Value is the best choice. Roughly speaking, the Net Present Value is the sum of money which, if invested in a bank at interest, would yield that flow of income. The higher the Net Present Value, the higher the flow of income.

Things are not always equal though. Even if a project has a high Net Present Value, the cash flow may be disastrous. For example, the following cash flow has a Net Present Value of £133,787 at a discount rate of 5%:

Year 0	Y1	Y2	Y3	Y4	Y5	Y6	Y7	Y8	Y9	Year 10
− £50,000	0	0	0	0	0	0	0	0	0	£200,000

This sounds good with the present value two and a half times as big as the investment, but it is not going to be acceptable to the average investor, as he would have to find £50,000 and wait 10 years before getting any return. For this reason, investors often calculate the *breakeven period*, the time it takes before all the costs are paid, after which all revenue is clear profit. In the example above, it is 10 years.

The breakeven period is just one consideration to take into account in planning a nursery and it is very much less important than the Net Present Value in most cases. However, the cash flow must be carefully examined to see that in each year the nursery has enough ready cash to pay its debts and service its overdraft. Any business needs cash to operate in the short term, however profitable it is in the long term. In the example of Table 10 for example, there are accumulated losses of £112,981 after three years and the business does not break even until the nursery is sold.

251

Objectives

In preparing a long term plan for a nursery it is important to be clear about one's objectives.

An ambitious young man setting up a nursery for the first time may plan to have a disposable cash income which is barely sufficient for his needs and to aim at maximum increase in the size of his firm so that he will be very well off in his 40s.

A man in his 40s with an established nursery may feel that his nursery is as big as he can handle. If there is any more expansion, he will have to work full-time in the office and he will have to employ an accountant, so he will plan for the maximum disposable income with the minimum growth — perhaps even a reduction in the size of the business.

A man who has just had a mild heart attack will want to replan his nursery to reduce the physical and mental strain of running it. He too will want the maximum disposable cash income, but the reduction of the size of his business is even more important.

A man approaching retiring age will live on a reduced income and plan his nursery in such a way that it will realise as much as possible when sold up. Here, of course, tax considerations are most important. The value of any investment or reinvestment will depend largely on whether the returns from sale will be taxed as income or as capital gains, or whether they will escape tax altogether. He may decide to draw a large income from the firm, putting as much as possible in the savings bank, in order to pay tax at the standard rate on it rather than to pay tax at a much higher rate in the year he sells the nursery, when he has a very high taxable income. This man is aiming at a very different kind of growth from that aimed at by the young man setting up in business. He is aiming at getting the maximum amount of money after tax and having no other assets when he retires. The young man is aiming at developing an asset that will only reach its full earning power after ten or fifteen years and he is not thinking of selling his business even then.

An old man with a son may aim at having as high an income as possible and, at the same time, at handing his son as much as possible of the nursery after paying estate duty, or after avoiding it.

An old man with no immediate heir may aim at enjoying the maximum income and at having no assets left when he dies. This is the principle of the annuity: one pays a sum to the insurance company which depends partly on the going interest rate and partly on one's life expectancy — the shorter the life expectancy the higher the income. The income is higher than the rate of interest, but the payments stop when one dies, and the insurance company keeps the original payment.

The plan chosen by each of these men will be quite different, so each must decide exactly what he wants to achieve and keep this aim constantly in mind. If he compares accounts with another nursery, he must remember that the other nursery may be aiming at the maximum after-tax profit, while he is aiming at the maximum growth, so the firm with the highest profit is not necessarily the most efficient.

Tax pays a large part in these aims — one man wants to get the maximum income after tax, while another wants to get the maximum lump sum after paying capital gains tax. Every nurseryman should consult a tax accountant. The cost is small in relation to the savings in tax the accountant should achieve. He is the best man to explain how to change a given cash flow, before tax, into the maximum cash flow, after tax. We will not give any advice on tax as so much depends on the family circumstances of the nurseryman, his aims, the type of nursery and the tax regulations currently in force.

One way of planning in order to achieve these aims is to use different discount rates for each aim.

The ambitious young man setting up a nursery for the first time will have a low discount rate. Present earnings do not mean any more to him than future earnings and they may even mean less. His discount rate will be somewhere near the rate of inflation, or, in the simple system where we ignore inflation, near zero.

The man planning to leave as much as possible to his heirs may be willing to sacrifice present income, investing his money in agricultural land, on which his heirs will pay a reduced rate of estate duty, instead of on a much more profitable industrial enterprise. This means that he too has a very low discount rate, below the rate of inflation and possibly even negative, with income earned by his son in 10 years being valued higher than income earned by himself now.

The man retiring in six years also has a low discount rate, preferring cash at his retirement to cash now.

The man in his 40s with an established nursery which he does not wish to expand will have a relatively high discount rate.

The old man with no heir will have an extremely high discount rate — present income being worth infinitely more than income after he dies.

Profits

The nurseryman is in business to make a profit and the economic planning methods presented here are designed to help him. When two very similar plans are compared, the difference in total returns may be as high as 25% and the difference in profit may be even higher. The nurseryman may increase his income over a five-year period by several thousand pounds, just by spending two or three weeks on making a first class plan for the nursery.

What is profit though? Profit is a loose term and accountants and farm management advisors have eight or ten definitions of profit which are widely recognised and widely used. It is important for the nurseryman to know what kind of profit he is talking about and why. If he does not, he may find his business is very 'profitable', but he does not have any spending money, or that his business is very 'profitable' in another way but after ten years all his assets have disappeared and he is bankrupt. Here are some of the common types of profit.

Cash trading profit is cash sales less cash expenses excluding capital expenses.

Before-tax profit is cash trading profit after making allowance for changes in the valuation of growing plants and making any permissable allowances for depreciation. A lot of this profit is book profit — increases in value of plants — which cannot be spent.

After-tax profit is before-tax profit less tax.

253

Disposable cash is after-tax profit less valuation increases (which are only paper profits) plus depreciation allowances (which are only paper costs) less repayments of loans. This is the amount of money the nurseryman has to spend or to invest.

Net farm income is used in farm management surveys in order to compare very different farms. Some farmers own their own land and capital while others rent their land and borrow their capital, so some pay rent and interest and the others do not. In order to compare the efficiency of the farm one adds interest charges and subtracts rent equivalent from before-tax profit to get net farm income. This is useful for comparisons of a lot of farms but nurserymen should avoid it: a high net farm income does not mean a high cash income.

Management and investment income is even more dangerous. It is net farm income minus the value of the farmer's labour. On small farms some of a farmer's time is used on labourers' jobs so the value of this is subtracted to make the figure comparable with that for a farm where the farmer works full time on management. This is valuable for comparing the efficiency of farms. It is not, however, the profit the nurseryman should try to maximise.

The definitions may be made even more complicated. There are different accounting conventions, depending on whether depreciation, undistributed profits, etc. should be included, so the quoted profit for a firm using the *Financial Times* definitions may not be the same as that when the firms uses its own definitions. Some refer to the world of big business where firms are owned by thousands of shareholders and are run by hired managers. Others are accounting concepts developed to make it easier to compare the efficiency of two firms. Most of these other definitions are meaningless to the nurserymen so we will not discuss them.

A nurseryman must know what he wants 'profit' to mean. Does he want it to compare his profit and efficiency with other firms? In practice this is very seldom possible as firms are secretive and as different accounting methods, from the minimum necessary to keep the taxman happy to the most sophisticated, are used. Does he want to use profit as a measure of what he can spend and save? This is usually the case but the definition of profit used by the accountant may hide this. Only if the nurseryman knows exactly what he wants to do, will the accountant be able to use a suitable definition of profit.

13
Planning your Planning

This chapter has some useful tips on how to organise your office work to make planning less trouble and to reduce errors. Some records are essential if a nurseryman is to plan his nursery at all. If he does not know how long it takes to lift plants or how many azalea cuttings he can get in a glasshouse, his planning cannot mean much. All management textbooks, all management specialists and all accountants have a lot to say about record keeping. If the nurseryman followed all their advice, he would have more people working in the office than in the nursery. Most of the records would be carefully kept but never used.

Why are records kept in the first place? Firstly, there are the records required by law to satisfy the requirements of the tax inspectors or the Companies Act. An accountant is the best person to advise on the minimum accounts needed to meet these requirements and he can also give extremely valuable information on how to arrange one's affairs to avoid taxation. The best system will depend on the family and finance of the individual nurseryman so individual advice is needed.

The other area in which accountants have been involved traditionally is in keeping accounts to detect or discourage theft. In the smaller nursery, all the money is handled by the owner so there is not much point in doing this. Even in the larger nursery, control of money is in the hands of one man and theft by the manager is very difficult for accountants to detect.

In presenting accounts for income tax, for company accounts, or to detect theft, 90% of an accountant's time is spent on seeing that the accounts add up the same each time, on seeing that the auditors will get the same answers. This is all very well but the message is clear. This is an expensive form of accounting and it should only be used where it is necessary. For most management accountancy, this accuracy is unnecessary so the system of double checks and cross checks and trial balances is unnecessary.

Accountants should have important management skills, and management accounting is now the major part of their job in most industries. In agriculture, however, management advice is given by farm management specialists, usually agricultural economists or agriculturists with farm management training. They have developed very effective techniques for planning farms. These techniques do not work when planning a nursery but the method developed in this book is based on the same principles. The farm management specialist bases much of his advice on figures obtained from the Farm Management Surveys. These figures vary from the purely financial, like profit and gross margin, to the physical efficiency factors like stocking rate, feed conversion rates, yields per acre. As the farm management survey covers 255 hundreds of farms of different sorts, varying from large dairy units to small market gardens, it is very difficult to get figures that mean the same thing to the dairy farmer and the market gardener. All the figures collected must be collected according to a carefully defined formula, which must be applied exactly, regardless of the peculiarities of the individual farm. Some of the results obtained as a result are ridiculous but, generally speaking, the survey serves its purpose. Here again, a lot of time and effort goes to getting figures that are comparable over a wide range of farms, and some of the definitions have to be made less meaningful for the individual farm, if they are to apply to the farming industry in general.

The system set out in this book is not expected to make comparisons possible over the whole nursery stock industry. There does not seem to be much point in comparing the efficiency factors or the profits per unit of glass of a garden centre and a wholesale nursery. Certainly the nurseryman can expect to gain a great deal from comparing his records with those of two or three nurseries in a similar line of business. He will quickly see whether he is devoting too much time to one part of his business or another or whether he is losing too many rhododendron cuttings. This comparison does not require as rigid a recording system as does an industry-wide comparison.

A lot of work is saved if three to five nurserymen with similar businesses use the same system and exchange figures. Because you will not be comparing garden centres with wholesale nurseries, the system does not have to be too complicated. Because there are only a few nurseries, everyone will know why Smith's nursery has an unusually high figure for glasshouse labour, so they will be able to allow for this, instead of thinking a mistake has been made in the statistics. Because there are only a few nurseries, the managers will be able to discuss each other's problems in detail and visit the nurseries, if necessary, to see how one nursery has economised in glasshouse space and another in planting-out labour.

In devising the system presented here, we have taken into account the following principles.

It is impossible to find the cost of producing a plant. Both in theory and in practice it is impossible to divide up the overheads between different subjects. The most that can be done is to divide up the *variable* costs between different crops to provide a type of Gross Margin.

Labour is an overhead and any attempt to cost labour, or to allocate labour cost to different subjects, will result in the nurseryman's losing money. This has been explained in more detail in Chapter 8.

High profit in the nursery not high profit per plant is the nurseryman's aim. Planning must be done for the business as a whole. It is pointless to concentrate on subjects with a high profit per plant if you can handle only a few of them. You would be better off growing a large number of plants with a low profit per plant.

Never collect any records you are not going to use.

Do not use one accounting system to collect different types of information.
It is convenient to use one accounting system for tax and company accounts.

If you try to make it do your management accounts too, all the double checks, etc. will be wasted effort as far as this is concerned. There are also two other dangers, first, that the right management-accounting information will not be collected, because it does not fit in with the financial accounting definitions — certainly some bending of definitions is to be expected. Secondly, tnere is the temptation to collect a little more information — 'now we have got the labour recording system organised, why not collect the hours spent on taking cuttings separately from the hours spent on preparing cuttings?' There is no end to the possibilities and a nurseryman might soon find he had superb records but no time to use them. If the recording procedure has a specific aim, and nothing is collected just in case it may be useful, one can cut this waste. With a mixed recording and accounting scheme it is difficult to separate the two.

Ideally, one would record each crop separately, noting the number of hours spent on each crop, at each time of the year, noting the amount of herbicide going on each crop. etc. To a nurseryman, growing one or two hundred crops, this would mean one or two hundred account books. The figures obtained would not be particularly accurate either — imagine calculating the amount of herbicide used on a plot 10 yards square.

Labour recording

The method of labour recording used for the planning system must also be simple. Recording is only really necessary when there is a shortage of permanent labour. During this period all workers fill in a worksheet stating what job they were working on and how long it took them. They also state what crop they were working on, eg. 'lifting 1,000 berberis 50 hours.'

These sheets are processed in the office. This information would be used to help get a figure for 'lifting, sorting, labelling and packing spiky or thorned plants'. The number of plant categories should be kept to a minimum: there is no point in keeping records for twenty different types of tree, when it takes much the same time to lift each of them. Similarly, there is no point in recording lifting, sorting, labelling and packaging separately, for each plant has to undergo all these processes.

This information would be sufficient for the planning system described in the last chapter, where we only want details of labour at those periods when labour is scarce.

It also provides supervisors with something to base their estimates of labour requirements on. If a supervisor can say 'lift those 1,000 ericas. It should take the two of you until 6 o'clock this evening' there is less chance that the job will be spun out for another day, so overtime will be reduced.

Planning office work

Calculating machines save a great deal of time, if used properly. It is important that the right methods are used to avoid errors and to speed up work.

Even the largest sums can be worked out rapidly with a calculating machine so there is no point in using the short-cut methods of school arithmetic, rounding to the nearest 1,000, cancelling out zeros, using logarithm tables or square root tables. It is *quicker* to punch the whole long sum on the machine and get an answer than it is to round the figures to the nearest hundred or thousand. It is *more accurate* to punch the full figures 1,783 × 1,973 = 3,517,859 instead of the rounded figures 1,800 × 2,000 = 3,6000,000. *Fewer errors* are made.

At the same time, get out of the habit of doing sums in your head. If, after a long string of additions, you come to a sum like 3,712 + 113 which you would normally do in your head, still do it on the machine. There are two reasons for this. First, if done in your head, it interrupts the rhythm and breaks your concentration, so it actually increases the time taken. Secondly, there is a high proportion of errors in even the simplest sums done in this way, because it is very difficult to switch concentration from operating a machine to mental arithmetic then back again.

This is not to say that you should not check the figures in your head, saying 5,760 × 263 is a bit higher than 6 × 2 with five zeros after it, 1,200,000, so an answer of 1,514,880 is roughly of the right size while an answer of 151,488 is clearly wrong. This type of rough calculation shows up many errors. It is also worth checking any unusually large or unusually small figures. When the answers to a series of sums are 4,728, 5,893, 6,320, 7,800, 13,630, 7,300 or 201, 402, 804, 1,005, 1,206, it is worth wondering why 13,630 is so much larger than the others or why the jump between 402 and 804 is twice as big as the jump between the other numbers.

Naturally, everyone makes a lot of mistakes the first time they use a calculating machine, pressing the wrong buttons or forgetting to press the right button. After a little practice though, calculations should be fairly accurate. We find though that some days, especially in the afternoon after a heavy lunch, we start to make a lot of mistakes. When this happens, there is no point in continuing — so many mistakes will be made that everything will have to be done again next morning.

Since mistakes will be made and figures will be changed as different plans are tried out, numbers should be written in pencil. A rubber should be readily at hand and there is no better place to leave it than on the end of the pencil. A right-handed person should work the machine with his left hand and keep the pencil in his right hand. This saves several seconds searching for a pencil to write down the answer.

If you are using the calculating machine a lot, it will pay to learn to 'touch type' on it, pressing the keys without looking, taking a quick look at the figures on the display, pressing the instruction key, touch typing the next number, checking the number on the display, pressing the instruction key and so on.

Everyone makes mistakes so all work must be checked. The simplest method is to make a rough mental check of the sort just described. Otherwise the calculation must be repeated, but it should be done differently, adding from the bottom not the top or multiplying by the second figure not the first. Even better is to have someone else check the calculation. If you once make a mistake, it is easy to make the same mistake again and again, so change the method of calculation or get someone else who has not made the same mistake to do the sum again independently. If the calculating machine prints out the figures entered and the answers, it is much easier to check.

Work should be laid out clearly to permit checking and to make calculations simple. Some time should be spent on preparing work sheets as it will save time later on. The first requirement is that the sheets are big enough. Large sheets of analysis paper, double foolscap size, should be bought. This paper is usually already ruled in columns. Do not be afraid to glue or staple two or three sheets together. When planning month by month for three or four years, this is necessary. If you try to cram too much information onto one small sheet of paper, the result will be a muddle.

Each column of the work sheet and the work sheet itself must be clearly labelled. It may be a year before the sheet is looked at again and then you will want to know exactly what you did at each stage of the calculation. It may also save time to put a note at the bottom of the page, saying what was done at various parts of the page. Headings may be written in ink but, if so, it is useful to have a bottle of Snopake or Tippex typing-correcting fluid, a white paint that goes over mistakes leaving a surface you can write on.

The work sheet can also be laid out so that the minimum of copying is necessary. It is not easy to copy a long row of figures without missing out one or copying down the wrong figures. If copying is unavoidable, the best system is to fold the paper so that the line on which you are going to write is immediately below the figures you are going to copy. This works very well if the headings are the same and the columns are the same size and both tables go across the page. If not, the figures being copied must be clearly marked, perhaps by being underlined with felt tip markers or by a ruler being held underneath the line of figures. If three or four rows of figures on a table are to be added, perhaps rows 1, 4, 9 and 12, the rows to be added should be underlined or marked with a felt-tip pen.

Checks should be made frequently. Every set of calculations should be checked immediately, as there is nothing more frustrating than to complete a day's work and then to find an obvious mistake on page 1 which makes all the rest of the work useless.

14

Computers are Easy

Today, computers are easier to use than calculators. They increase accuracy and they cut weeks off the time needed to plan a nursery.

You do not need to know anything about programming to work a computer. You buy the program already written, plug it into the computer and start writing in your plans today.

You do not need to be a mathematician to use a computer. In fact for this whole planning exercise nothing more is needed than the ability to add, subtract, multiply and divide. It is no more difficult to tell the computer to do this than it is to tell your calculator to do it.

When should you buy a computer?

In the first edition of this book, in 1975, we were encouraging nurserymen to invest in that new, but very expensive, miracle of science, the electronic calculator. Within five or six years, these were being produced so cheaply that every schoolchild had one and that they were being thrown away instead of being repaired. The same thing is happening today with computers. Every year a new, smaller, more powerful and, above all, cheaper machine hits the market. At some stage in the next ten years every business in the country will have its own computer and most secondary schoolchildren will have them.

The fall in price means that there is a temptation to put off buying a computer — 'If I wait until next year, the price will be down 25%.' True, but the £300 saved is small compared with the time you are wasting by doing all your calculations by hand. More important, it is very small indeed compared with the money you lose by not bothering to plan your nursery at all, because it will take too long. At any time in the next twenty years, you will be able to say to yourself that you could get a more powerful, better and cheaper model next year. At some time though, you will have to make the decision.

What kind of computer?

If you already have a home computer, you can start your planning with it. The 8-bit, 64K, mini-computer (your computer salesman will explain these terms) which was the standard home computer in the early 1980s is adequate for a first attempt at planning. However, you will soon find it infuriating. It does not have enough machine memory to hold all the information you want — and it takes a surprising amount of memory to store all the information on each

260

line you grow. You keep getting 'memory full' messages. You will find it irritatingly slow in calculating. You will see how valuable a computer can be, and be annoyed that yours is not better.

If you are buying a computer, a better choice is a 16-bit computer with as much memory as you can get — say 256K RAM plus 340K disc memory. 32-bit home computers are starting to hit the market, machines with an add-on memory of 980K RAM. Already you can buy these for little more than the old home computers.

As well as machine memory, you need disc memory, so that you can store all your records on a magnetic disc. Surprisingly, for planning you do not need a lot of disc memory. However, you will probably be switching your accounts to the computer, and perhaps using it as a word-processor, and for these you will find that the more storage you have the happier you are. For the rich, a Winchester disc is an added luxury, giving you all the storage space you need and saving time.

It is sometimes said that an 8-bit computer is better because there are more programs available for it. This is becoming less and less true. Anyway, I have not been able to find any program specifically designed for the nurseryman's planning. What the nurseryman needs is a spreadsheet program, and the ones for 16-bit or 32-bit machines are far better. He may also want an accounting program, and those for 16-bit machines are more than adequate.

There is not a lot to choose technically between computers of similar specification. Look for a large, comfortable screen (*not your television set*), a well-designed keyboard, a silent keyboard (some machines go 'ping' every time you touch a button, which can be infuriating, and, contrary to what the salesman tells you, this cannot be turned off with a program). Do not worry about coloured screens and games playing ability — you want a different sort of machine for that. It is cheaper to get the right machine for your business and a small Atari for games.

Some firms will hire out a small computer to you. It pays handsomely to take advantage of this. You may find that the machine you wanted had a bad screen, a poor keyboard, or insufficient memory. After you have had the machine for a couple of months, you will know what it can do for you, and you will have a good idea of what your ideal machine is and how much you are willing to pay for the extras.

For the nurseryman a wide, dot-matrix printer like the Epson FX 100 is best. It can print 236 characters across the page so it can handle tables covering several years, month by month. It is also faster, cheaper and more reliable than the 'letter-quality' printers.

Who to buy it from

When you look through the computer magazines, you will find that there are firms in London or in isolated parts of the country that sell computers at a lower price than your local computer shop. By all means use this information when negotiating a discount from your local computer shop (and you should get one) but do not buy from them. It means a lot to you to be able to go to your local shop for advice or for repairs rather than going to London. If you cannot understand the instructions, or a program does not work, it is important to be able to get expert advice locally. The time and money you save by not having to travel to London will soon compensate for any higher price.

Get the salesman to set up your machine for you and show you how it works. Spend two hours a day for a week learning to use your computer and your Calc program properly. The shop is empty most of the day and they can spare the time. Even if you had to pay for this service, it is worth it for the time you save — there are always some problems which are easily solved but which are not explained clearly in the manual or in the lessons program.

The program

You will probably be given a spreadsheet program, VisiCalc or Perfect Calc or one of the other Calc programs, with the machine. If not, you can buy one. The description given here is based on a Perfect Calc program running on an 8-bit machine. The VisiCalc program is very similar. Perfect Calc has some features that make it especially useful for nursery planning, but VisiCalc and the other Calc programs have their own special features. The market for programs is highly competitive and these will improve still further in the future, while new and different programs are about to hit the market.

Our experience is that it is possible to teach someone who has never seen a computer before to use such a spreadsheet program adequately in half an hour. The program comes with its own 'programmed learning' course, and this will make you a complete expert in about 8 hours. By the time you have done a table or two you will have no problems.

The program comes on a disc like a 45 r.p.m. gramophone record. You put this into the disc drive slot, and type in a few letters (e.g. 'pc Table1') to call your spreadsheet to the screen. The spreadsheet is like a large sheet of paper ruled into rows and columns. There are 52 columns, marked 'a' to 'z' and 'A' to 'Z' running across the page. There are 126 rows, marked '1' to '126'. As with a sheet of paper, there are 'cells' where the rows meet the columns. These cells are referred to by the column letter and row number. For instance the top left hand cell is 'a1', while the bottom right hand cell is 'Z126'.

The first thing to do is to type in the column headings — nothing could be easier. Move the cursor (the flashing light which indicates where on the screen you will be writing) to the top of the column. Type your heading, and it appears written on the screen.

You can then start entering the numbers. Move to the right cell, enter the number as you would with a calculator, and it appears on the screen. Again, nothing could be simpler.

When you reach the bottom of the column, you want the computer to do the adding up for you so you enter a simple formula by writing 'sum'. For instance the entry 'sum(b5:b12)' means 'write in this cell the sum of all the numbers in cells b5, b6, b7, b8, b9, b10, b11 and b12.

You can now see some of the big advantages of the spreadsheet. It is much quicker to write down 'sum(b5:b12)' than it is to add all the numbers with a calculator, and there is no chance at all of making a mistake in entering the figures. More exciting still, you can go back to b5 and change the figure there to see what happens if you grow more rhododendrons, and the machine automatically changes the total.

Another command you may give for this planning exercise is 'g20 = b5 × f19' where for example b5 is the cell showing the number of rhododendrons you have decided to grow and f19 is the cell showing the mount of bench space you need for each. Cell g20 then shows you the total amount of bench space you need. Again, you can change the figure at b5 or at f19 and the new answer will be worked out automatically. (In fact the computer uses * as a multiply sign, so you would enter the formula as 'g20 = b5*f19'.)

The computer will also work out the Net Present Value of a cash flow, which means that all the calculations set out in the last chapter are done automatically.

The computer makes the planning system very quick and easy. Once you have set up your tables showing labour needs, prices, glasshouse space etc., it is a matter of a few moments to work out the effect of a new plan. Just enter the new plant numbers and in a few seconds it will come up with a new Net Present Value to show if the new system is more or less profitable than the old one.

Table 16 shows the spreadsheet used for calculating Table 10. Cell g13, for instance, is 'c13*d13' (with the * being a multiply sign). In this cell, therefore, goes the number in c13 (21,000 plants) times the number in d13 (the price £1.30) to give the total revenue from deciduous azaleas. If the numbers, 21,000 or 1.30 are changed, the formula changes the number that appears in cell g13.

At the bottom of the column the amounts in cells g10 to g21 are added up, with the answer appearing as 'TOTAL REVENUE' in column g23, with the formula 'sum(g10:g21)'. The costs are subtracted from this to give the 'NET REVENUE' by the formula 'g23-g26'. Finally, in cell b32, the 'NET PRE-SENT VALUE' of all the 'NET REVENUE' from e28 to o28 is worked out by a formula. If any of the numbers of plants, or prices are changed, all the totals down to the 'NET PRESENT VALUE' are reworked instantly. Similarly, any of the formulas can be changed at any time, and all the totals will be reworked automatically.

It is easy to insert a new line at say, line 15, to give details of another crop. The computer automatically changes all the other formulas to include this. The column total moves down one line and becomes 'sum(g10:g22)' instead of 'sum(g10:g21)'.

The table looks complicated and it looks as though it would take an expert typist hours to type it all into the computer. In fact, it does not take long. You type in the first formula in a row, e.g. 'c16*d16' and the computer will copy the formula all along the row. This saves a lot of time, and it also saves the possibility of copying down the formula wrongly. If you prefer, the computer will copy the formula, changing it to fit in its new place. For example the TOTAL REVENUE formula 'sum(e10:e21)' was copied along the whole row, changing so that each column was totalled. In column f, for example, it added up column f with the formula 'sum(f10:f21)'. The computer will copy whole columns of figures or blocks of figures from one part of the table to another, or even from one table to another.

With a 16-bit or 32-bit machine, it is possible to save time by putting all the tables on one enormous spreadsheet. At the top of the table put the number of plants and the information in Table 6. For the later tables refer back to these tables. In Table 10, for example, instead of writing down 8,400 for the number of rhododendrons, put in the cell number of this figure in the first table. Instead of a price of £2.00, put in the cell number of this in Table 6. This means that all you have to do is to change the price, or number of plants, or plant spacing, in the first table, and all the other tables in the plan are worked out automatically. You can then have, right at the bottom of the sheet, a summary table showing number of plants, total bench space used, total frame space used, total ground used, net revenue and Net Present Value. More often than not this summary table will show you all you want to know.

263

Something very similar can be done on a 8-bit machine with Perfect Calc, but not with all Calc programs. The tables on different files can be linked so that Tables 2, 3, 4, 5 and 6 depend on Table 1 and Table 7 depends on Tables 2, 3, 4 and 6. The basic information is then put in Table 1. The calculations are done in Tables 2, 3, 5, and 6, and the summary is presented in Table 7.

Quadratic programming and linear programming

It is possible to do linear or quadratic programming of a nursery, but there are only a handful of people who have the necessary mathematical skills, economic training and understanding of nursery stock techniques to do it. They do not have much spare time and their time is not cheap. Only the very large nursery stock producers could afford such an exercise.

The linear programming and quadratic programming techniques used for farm management are hopelessly inadequate for nursery stock. It needs an expert to run a program on a simple farm with half a dozen enterprises and with all the production processes taking place within a single year. A nursery might have hundreds of different crops (with the computer taking October propagation and February propagation as different crops, and sale as liners and sale as two-year olds as different crops). The returns seldom come in the same year as the costs. The computer does not know whether it is possible to postpone planting or the taking of cuttings to avoid a clash, and whether this would have any effect on the growth or the price of the plant.

Even if linear programs for nursery stock could be as routine as those for farms, we would not be wild about planning done entirely by outside experts, as opposed to planning done by the nurseryman himself with or without outside help. The nurseryman learns a lot from doing his own planning. He learns how important frame space is. He learns how much he depends on casual labour. He finds out what are the difficulties and bottlenecks. He can see on the screen in front of him the results of any changes he may try. He does not have to rely on a computer printout giving a recommended plan without any explanation.

TABLE 16   SHOWING THE FORMULAS USED TO WORK OUT TABLE 10—TOTAL REVENUE FROM THE PROPOSED PLAN

Col.	b	c	d	e	f	g	h	i	j	k	l	m	n	o
row		No. of Plants	Price in pounds	Year 0	Year 1	Year 2	Year 3	Year 4	Year 5	Year 6	Year 7	Year 8	Year 9	Year 10
10	Rhododendrons	8,400	2.00				c10*d10	c10*d10	c10*d10	c10*d10	c10*d10	c10*d10	c10*d10	2*c10*d10
11	Ericas (glass)	54,890	0.15	.5*c11*d11	.5*c11*d11									
12	Dwarf Rhodos.	21,700	0.85				c12*d12							
13	Decid. azalea	21,000	1.30			c13*d13	c13*d13	c13*d13	c13*d13	c13*d13	c13*d13	c13*d13	c13*d13	2*c13*d13
14	Jap. azaleas	16,800	0.45			c14*d14	c14*d14	c14*d14	c14*d14	c14*d14	c14*d14	c14*d14	c14*d14	2*c14*d14
15	Viburnum	13,580	0.85				c15*d15	c15*d15	c15*d15	c15*d15	c15*d15	c15*d15	c15*d15	2*c15*d15
16	Ericas	15,000	0.15		.5*c16*d16	c16*d16	c16*d16	c16*d16	c16*d16	c16*d16	c16*d16	c16*d16	c16*d16	2*c16*d16
17	Prunus	15,000	0.40				c17*d17	c17*d17	c17*d17	c17*d17	c17*d17	c17*d17	c17*d17	2*c17*d17
18	Viburnum	15,000	0.40				c18*d18	c18*d18	c18*d18	c18*d18	c18*d18	c18*d18	c18*d18	2*c18*d18
19	Cotoneaster	15,000	0.30			c19*d19	c19*d19	c19*d19	c19*d19	c19*d19	c19*d19	c19*d19	c19*d19	2*c19*d19
20	Santolina	40,000	0.20		c20*d20	c20*d20	c20*d20	c20*d20	c20*d20	c20*d20	c20*d20	c20*d20	c20*d20	2*c20*d20
21	Sale of nursery													250000
22														
23	TOTAL REVENUE			sum(e10:e21)	sum(f10:f21)	sum(g10:g21)	sum(h10:h21)	sum(i10:i21)	sum(j10:j21)	sum(k10:k21)	sum(l10:l21)	sum(m10:m21)	sum(n10:n21)	sum(o10:o21)
24														
25	less NET CURRENT VALUE			200000										
26	less TOTAL COSTS			70000	70000	70000	70000	70000	70000	70000	70000	70000	70000	70000
27														
28	equals NET REVENUE			e23-e25-e26	f23-f26	g23-g26	h23-h26	i23-i26	j23-j26	k23-k26	l23-l26	m23-m26	n23-n26	o23-o26
29														
30	Discount rate 5%													
31	NET PRESENT VALUE £													
32	npv (.05,d28:n28)													

15

Planning Labour

In this chapter we show how the nurseryman can check to see how much labour a proposed production plan will use, and whether he will need to take on more labour to work it. There is no point in making a plan which needs ten workers when there are only six available. Labour planning is done in much the same way as frame space planning, but it is more time consuming, a bit more complicated and a lot less accurate. For this reason we suggest that the nurseryman should not start on this aspect of planning until he is satisfied that he has mastered the planning system already presented.

If a nurseryman were willing to employ a staff of cost accountants with stopwatches, he could work out exactly how much time was spent on each crop and how much was spent on the nursery as a whole. This is quite impractical: nobody could afford to collect these figures and nobody could spare the time to analyse them.

In the simple planning system, we do not try to time everything. We time only the big jobs, which use most labour, jobs like:

Labour per square foot for preparing benches

Labour per square foot for preparing frames

Labour per square foot for preparing land

Labour per 1,000 cuttings for taking and preparing cuttings

Labour per 1,000 plants for transplanting to frame

Labour per 1,000 plants for transplanting to land

Labour per 1,000 plants for lifting, packing, labelling and grading

Labour per 1,000 plants for pruning or root pruning (but only when this is substantial)

We do not bother timing all the little jobs, a few hours here, a day or two there, an hour or two a day inspecting frames etc. It is too time consuming to record all these labour inputs and there is no useful way of using the figures even if we had them. Instead, in the simple system we assume that the nursery uses a fixed amount of labour for odd jobs, routine tasks etc. and that the amount remains much the same throughout the year. In fact, a full analysis of the labour input on large jobs and small ones in one nursery showed that, in any one of the months when labour is short, at least seven-eighths of the labour input was on these major operations. This suggests that we might ignore the minor operations as long as the major operations do not use more than seven eighths of the available labour. Of course, the figures will vary from nursery to nursery, so, to be on the safe side, it is worth working out a more accurate figure for a particular nursery. This means working out, for the peak periods of the year, how much time must be spent on running the

266 glasshouse, inspecting the frames and beds and also the time that is spent on

TABLE 17   NUMBER OF CUTTINGS AND AMOUNT OF GLASS, FRAME SPACE AND GROUND NEEDED TO PRODUCE 1000 PLANTS FOR SALE

	No. of cuttings	Cuttings per sq. ft	Sq. ft glass needed	Glass for growing on	Frames for cuttings	Plants put in frames	Plants per sq. ft	Sq. ft frames needed	Plants into ground	Sq. ft ground needed	Replanting ground needed	No. plants sold
Ericas (a)	1543	100			16	1111	12	92	0	0		1000
Ericas (b)	1543	100	16			1111	12	92	1000	111		1000
Prunus	1307	40			31	1176			1176	98	392	1000
Viburnum (a)	1237	25			50	1176			1176	98	392	1000
Cotoneaster	1384	75			19	1176	20	58	1176	98	236	1000
Santolina	1221	35			35	1111			1000	333	750	1000
Dwarf Rhodo.	1760	45	40			1144	20	57	1000	100		1000
Rhododendrons	2286	23	100	102		1371	6	228	1111	179		1000
Decid. Azaleas	1667	42	40			1167	11	111	1000	167		1000
Jap. Azalea	2075	42	50			1494	9	166	1000	111		1000
Viburnum (b)	1562	25	62			0			1249	156	312	1000

Note: This table is just a reworking of Table 6

267

absolutely unavoidable weeding, spraying and general maintenance. By unavoidable work we mean work that could not be done equally well, or nearly as well, when labour is not so short. Once this has been worked out, a figure can be put in for each month in the plan. It is not necessary to take any trouble about labour needed in the slack season, as labour supply is not a problem then.

Information needed

For the planning exercise we need the basic information presented in an earlier chapter on the number of cuttings etc. that must be taken to produce 1000 saleable plants. For convenience, this is presented here as Table 17.

The other information we need is the labour requirements for the important jobs, as set out in Table 18. This table gives the sort of detail that might be used by a nurseryman planning for the first time. Obviously, as he keeps more records and as he times more operations over the years he will have more information and more accurate information for a wider range of crops. For instance, he will want to allow for the difference between the time needed for taking erica cuttings with garden shears and the time taken to trim and wound rhododendron cuttings.

TABLE 18   LABOUR REQUIREMENTS FOR VARIOUS JOBS

Taking, preparing and inserting cuttings	8.48 hours per 1,000 cuttings
Transplanting rooted cuttings in glasshouse	5.28 hours per 1,000 plants
Transplanting to frame	5.71 hours per 1,000 plants
Transplanting from frame to ground	10.00 hours per 1,000 plants
Lifting, grading, packing and loading	33.00 hours per 1,000 plants
Glasshouse preparation = 64 hours for 840 sq feet	0.008 hours per sq foot
Frame preparation	0.04 hours per sq foot
Running glasshouse, frames and fields: essential work	160 hours per month.

Note: These are based on figures obtained in various Irish nurseries but they are in no sense averages and they might be quite wrong under different management systems.

This information must be collected in a way that is simple and that does not throw too much strain on the office staff. All that is necessary is that the workers should fill in a worksheet, saying what crop they were working on, what job they were doing and how long it took them e.g. 'lifting berberis 50 hours'. This information would be used to work out a figure for 'lifting, sorting labelling and packing spiky or thorned plants. Other standards may be needed for plants that need their roots burlapped. The number of different plant categories should be kept to a minimum: there is no point in keeping records for twenty different types of tree when it takes much the same time to lift each of them. Similarly, there is no point in recording the operations of lifting, sorting, labelling and packaging separately, for each plant has to undergo all of these operations.

In the first runs of the plan we take account of all labour usage. Soon, however, it will become obvious when there are labour peaks that makes it necessary to plan carefully. It will then be possible to ignore the slack season when planning.

These figures are useful for supervision as well as for planning. Remember the supervisor who said 'Lift those 1000 ericas. It should take the two of you until 6 o'clock tomorrow'; there is less chance that the job will be dragged out for another day.

Labour inputs for each crop

The next step is to prepare a table of standard times for each crop. This shows the amount of labour needed each month to produce, say, January-propagated ericas. The times are set out as in Table 19. In January the cuttings go into the glasshouse, needing 13 hours per 1000 saleable plants. In February they are transplanted to a frame, a task needing 8 hours. In April they are planted out, using 6 hours, and in October they are lifted for sale, using 33 hours. All this is in a single year. The table is long, spreading over four years or more, because some crops are not harvested until then.

To make calculation easier, all these tables are presented per thousand finished plants. This means that allowance is made for the number of cuttings that do not take and the number of plants that do not survive. For example, Table 17 shows that 2286 rhododendron cuttings are needed to produce 1000 finished plants, while only 1237 viburnum cuttings are. This means that nearly twice as much labour is needed. The figures in Table 19 have taken this into account. They are worked out by taking the figure of 8.48 hours per 1000 cuttings in Table 17. The result is 19 hours ($8.48 \times 2286 \div 1000$) for rhododendrons and 10 hours ($8.48 \times 1237 \div 1000$) for viburnums, in each case to take and prepare enough cuttings to produce 1000 finished plants.

In the same way, the number of hours needed to transplant 1000 rooted cuttings (Table 18) is multiplied by the number of cuttings that take (Table 17) and the figure is entered for the month when the job is done.

Table 19 is a table which sets out information so that it can be conveniently applied to the planning process in the next section. No conclusions can be drawn from it alone.

What labour is needed for the complete plan

Now is the time to put the labour usage figures into a real plan. The figures from Table 19 are used to provide the total nursery labour requirements in Table 20.

The first line shows the labour requirements for rhododendrons. 8400 finished plants are to be produced, so the figures in Table 19 are multiplied by 8.4 and are entered in the appropriate month.

The second line shows the second crop, planted a year later. This is put on a new line, to avoid the confusion that would arise if the figures were all on the same line. Again, it is the number of finished plants multiplied by the figures in Table 19. Another new line is taken for the crop planted in the next year, and another for the crop taken in the following year.

With ericas, 54,000 are produced in the first year, before the glasshouses are filled with more valuable crops, but after this none are grown under glass, so zeros appear in the table.

After the hours taken for each crop have been written down, a figure for work done in inspecting the cuttings, watering, ventilating, removing dead leaves, inspecting the frames, ventilating, shading, weeding, spraying the 269 beds, etc. is put down. This figure is meant to cover those jobs that must be done in this month. If the job can be done equally well in a month when there is no great demand for labour, then it is not included. The figure that has been put down, 160 hours for the nursery as a whole, would depend on the size of the nursery, the amount of glasshouse space, the number of frames etc. It is simple enough to record the time actually spent on jobs of this type in a few months of the year.

Finally, at the bottom, the columns are totalled to give the labour utilisation of the plan as a whole. To simplify presentation Table 20 gives only the labour for the glasshouse crops — a much longer table would be needed to cover everything.

Juggling with the figures

Table 20 shows very sharp labour peaks in October. When the plan gets fully under way in Year 3, 3483 hours are needed in this month alone, while only 160 hours are needed in April. This is because we have assumed so far that all crops are planted or transplanted in October and that they are lifted for sale in October. This assumption has saved work so far, but now it must be seen how realistic it is.

In some areas with favourable climate it may be possible to postpone taking cuttings as late as December without risk of frost damage.

Technical considerations will determine when the plants can be lifted and when they cannot. Plants like cotoneaster, santolina, viburnum and ericas can be lifted all through winter, while others must be lifted either very early or very late. In areas with a harsh climate, plants may be frozen in the ground, making it impossible to lift them. In Europe where winters are hard nurserymen find it much harder to smooth out this labour peak than in Ireland or Southern England.

Containerisation can help change labour peaks, so that lifting and packing is not such a critical constraint.

Marketing also plays its part. A retail nurseryman can sell plants right up to the end of the transplanting season. A wholesale nurseryman must have plants delivered to customers so they have a reasonable time to sell them — the last plants should arrive at the retain nursery by the first week in March. Transport costs are smaller if a larger consignment is sent, so the customer who is paying transport costs prefers to get all the plants he has ordered in one delivery, rather than in several.

Bottlenecks can be tackled in several ways. First the jobs can be examined. Ask yourself 'Need the job be done at all? Could it be done at another time of the year when there is labour available?' Many of the jobs in a nursery are not directly productive. Keeping the machinery painted, weeding the drive and so on are useful jobs, but they should be done when there is labour to spare, rather than at peak periods.

If the job is necessary, ask yourself what can be done to speed it up. Machinery might be used for the job. More commonly, a more efficient method can be devised. For instance, if trailers are parked at both ends of the row instead of just one during harvesting, less time is spent carrying. Work study can be used to develop more efficient ways of digging, packing, labelling, taking cuttings etc. There are a large number of books available on work study and method study and most public libraries have several. It is surprising

TABLE 19   LABOUR INPUTS PER 1000 PLANTS

Year 0

	No of plants (000)	J	F	M	A	M	J	J	A	S	O	N	D
Rhododendrons	1	13										19	
Ericas	1		8		6						33		
Dwarf Rhodos.	1		15		7						10		
Decid. azaleas	1					14			7		10		
Jap. azaleas	1						18		9				
Viburnum	1								13	12			
Ericas	1										13		
Prunus	1										11		
Viburnum	1												
Cotoneaster	1										12		
Santolina	1										10		

Year 1

	No of plants (000)	J	F	M	A	M	J	J	A	S	O	N	D
Rhododendrons	1		7				8					11	
Ericas	1												
Dwarf Rhodos.	1												
Decid. azaleas	1											10	
Jap. azaleas	1												
Viburnum	1											22	
Ericas	1				6								
Prunus	1				12								
Viburnum	1												
Cotoneaster	1					7							
Santolina	1					10						33	

Year 2

	No of plants (000)	J	F	M	A	M	J	J	A	S	O	N	D
Rhododendrons	1												
Ericas	1												
Dwarf Rhodos.	1												
Decid. azaleas	1										33		
Jap. azaleas	1										33		
Viburnum	1												
Ericas	1												
Prunus	1										17		
Viburnum	1												
Cotoneaster	1										33		
Santolina	1												

Year 3

	No of plants (000)	J	F	M	A	M	J	J	A	S	O	N	D
Rhododendrons	1										33		
Ericas	1												
Dwarf Rhodos.	1										33		
Decid. azaleas	1												
Jap. azaleas	1												
Viburnum	1										33		
Ericas	1										33		
Prunus	1												
Viburnum	1												
Cotoneaster	1												
Santolina	1												

TABLE 20   LABOUR INPUTS FOR A FEASIBLE PLAN — GLASSHOUSE CROPS ONLY

	No of plants (000)	Year 0												Year 1											
		J	F	M	A	M	J	J	A	S	O	N	D	J	F	M	A	M	J	J	A	S	O	N	D
Rhododendrons	8.40	0	0	0	0	0	0	0	0	0	0	0	0	0	61	0	0	0	66	0	0	0	93	0	0
	8.40	0	0	0	0	0	0	0	0	0	0	0	0	0	0	0	0	0	0	0	0	0	163	0	0
	8.40																								
	8.40																								
Ericas (glass)	54.89	718	447	0	348	0	0	0	0	0	1,811	0	0	0	0	0	0	0	0	0	0	0	0	0	0
	0																								
	0																								
	0																								
Dwarf Rhodos.	21.70	0	324	0	142	0	0	0	0	0	217	0	0	0	0	0	0	0	0	0	0	0	0	0	0
	0																								
	0																								
	0																								
Decid. azaleas	21.00	0	0	0	0	297	0	0	140	0	210	0	0	0	0	0	0	297	0	0	140	0	210	0	0
	21.00																								
	21.00																								
	21.00																								
Jap. azaleas	16.80	0	0	0	0	0	296	0	143	0	0	0	0	0	0	0	0	0	296	0	143	0	168	0	0
	16.80																								
	16.80																								
	16.80																								
Viburnum glass	13.58	0	0	0	0	0	0	0	180	170	0	0	0	0	0	0	0	0	0	0	180	170	0	0	0
	13.58																								
	13.58																								
	13.58																								
Glass and frame inspection etc		160	160	160	160	160	160	160	160	160	160	160	160	160	160	160	160	160	160	160	160	160	160	160	160
TOTAL		878	931	160	650	457	456	160	623	330	2,398	160	160	160	221	160	160	457	521	160	623	330	794	160	160

	No of plants (000)	Year 2												Year 3											
		J	F	M	A	M	J	J	A	S	O	N	D	J	F	M	A	M	J	J	A	S	O	N	D
Rhododendrons	8.40	0	0	0	0	0	0	0	0	0	0	0	0	0	0	0	0	0	0	0	0	0	277	0	0
	8.40	0	61	0	0	0	0	0	0	0	0	0	0	0	61	0	0	0	0	0	0	0	0	0	0
	8.40	0	0	0	0	0	66	0	0	0	93	0	0	0	0	0	0	0	66	0	0	0	93	0	0
	8.40	0	0	0	0	0	0	0	0	0	163	0	0	0	0	0	0	0	0	0	0	0	163	0	0
Ericas (glass)	54.89	0	0	0	0	0	0	0	0	0	0	0	0	0	0	0	0	0	0	0	0	0	0	0	0
	0	0	0	0	0	0	0	0	0	0	0	0	0	0	0	0	0	0	0	0	0	0	0	0	0
	0	0	0	0	0	0	0	0	0	0	0	0	0	0	0	0	0	0	0	0	0	0	0	0	0
	0	0	0	0	0	0	0	0	0	0	0	0	0	0	0	0	0	0	0	0	0	0	0	0	0
Dwarf Rhodos.	21.70	0	0	0	0	0	0	0	0	0	0	0	0	0	0	0	0	0	0	0	0	0	716	0	0
	0	0	0	0	0	0	0	0	0	0	0	0	0	0	0	0	0	0	0	0	0	0	0	0	0
	0	0	0	0	0	0	0	0	0	0	0	0	0	0	0	0	0	0	0	0	0	0	0	0	0
	0	0	0	0	0	0	0	0	0	0	0	0	0	0	0	0	0	0	0	0	0	0	0	0	0
Decid. azaleas	21.00	0	0	0	0	0	0	0	0	0	693	0	0	0	0	0	0	0	0	0	0	0	693	0	0
	21.00	0	0	0	0	0	297	0	0	0	0	0	0	0	0	0	0	297	0	0	0	0	0	0	0
	21.00	0	0	0	0	0	0	0	0	140	0	0	0	0	0	0	0	0	0	0	140	0	0	0	0
	21.00	0	0	0	0	0	0	0	0	0	0	210	0	0	0	0	0	0	0	0	0	0	210	0	0
Jap. azaleas	16.80	0	0	0	0	0	0	0	0	0	554	0	0	0	0	0	0	0	0	0	0	0	554	0	0
	16.80	0	0	0	0	0	0	0	0	0	168	0	0	0	0	0	0	0	0	0	0	0	168	0	0
	16.80	0	0	0	0	0	0	0	143	0	0	0	0	0	0	0	0	0	0	0	143	0	0	0	0
	16.80	0	0	0	0	0	296	0	0	0	0	0	0	0	0	0	0	0	0	0	0	0	0	0	0
Viburnum glass	13.58	0	0	0	0	0	0	0	0	0	0	0	0	0	0	0	0	0	0	0	0	0	448	0	0
	13.58	0	0	0	0	0	0	0	0	0	0	0	0	0	0	0	0	0	296	0	0	0	0	0	0
	13.58	0	0	0	0	0	0	0	180	0	0	0	0	0	0	0	0	0	0	0	180	0	0	0	0
	13.58	0	0	0	0	0	0	0	0	170	0	0	0	0	0	0	0	0	0	0	0	170	0	0	0
Glass and frame inspection etc		160	160	160	160	160	160	160	160	160	160	160	160	160	160	160	160	160	160	160	160	160	160	160	160
TOTAL		160	221	160	160	160	818	160	483	470	1,832	370	160	160	221	160	160	457	521	160	623	330	3,483	160	160

that Zimbabwean tobacco farmers who paid their workers less than £300 a year had a work study book three inches thick on this one crop, while few British and Irish horticulturists have thought it worthwhile to investigate work study at all, though they pay wages twenty times as high.

Where there is a major labour peak and there is no easy way to overcome it, it will pay to do a week by week plan covering the critical time. The schedule must not be too tight, or else total confusion would be caused by a change in the weather or an unexpected order.

If the plan cannot be managed with the labour available, it is back to the drawing board, to try another plan which uses less labour in the critical period. It may use propagation at other times of the year or it may use plants that are easier to harvest or that need less complicated packing.

Using computers

Labour planning with a computer really needs a 16-bit or bigger computer with 256K or more. The tables are big and they use a lot of formulae to save calculations, so a lot of machine memory is needed. However, you can get by with an 8-bit computer if you work out the tables separately and break big tables into smaller tables of manageable size.

The tables shown in this chapter, Tables 17, 18, 19 and 20 can all be put on the same spreadsheet (or, with an 8-bit computer, linked together). Table 19 is worked out with formulae. For the example the figure for labour needed to take rhododendron cuttings is a formula — the number of hours per 1000 cuttings (from Table 18) times the number of cuttings (from Table 17). This means that you can change the figures in Tables 17 or 18, to reflect more efficient labour usage or a propagation method that has a higher take, and the figures in Table 19 will be changed automatically.

Table 20 is worked out directly from Table 19. Multiply the number of finished plants, shown in column *b* by the appropriate figure in Table 19. This formula has only to be worked out for the first figure in each row. The formula is then replicated across the spreadsheet through the life of the crop (the number of plants in column *b* is not relative, but the other figures are). The second crop is worked out the same way, with the entry starting a year later.

Finally, at the bottom, the column total is worked out and the formula is replicated across the page.

Setting up the spreadsheet like this may take a few hours, especially if you are not used to the program. Once it has been set up, though, it is very easy to use. You can change the survival rate of cuttings, or the hours taken to prepare cuttings or the number of plants produced. The computer then thinks away for a couple of minutes and comes up with a totally new plan with all the labour requirements worked out.

It is possible to link the labour calculations with the tables for the space requirements and the revenue, so that a summary of the plan as a whole appears. Again, it takes a little longer to set up the whole spreadsheet, but it then takes only minutes to look at a whole new plan, and to see its revenue, as well as its feasibility in terms of labour, bench space and frame space.

Labour costs

We have said above that it is wrong to cost out the labour input for each crop: it produces the wrong answers.

However, when you are comparing a plan that requires 6 men with one that requires 10 men or with one that requires a lot more overtime or casual labour, you should take labour costs into account, charging each plan with the labour costs incurred. This can only really be done after the detailed week by week calculation of labour utilisation during the peak periods.

Of course, if the labour, especially the skilled labour is not there, the plan cannot be done, and it is pointless to work out the labour costs.

16

Allowing for Inflation

So far, the planning has been done on the assumption that all costs and prices remain at today's level. A very low discount rate has been used, 5%. This is perfectly adequate for most purposes. It will show which plans are most profitable and it will show where cash flow is likely to be a problem. Most important, perhaps, the assumptions are quite clear and there is no temptation to imagine that vast inflationary increases in price will compensate for present losses.

However, we can be certain that there will be at least a moderate rate of inflation throughout the next twenty years and we can expect some periods of rapid inflation. Naturally, this will have some effect on the profitability of the nursery, and this chapter shows how to allow for it.

Even if the nurseryman decides that it is too much trouble to allow for inflation when planning — and we would give a low priority to the task — he will have to produce at least one cash flow allowing for price changes, for the bank manager. The bank manager will want to know how the nursery is going to manage interest and loan repayments, and how serious the cash flow problem will be.

Financial charges

Financial charges, such as interest payable on bank loans and repayments to the bank, are put into the cash flow as payments and the loans themselves are put into the cash flow as revenue to the firm. They fall into the categories of revenue and expenditure as follows:

Revenue	*Expenditure*
Loan from bank	Bank interest
Interest received from outside investments.	Repayments made
Repayments to the firm of outside investments.	Investments made
Tax recovered.	Tax payments.

The interest rates have been arrived at taking inflation into account, so they cannot be used without change when planning at today's prices. It is most unlikely that a new nursery could be profitable paying high, inflationary, interest rates. Instead, the figures should be discounted by the rate of inflation to get repayments at today's prices. For example, if the rate of inflation is 10% and financial charges are £10,000 a year, these can be put in as £9,000 next year (90% of £10,000) and as £8,100 (90% of 90% of £10,000) the following year. Of course, if inflation is less than you expected, these repayments are more of a burden.

When preparing a plan taking inflation into account, it is not necessary to make these changes. The figures can go in as they are.

Depreciation

Depreciation is ignored in all planning. The full cost is put in for the year the tractor is bought and for the year it is replaced. This gives the actual cash flow, which is what the nurseryman wants to know. Depreciation is merely an accountant's device for working out tax etc. It does not show actual expenditures.

The discounting period

It is important that the period of analysis is the same for all the investments considered, and that a 2-year project and a 20 year project are not compared. If they are compared it is implicitly assuming that all the profits from the 2-year project can be re-invested in equally profitable projects for the next 18 years, which is unlikely. Other problems also arise. The way to make the comparison is to follow up the 2-year project for the full 20 years, showing how the profits are reinvested, and then to compare the two 20-year cash flows.

The plan for the firm could be made to cover 100 years, but this would be unrealistic. It is unlikely that a nurserymen can forecast as far as 15 years ahead with any accuracy. Perhaps the best plan is to forecast 10 or 15 years ahead, the time at which a lot of new expenditure, such as the purchase of a new glasshouse, might become necessary.

The discount rate

We suggest that, initially, the planner should use a discount rate 5% over the actual interest rate.

The rate of interest charged on any money borrowed by the nursery is likely to prove too low to be used as a discount rate for several reasons. First, the bank has good security for its loan to the nursery, so the risk is not high. The nurseryman, on the other hand, has fairly substantial risks and must allow for them. Second, if the nurseryman borrows at 10% and discounts at 10%, he may find that there is very little left for himself — if a nurseryman cannot find investments which pay considerably more than the bank loan rate, then he has no business to be investing. Third, the interest rate bears no relation to the rate of return on other investments made by the firm.

277

A higher discount rate may be charged — the rate of return the firm is getting on its current investments. If the firm has found from experience that it can expect to get an internal rate of return of at least 20% on its investments, then this is the rate to use.

As it is impossible to choose a discount rate that is exactly right, it is worth calculating the present value at several rates. This will show whether a relatively small change in discount rates would make another project have a higher net present value. (This is all that is meant by 'sensitivity analysis' — seeing how sensitive your choice is to a change in discount rate, wage rates, prices etc.) If 20% seems to be the right discount rate, and Project A is the most profitable at this rate, the nurseryman should still consider Project B, which is the more profitable at 17%. It would be foolish to say that any one discount rate or any one estimate of costs will be exactly right, so several alternatives should be considered.

Risk must then be taken into account. Once it has been decided that, say, 20% is a suitable discount rate for a zero risk project, a suitable discount rate must be chosen for the project being considered. Usually a high discount rate is chosen for a high-risk project, so the planner does not place much importance on revenue obtained in the distant future when the project may well have collapsed. This is not entirely satisfactory for long-term businesses like a nursery, as it makes high-risk, short-term crops appear to be safer than equally high-risk, long-term crops. Nor is there any satisfactory way of saying how much higher the interest should be for a high-risk project.

An alternative system is to charge the zero-risk discount rate, but to reduce the expected revenue from a crop according to the risk — if there is a one in four chance that the crop will fail completely, reduce the expected price by 25 per cent. This deals with the risk as far as individual crops are concerned, but not the risk to the firm if frost hits all the crops in the same year and the nursery cannot obtain enough cash to stay in business. This risk the nurseryman must work out for himself: it is worth getting 10 per cent more revenue from tender plants and facing a one in five chance of going bankrupt in the next ten years?

The value of the nursery

The final entry in the cash flow is the value of the nursery. The nursery is valued as though it is going to be sold. All mother stock and growing plants are valued at their market price. All outstanding debts are paid.

We recommend that it is valued using today's prices, without any allowance for development value. The figure can then be brought up to the future price by applying the inflation rate. There are three reasons for this. First, the current price for land in the area already takes into account its possible development value. Second, the speculator bases his price on the possibility of getting planning permission to develop the land. The nurseryman is not likely to have the same skill in obtaining planning permission, so it would be unwise for him to forecast that his land would increase in value to the same extent. Third, fortunes have been lost as well as made by land specuiation.

It is worth remembering that, if the nursery is sold at an inflated price in ten years, the nurserymen can expect to have to buy his new nursery at an

equally inflated price.

Costs and prices

The only justification for using current costs and prices instead of today's costs and prices is the planner's belief that some costs and prices are going to rise faster than others and that they will not rise in line with inflation. We believe, for example, that improved efficiency in the industry means that prices will not rise as fast as costs: improved productivity will be needed to maintain profitability. If this is so, it would be foolish to make forecasts that assume both constant real prices and improved efficiency.

The planner may also want to write into the plan his forecast that the price of oil and labour will rise faster than inflation, and that the price of machinery and peat will rise slower. He may be relying on his prediction that the prices of specimen trees will rise much faster than the prices of liners. Again, this is easiest to do with a plan that takes into account inflation (though it can be done on the plan using today's price, by assuming a lower or higher price in the later years).

It must be emphasised that the planner who makes all these assumptions is making forecasts that the Treasury with all its economists and computers is afraid to make. There is a serious danger that he will, quite unconsciously, make unduly optimistic forecasts.

Calculating the price changes

To show the method of making the calculations we will make the calculations for the following rates of price increase:

Rhododendrons and dwarf rhododendrons: 15% per year until the end of year 5 and 10% per annum after that.

Deciduous and Japanese azaleas: 10% per annum then 5% from year 6.

Viburnum: 5% per annum.

Prunus, ericas, santolina: 10% per annum.

Cotoneaster: no changes in prices.

These figures are not intended to be realistic. They have been selected to show the method of allowing for different rates of price change.

A factor is now calculated to allow for the price change. With rhododendrons it is calculated as in Table 21.

Where the prices are expected to increase by the same percentage each year, the factor can be calculated very quickly, by putting the first number (say

TABLE 21

Year	Rhododendrons	Factor	Azaleas	Viburnum
Y0	1.15 =	1.15	1.10 = 1.10	1.05 = 1.05
Y1	1.15 × 1.15 =	1.32	1.10 × 1.10 = 1.21	1.05 × 1.05 = 1.10
Y2	1.32 × 1.15 =	1.52	1.21 × 1.10 = 1.33	1.10 × 1.05 = 1.16
Y3	1.52 × 1.15 =	1.75	1.33 × 1.10 = 1.46	1.16 × 1.05 = 1.22
Y4	1.75 × 1.15 =	2.01	1.46 × 1.10 = 1.61	1.22 × 1.05 = 1.28
Y5	2.01 × 1.15 =	2.31	1.61 × 1.10 = 1.77	1.28 × 1.05 = 1.34
Y6	2.31 × 1.10 =	2.54	1.71 × 1.05 = 1.86	1.34 × 1.05 = 1.41
Y7	2.54 × 1.10 =	2.79	1.86 × 1.05 = 1.95	1.41 × 1.05 = 1.48
Y8	2.79 × 1.10 =	3.07	1.95 × 1.05 = 2.05	1.48 × 1.05 = 1.55
Y9	3.07 × 1.10 =	3.38	2.05 × 1.05 = 2.15	1.55 × 1.05 = 1.63
Y10	3.38 × 1.10 =	3.72	2.15 × 1.05 = 2.26	1.63 × 1.05 = 1.71

TABLE 22   TOTAL REVENUE FROM THE PROPOSED PLAN — ALLOWING FOR INFLATION

	No. of Plants	Price in Year 0	Year 0	Year 1	Year 2	Year 3	Year 4	Year 5	Year 6	Year 7	Year 8	Year 9	Year 10
Rhododendrons	8,400	2.00				29,400	33,768	38,808	42,672	46,872	51,576	56,784	124,992
Ericas (glass)	54,890	0.15	4,528	4,981									
Dwarf Rhodos.	21,700	0.85				32,279							
Decid. azaleas	21,000	1.30			36,309	39,858	43,953	43,953	50,778	53,235	55,965	58,695	123,396
Jap. azaleas	16,800	0.45			10,122	11,111	12,253	13,014	14,155	14,840	15,601	16,362	34,399
Viburnum	13,580	0.85				14,082	14,775	15,468	16,276	17,084	17,892	18,815	39,477
Ericas	15,000	0.15		1,361	2,993	3,285	3,623	3,983	4,388	4,815	5,288	5,828	12,825
Prunus	15,000	0.40				8,760	9,660	10,620	11,700	12,840	14,160	15,540	34,200
Viburnum	15,000	0.40				7,320	7,680	8,040	8,460	8,880	9,300	9,780	20,520
Cotoneaster	15,000	0.30			4,500	4,500	4,500	4,500	4,500	4,500	4,500	4,500	9,000
Santolina	40,000	0.20		9,680	10,640	11,680	12,880	14,160	15,600	17,120	18,880	20,720	45,600
Sale of nursery													1,276,900
TOTAL REVENUE			4,528	16,023	64,563	162,275	143,091	152,545	168,528	180,186	193,161	207,024	1,721,309
less NET CURRENT VALUE			200,000										
less TOTAL COSTS			70,000	70,000	70,000	70,000	70,000	70,000	70,000	70,000	70,000	70,000	70,000
equals NET REVENUE			−265,472	−53,977	−5,437	92,275	73,091	82,545	98,528	110,186	123,161	137,024	1,651,309

Discount rate 12%
NET PRESENT VALUE £   510,323

Discount rate 15%
NET PRESENT VALUE £   346,429

Discount rate 20%
NET PRESENT VALUE £   161,030

1.10) on the calculating machine, squaring it to get the figure for Y1, pressing the equals button to get the figure for Y2, pressing the equals button again to get the figure for Y3 and so on.

The factor shows the amount prices are expected to rise. Taking the 10% column, for example, prices in one year's time, at the end of Y0 are expected to be 1.10 times as much as now and prices at the end of year 10 are expected to be 2.15 times as big as they are now. (There are slight rounding errors as the factors are calculated to only two decimal places but they may be ignored.)

These inflation factors are applied to the figures in Table 10 'Total revenue from the proposed plan' to get Table 22. For example, Table 10 shows the revenue at today's prices from rhododendrons in Year 3 to be £16,800. This figure is multiplied by the inflation factor for rhododendrons in year 3, which is 1.75 (Table 21). The result is the revenue allowing for inflation £29,400 (Table 22).

This is a simple calculation with a calculator and it probably takes a little longer with the computer. However, the joy of the computer table is that Table 22 is linked to Table 10, so that any changes made to Table 10 automatically lead to changes in Table 22. In fact, since Table 10 itself is based on other tables, a series of tables is linked in this way. Each cell in Table 22 is calculated by the computer according to a formula. First comes the inflation factor, 1.32 or 1.75 or whatever, from Table 21. Then comes the multiplication sign *. Then comes 'rev1' which is the name we used for the computer file which became Table 10 in this book. Then comes (g10) or (h16), the number of the cell in Table 10 which gives the revenue at constant prices. The computer reads the formula as multiply the revenue from Table 10 by the inflation factor in Table 21 to get the revenue at current prices.

At the bottom of Table 22 the Net Present Value is given at three different discount rates. This is done so that the planner can rank the different plans using different discount rates. If one plan is more profitable at all the rates, there is no more to be said. If, however, one plan is more profitable at a low interest rate and another at a high one, then the planner must sit back and think what it is he really wants. He must go back to Chapter 12 and think out his objectives.

17

Setting up in Business

The planning system shown so far was designed for an existing nursery, so it was possible to ignore many of the problems that are crucial for a new business.

Mother plants

The cash flows in the previous chapter ignored mother plants entirely. It may be safe for an established nurseryman to do this, because his mother plants are mature and they do not need a lot of attention. The man setting up a nursery is in a very different position as mother plants are his chief limiting factor and investment in mother plants can amount to many thousands of pounds at a time when the business can least afford it. The mother plants should be grown for a season before cuttings are taken and this imposes a resource limit. The nursery plan must be started a year earlier, in Y-1 instead of Y0. (We usually give the years of preparation before the production process starts, while the equipment is being assembled and the raw materials gathered, a minus number, so Y-1 is the year before production starts.) It is impossible to grow plants unless cuttings are available, so one cannot suddenly introduce a crop like dwarf rhododendrons in the middle of a production system which has ignored this crop previously. Either there must be a supply of cuttings available locally or the nurseryman must buy and plant mother stock well in advance.

The mother plants may be bought as young plants and, as they get bigger and more cuttings per plant can be taken, the surplus can be sold. There are two elements in growing mother plants: firstly, providing cuttings for another crop and, secondly, growing on young mother plants for sale as mature plants. Fortunately, under the planning system described here, we do not allocate costs between the two elements, saying the cost of cuttings is £x per 100 and the cost of growing a mature plant is £y. That would be as difficult and as useful as the medieval arguments on how many angels can sit on the point of a pin.

Mother plants fit very easily into our system. After the plan has reached the stage where the best cropping systems have been identified, the number of mother plants needed for the system are worked out. To take an example, 5,000 mother plants are bought in Y-1 and are planted in October. In February Y0, 25,000 cuttings can be taken from these plants. In June, some mother plants are trimmed to provide shoots for the next year's cuttings. By October Y0 they have increased to the size where twice the number of cuttings can be taken, so half the original stock can be sold off. One year later the plants are

282

bigger still and 40% (1,000) can be sold off as surplus. After this, there is an established mother-stock bed which needs little attention. The cash flow for mother stock to provide 25,000 erica cuttings would be:

Dec. Y-1 *	5,000 plants purchased	– £1,075
Dec. Y0 *	2,500 plants sold	+ £ 619
Dec. Y1 *	1,000 plants sold	+ £ 284

Assuming payment three months after sale

Mother stock purchases are a severe strain on the finances of the nursery at the beginning, but the sales of surplus plants can provide a useful addition to cash flow in the early years. It does not take long to adjust the cash flow for purchase and sale of mother plants.

The chief labour input for the mother stock comes from planting out in the spring or autumn of Y-1 and in lifting the plants in October Y0 and Y-1. This can be handled by casual labour or even, in Y0 and Y-1, by permanent labour, so it need not affect the labour availability table under the circumstances we describe — in other nurseries labour shortage may limit the output in the first few years.

In addition to the normal costs, one must allow for the cost of purchase of the mother plants, the cost of erecting a plastic house for forcing, if this is necessary, and returns from selling surplus mother plants. When fitting in the mother plants with the rest of the nursery, simply put them in as a third or fourth crop in the cycle. In Table 20 for example, the first line would be for planting, harvesting and care of the rhododendron mother crops, and only after this would come crops 1, 2 and 3.

Anyone thinking of starting his own nursery in the next few years would be well advised to set up his own mother stock beds on a small piece of ground, propagating and caring for the plants in his spare time. This would mean that a few large plants would provide the cuttings instead of a large number of small plants and it would make it unnecessary to buy several thousand pounds worth of plants when the nursery starts. It also reduces the risk of introducing diseased plants into a new nursery.

Estimating costs of production

When a nursery is being planned from the start, a lot of the value of the plan depends on the accuracy of the costs used. For an established nursery this is not nearly so important, as the costs for the present system are known and as the costs are usually much the same for all other feasible plans so all plans will be equally miscosted.

The first step is to choose the right production process. In this book we have described several production processes for the crops including mist propagation, frame propagation, grafting, warm bench and plastic. Even when one system is clearly the best from one point of view, as it produces most plants in the shortest time and with the least costs, the other systems may be preferable from the economic point of view. For example, warm bench and plastic in January may be more efficient, technically, for producing ericas, than the traditional method of taking cuttings in July but if a more profitable crop, such as rhododendrons, is taking up the glasshouse space at the beginning of the year, it may be best to use the traditional system for ericas. It is important, therefore to have a wide choice of processes available and to consider the possibilities of each process.

Secondly, the machinery, the glasshouse, the frames and the plastic houses should be carefully chosen for the crops planned. For example, mist propagation, though spectacular, is expensive and is dependent on lime-free water and an electricity supply, so investment in this should be avoided if all the plants can be produced with warm bench and plastic.

The detail of the costing, the cost of spades, fences, gates, bridges, drains, lavatories, telephones, etc. is worth some attention. These odds and ends amount to a considerable proportion of total investment and it is easy to leave out costs. Power and water costs may be very high indeed if the nursery is far from the existing mains. It is worth getting a fellow nurseryman's advice on these costs. However, at the present rate of inflation, his experience of how much it cost him to set up a nursery is hopelessly out of date: all he can do is say what he spent the money on and leave it to you to see what is the present price. Even so, the cost of a glasshouse may go up 10–30% between the time the loans are arranged and the time the glasshouse goes up.

Forecasts of the time taken to get grants and loans and of the time taken to complete the packhouses and glasshouses are almost invariably wrong. If a flow chart is drawn up, with the latest times at which each operation is to be completed, some control is possible. It is also possible to plan the development so each item of equipment is bought only when needed. This may not be safe, however: if the plan says that the glasshouse is not needed until January of the second year of operation, it usually happens that it is not ready until mid-March and a whole crop has been lost. It is wiser to plan for the glasshouse to be ready some months before it is needed.

The choice of a site is important, particularly for the retail nursery and garden centre. These should be near a large town, and readily accessible from a main road. When considering a site, one should count the number of cars travelling past on a weekend and try to make some estimate of the number of people who are out for a drive and might stop to look at a garden centre. Suitable soils and low production costs are more important for the production nursery than for the garden centre. In the past, transport costs have not been critical: the Dutch have shown that even cross-channel transport costs do not seriously hinder competition. A nurseryman who can buy peatland at £500 per acre in Ireland will not find the transport cost to England, £5.00 a container, a serious problem. Nevertheless, in any forecast, it is important to allow for the fact that transport costs will rise faster than most other costs.

The transport costs for the different plants depend largely on the number that can be fitted in a container safely and this is something you can find out only by practical experience, so it is worth taking a note of the way in which any containers arriving at or leaving the nursery are packed. Correct packaging could easily reduce transport costs by 20%. Different transport companies will give different quotations, depending on the backload capacity available and how busy they are. The cheapest firm at one time of the year may be the most expensive at others. However, the cost of transport is a small proportion of the value of the plants and it does not pay to be mean. If you can find a small firm with a driver who knows something about plants, who is interested in handling them properly and who will take a little extra effort to see that they are delivered in good condition, it is worth paying him well over the going price.

Naturally one looks at availability of labour when deciding to set up the nursery in any area. Cheap labour and skilled labour are not usually found in the same area, so, if labour is cheap, the nurseryman may have to start his own training scheme. The labour requirements in the first few years are likely to be higher as unskilled workers are slow and a nurseryman who has been used to working with skilled workers will find jobs taking two or three times as long as he expected. Cheap labour may attract a factory to the area so the nurseryman finds that, instead of having cheap unskilled labour, he has to pay high wages and has expensive unskilled labour. As a result, labour inputs and labour costs are particularly difficult to forecast.

Forecasts of output may also prove optimistic, as unskilled workers will have a lower success rate when planting, grafting or inserting cuttings. The output would be reduced by one quarter if the success rate for cuttings was 60% instead of 80%.

Detailed cost-of-production studies of vegetables and field crops are useful to the farmer as a comparison for checking labour, fertiliser and spray requirements but nurserymen do not have the same support.

The trends in costs are even more difficult to forecast. One can assume, as a broad generalisation, that fuel costs are going to keep rising for the foreseeable future. Labour costs will continue to rise at about the same rate as inflation. Cost of labour employed in a nursery will be affected by labour costs locally and the supply and demand for labour in that area.

The most common mistakes in forecasting costs are due to insufficient analysis. Sometimes a soil analysis is not carried out, the drainage is not allowed for or secondary factors, such as labour and mother plants, are forgotten. Often too, only one approach is examined and the alternatives are not even considered. Time spent on planning is seldom wasted.

Cash flow

The new nursery is particularly vulnerable to a breakdown of cash flow, as it is totally reliant on credit. This means that cash flow should be worked out on a monthly basis, not on an annual basis as shown in Table 10. A well prepared cash flow table identifies cash crises soon enough for action to be taken on them and for plans to be changed. The bank manager will also be more willing to lend on a prepared cash flow and he will be more willing to extend emergency aid if he is given reasonable warning and a new cash flow table.

In preparing the table full allowance should be given for the delays in payment, perhaps a 3 to 6 month delay in getting payment for plants, while the new nursery with no credit rating will have to pay cash for all its inputs.

In the first years of the nursery's existence the problem is survival not profit maximisation. Plans which build up the nursery to a vast, profitable business in year 15 are out of the question if they do not keep body and soul together and the bank manager happy in the establishment period. The new nursery is operating on a tight margin and cannot afford to take the risks an established nursery can.

Cash flow problems may force the nursery to concentrate on plants which can be produced rapidly rather than on more profitable, longer-term plants like rhododendrons. Similarly, the nursery may have to sell off plants as liners, rather than grow them on for a larger profit.

285

Planning

The new nursery needs the closest possible planning. The established nursery-man may be willing to assume that if he goes on as before he cannot go far wrong (ignoring both the risk that things will go wrong and the possibility that he could make a lot more with a different plan). The newcomer has no experience to go on: he must plan. The planning system presented here can be used by most nurserymen without the help of a professional accountant. It is simple and straightforward, and could only be further simplified with a great loss in accuracy. It should increase profits by identifying those plans which are not feasible with the resources available, by identifying the plans which are definitely not attractive financially, and by identifying several plans which appear to be well above the average in profit. The payoff from planning is far more than that from most of the non-essential work the nurseryman does.

Good luck!

Index